Coyotes Still Sing in My Valley

Conserving Biodiversity in a Northern City

Ross W. Wein, Editor

© 2006 Spotted Cow Press

4216 – 121 Street

Edmonton, Alberta Canada T6J 1Y8

www.spottedcowpress.ca

Library and Archives Canada Cataloguing in Publication

Coyotes still sing in my valley : conserving biodiversity in a northern city / Ross W. Wein, editor.

Includes bibliographical references.

Also available in electronic format.

ISBN 0-9733864-8-7

1. Biological diversity conservation--Alberta--Edmonton. 2. Urban ecology (Biology). 3. Natural areas--Alberta--Edmonton. I. Wein, Ross W., 1940-

QH77.C3C69 2006   333.95'16'09712334   C2006-900932-5

Printed and bound in Canada.

Preface

The City of Edmonton (capital of the Province of Alberta), located at 53° 32'N, 113° 30'W, is the sixth largest city in Canada with a population of about 783,000 people; the region swells this population to about one million. This western Canadian city is near the centre of the Province of Alberta, which is bounded by latitudes 49°N and 60°N, and longitudes 110°W, and 120°W (and partly by the Rocky Mountains).

Edmonton is a winter city with a dry climate and clear skies year round. Snow and ice cover characterizes winter from November through mid-March. Summers are generally dry and sunny. Average monthly temperatures range from 17°C in the summer months to −15°C in the winter months.

Edmonton was established on the North Saskatchewan River Valley, which drains water from the Columbia Ice Fields of the Rocky Mountains. The city of 700 km² straddles the valley that is known as a 'ribbon of green,' which is the largest natural river valley urban park system on the continent. More than 100 km of biking, hiking, skiing, walking and snow-shoeing trails introduce visitors to the wildlife species that represent the prairies to the south and boreal forests to the north. Visitors and residents alike are thrilled at the sight of hundreds of bird species (including owls, pilated woodpeckers) and mammal species (including deer, coyotes, porcupines).

We are a young city, only founded in 1904, so we are not much older than a human life span as illustrated by my meeting with an elderly resident of my community.

As I approached he was leaning on his cane, facing into the setting sun, and overlooking the Whitemud Riding Stables in the North Saskatchewan River Valley. He stated, "It's my valley." He was well over ninety years old and his dog must have been just as old in human-years. He continued to acknowledge my presence by saying "I used to trap along Whitemud Creek and the Big Valley when I was a kid – the city sure has changed". He creaked over to the park bench; "Boy" followed him and so did I. He ruminated about his family at the early part of the century, about trapping as a teenager, about the wars, about raising a family through hard times, about his children, grandchildren, and great-grandchildren who still hike the valley. His life experiences were a sampling of Edmonton's history. "Yes, the city sure has changed. Belgravia used to be all farmland and bush; but, you know, you can still hear the coyotes sing at night. I live for that."

The contents of this volume address subjects related to urban protected areas that range from celebrations of special features to approaches that will protect natural areas for future generations. We expect the readership to be naturalists, historians, city planners, teachers and students of environmental studies, and others who are interested in the quality of life issues of their cities. We hope that post-secondary students will be stimulated to conduct studies on the subjects explored in this volume; this is why we have included source materials for further study.

This volume is offered as a celebration of the past 100 years and as a contribution toward maintaining the quality of life in our "River City," our "Winter City," and our "City of Champions" and just as importantly in our sister urban areas of Alberta, Canada, and the World.

Ross W. Wein
Edmonton, Alberta, Canada

Acknowledgements

It was through the energy and good will of contributors that this volume was brought together beginning in mid-November of 2003, in anticipation of centennial celebrations for Edmonton in 2004 and the centennial celebrations for the Province of Alberta in 2005. All authors had opportunities to review the contributions of other authors. The reviews were guided by an editorial panel with members that included, in alphabetical order, Lu Carbyn, Tara McGee, Grant Pearsell, Mike Salomons, Guy Swinnerton, and John Wood and also anonymous reviewers.

The assistance of Provincial Archives staff to locate historical photographs and support of Legacy Lands Conservation Society was appreciated. Conservation Society members Doris Kramm, Shannon Ripley, and Mike Salomons assisted with the communication among contributors and the development of the manuscript. The guidance of the Spotted Cow Press team throughout the development of the book was professional and personable; book design and layout were provided by Melanie Eastley and Lu Ziola, while Jerome and Merle Martin provided friendship and support for a myriad of details.

On a personal level, my undergraduate and graduate students taught me a great deal about the valley ecosystems. I value the enthusiasm of my university, government, and NGO colleagues, other friends and neighbours, who study and enjoy our ribbon of green.

Funding contributions toward the editing and publishing of the volume were made available from the Edmonton Natural History Club (renamed Edmonton Nature Club), through the Office of the Conservation Co-ordinator, City of Edmonton and through the University of Alberta.

Foreword

I consider myself most fortunate. As the son of one of the last of the Hudson's Bay fur traders I have lived in some of the most beautiful areas Canada has to offer. My dad's postings took our family from Fort Resolution and then Fort Smith in the North West Territories through a number of small settlements in northern British Columbia and finally to Fort Vermilion, a small town in northern Alberta where I lived until I was 16 years old. Living in small towns in remote areas as a young boy was a true learning experience that taught me to not only appreciate and value our pristine environment and natural wilderness, but to preserve it so that those who follow in our footsteps may enjoy its beauty just as we have.

As Albertans, our ability to enjoy our province's beautiful natural wilderness is not limited to small towns in northern Alberta. Anyone who has ever lived in Edmonton knows what I am talking about. Our river valley, which is considered one of the largest urban forests in North America, is a jewel to be cherished. It, together with the many other wilderness areas within our city's region, are fundamental to the quality of life we enjoy in our city.

Coyotes Still Sing in My Valley, using Edmonton as a backdrop, is a superb compilation of essays that speak to the importance of conservation of our environment particularly urban settings and the natural areas within them. The book includes many illustrations highlighting this area's biodiversity, landscape and wilderness that will leave readers with a new found appreciation for all that we have as Edmontonians and Albertans.

I have always said that scratch any Albertan and underneath you will find an environmentalist. By that I mean you will find a person who is concerned about the air they breathe, the water they drink and the land they walk. This book will appeal to everyone interested in the environment and its sustainability especially in this time of unprecedented growth in Alberta.

I commend Dr. Ross W. Wein for his dedication and tireless work in putting this book together. *Coyotes Still Sing in My Valley* is a wonderful way to commemorate Alberta's Centennial and, more importantly, to pass on important messages about our environment and our duty to preserve and protect it for future generations.

Dave Hancock, Q.C.

Contents

Contributors

Abma, Geoff S., Faculty of Environmental Design, University of
Calgary, 2500 University Drive NW, Calgary, AB T2N 1N4
Email: geoff.abma@gbj-eidos.com

Adshead, Karin, The Earth Challenge Project, 9829-74 Ave.,
Edmonton, AB T6E 1G1
Email: karin.adshead@earthchallenge.com

Amell, Bernard, Calgary, AB
Email: bamell@home.ca

Butler, Jim, University of Alberta, Edmonton, AB T6G 2H3
Email: butleruofa@aol.com

Carbyn, Lu, Clifford E. Lee Nature Sanctuary, 51306 Range Road
264, Spruce Grove, AB T7Y 1E7
Email: lu.carbyn@ec.gc.ca

Chapman, Ross, Elk Island National Park, Site 4, RR#1,
Fort Saskatchewan, AB T8L 2N7
Email: ross.chapman@pc.gc.ca

Cotterill, Patsy, Edmonton Natural History Club, 7401 – 156 St.,
Edmonton, AB, T5R 1X4
Email: nutmeg@planet.eon.net

Ewaschuk, Ernie, Land Stewardship Centre of Canada,
17503 – 45 Ave., Edmonton, AB T6M 2N3
Email: ernie@landstewardship.org

Girvan, Locke, Strathcona County, 2001 Sherwood Dr., Sherwood
Park, AB T8A 3W7
Email: girvan@strathcona.ab.ca

Horstman, Louise, Big Lake Environmental Support Society,
P.O. Box 65053, St. Albert, AB T8N 5Y3
Email: pecaninc@compusmart.ab.ca

Johnson, J. Derek, Canadian Forest Service, 5320 – 122 St.
Edmonton, AB T6H 3S5
Email: dejohnso@nrcan.gc.ca

Mandryk, Adele M., Department of Renewable Resources,
University of Alberta, Edmonton, AB T6G 2H1
Email: amandryk@ualberta.ca

Martell, Kathryn, Department of Renewable Resources,
University of Alberta, Edmonton, AB T6G 2H1
Email: katemartell@wildmail.com

Noble, Elizabeth, Learning Network, Faculty of Education,
University of Alberta, Edmonton, AB T6G 2E3
Email: elizabeth@ereb.com

Neupane, Anish, Department of Rural Economy, University of
Alberta, Edmonton, AB T6G 2H1
Email: aneupane@ualberta.ca

Priebe, Bob, Northeast Planning and Development, Natural Areas
Planning Co-ordination, Parks Development Branch, Edmonton
Community Services, City of Edmonton, Revillon Building,
Edmonton, AB T5J 2R7
Email: priebe@strathcona.ab.ca

Pyszcyzk, Heinz W., Heritage Resource Management Branch, Alberta Community Development, Old St. Stephen's College, 8820 – 112 St. Edmonton, AB T6G 2P8
Email: heinz.pyszczyk@gov.ab.ca

Reine, Marg, Clifford E. Lee Nature Sanctuary, 51306 Range Road 264, Spruce Grove, AB T7Y 1E7
Email: mreine@telusplanet.net

Salomons, M. J., Department of Renewable Resources, University of Alberta, Edmonton, AB T6G 2H1
Email: mikeandmaguy@gmail.com

Swinnerton, Guy, Faculty of Physical Education and Recreation, University of Alberta, Edmonton, AB T6G 2H9
Email: guy.swinnerton@ualberta.ca

Tomiyama, Kimberley, King's University College, Edmonton, AB T6B 1A6
Email: sunflowergirlofgod@yahoo.com

Truscott, Jeff, Banff National Park, Banff, AB T1L 1K2
Email: jeff.truscott@pc.gc.ca

Wein, Ross W., Department of Renewable Resources, University of Alberta, Edmonton, AB T6G 2H1
Email: rosswein@shaw.ca

Westworth, Dave, Westworth Associates Environmental Ltd., #140, 9405 – 50 St., Edmonton, AB T6B 2T4
Email: westworth@compusmart.ab.ca

Wood, John R., King's University College, Edmonton, AB T6B 2H3
Email: john.wood@kingsu.ca

Celebration of the
Natural Environment

Setting the Stage

Ross W. Wein, University of Alberta

Urban planning has long been an important discipline and a profession that is changing rapidly as it continues to enhance the lifestyles of urbanites (Ravetz 2000, Macionis and Parillo 2001). There is increasing emphasis that culture and conservation are closely linked (Kaplan *et al.* 1998, Green and Vos 2001). Canadian city planning has been synthesized in books, such as Bunting and Filion (1991), Hodge (1998) and Roseland (1998). With the increasing interest in applying the principles of landscape ecology (Forman 1995) to cities, the field of greenways studies has emerged (Fabos and Ahern 1995, Flink and Searns 1993). Conservation in the old cities of Europe has been part of cultural landscape studies (von Droste, Plachter and Rössler 1995). Wildlife of cities has always been the most high profile aspect of biodiversity protection (e.g. Adams 1994, Traut and Hostetler 2003, Tigas, Van Vuren and Sauvajot 2002, Fernandez-Juricic and Jokimaki 2001, Grinder and Krausman 2001, Lawton and Wiken 2000). Concurrently, there has been increasing emphasis on cities as ecological systems (White 2002, Berkowitz 2002, Arendt *et al.* 2001, Sabloff 2001, Beatley 2000,

Hough 1995, Arendt and Harper 1996, Arendt 1999, Gilbert 1991, Gordon 1990, Sukopp, Hejny and Kowarik 1990, Nicholas-Lord 1987) with resource extraction footprints that extend to far corners of the world (Wackernagel and Rees 1996).

With this wealth of background information it should be possible to incorporate protected areas in urban development to maintain and enhance the quality of life for our citizens.

Cities in Canada have been receiving media attention over the past few years because there is an increasing need for the upgrading of infrastructure at the same time as cities are expanding so rapidly that urban sprawl is an issue. The Canadian government has been exploring urban development issues with increasing vigour (Sgro 2002). In September, 2003 an international conference entitled "Strategies for urban sustainability" was held in Edmonton to explore the needs of cities in Canada. Quality of life issues related to protected areas underlie these efforts because many citizens appreciate protected areas.

Alberta cities are some of the fastest growing cities in Canada and with this comes the difficulty of efficient long-term planning. Our cities have special features that require special planning. We are winter cities and we celebrated this through the hosting of the 1998 Winter Olympics (Calgary) and the 1998 Winter Cities Conference (Edmonton).

Development of Edmonton has been rapid. In our rush for development some citizens are concerned that we have ignored protected areas. They point to the lack of emphasis on conservation and protected areas in such reports such as the City of Edmonton's "Plan Edmonton" (The City of Edmonton 1998). Others point out that there is evidence of increasing interest in protected areas. Recently, a review of special protected areas has been published (Westworth Associates Environmental Ltd. 2001) and even more recently a Conservation Co-ordinator Office has been established by the City of Edmonton. The North Saskatchewan River is being nominated as a Heritage River; the nomination developed, in part, out of a book published by the North Saskatchewan Watershed Alliance (Milholland 2002). Recently, the City has published a "State of the Environment" report (Anonymous 2003). These activities are indications that citizens are more aware of the quality of life of their city.

It should be noted that parks were seen as important components of city boosterism in Canada in the latter part of the 19th and early 20th centuries (Markham 1988). These protected areas, along with other conservation areas provided opportunities for recreation and were symbols of civic pride and quality of life (McNeely 2001).

Protected areas today reflect our historical activities. If you canoe the North Saskatchewan River, you may still see evidence of mining for gold, coal, and clay. If you walk through the forests of the valley sides you may find old foundations of farm buildings. If you dig into the soil in the right place you will certainly find evidence of brickyards and even sawmills. We celebrate our history of exploitation for furs in the reconstructed Old Fort Edmonton. The Royal Alberta Museum holds a wealth of prehistoric and historic information and displays. While we recognize the valuable efforts by natural history groups such as the John Janzen Nature Centre and others, some citizens believe that much more could be done to celebrate our natural ecosystems. A celebration of the Aboriginal cultures that depended on the original ecosystems is more difficult to find.

Our ecosystems are still influenced by the physical environment of geology (Godfrey 1993), soils (Bowser, Kjearsgaard, Peters and Wells 1962), and climate (Wheaton 1998). Edmonton is a winter city (Halfpenny and Ozanne 1989) and we celebrated this through the hosting of the 1998 Winter Cities Conference. A wide range of transportation, energy conservation, and people issues are discussed at these Winter Cities biennial conferences, including winter sports (Pressman 1995, 1999). However, protected areas in winter have been almost ignored; this topic deserves exploration and celebration.

Our city and surrounding landscape have been described as aspen parkland that lies between the Grassland Natural Region (Anonymous 1997) to the south and the Boreal Forest Natural Region (Anonymous 1998) to the north. We are a river city and the North Saskatchewan River, the valley, and the ravines give character to our city and connects us to the Rocky Mountains, the origin of much of the water that supports the Greater Edmonton region. The valley provides the connectivity for biodiversity protection and also provides recreation, education, and health support for our citizens.

References

Adams, L W. 1994. In our own backyard - conserving urban wildlife. Journal of Forestry 92 (10): 24-25.

Anonymous. 2003. Edmonton's environment: a snapshot 2002. Office of the Environment, City of Edmonton, Edmonton, AB. 82 pp.

Anonymous. 1998. The boreal forest natural region of Alberta. Alberta Environmental Protection, Edmonton, AB. 312 pp. plus maps.

Anonymous. 1997. The grassland natural region of Alberta. Alberta Environmental Protection, Edmonton, AB. 229 pp. plus maps.

Arendt, R G. 1999. Growing greener – putting conservation into local plans and ordinances. Island Press, Washington, DC. 261 pp.

Arendt, R G and H Harper. 1996. Conservation design for subdivisions: a practical guide to creating open space networks. Island Press, Washington, DC. 203 pp.

Arendt, R G, M Clarke, A Hutchinson and K Foster. 2001. Growing greener ordinance language visually enhanced zoning and subdivision models. Island Press, Washington, DC.

Beatley, T. 2000. Green urbanism: learning from European cities. Island Press, Washington, DC. 308 pp.

Berkowitz, A R, C H Nilon and K S Hollweg (eds.). 2003. Understanding urban ecosystems: a new frontier for science and education. Springer-Verlag, New York, NY. 523 pp.

Bowser, W E, A A Kjearsgaard, T W Peters, and R E Wells. 1962. Soil Survey of Edmonton Sheet (83-H). University of Alberta Bulletin No. SS-4 and Alberta Soil Survey Report No. 21. 36 pp plus map.

Bunting, T and P Filion (eds.). 1991. Canadian cities in transition. Oxford University Press, Toronto, ON. 555 pp.

City of Edmonton. 1998. Plan Edmonton: Edmonton's municipal development plan. (Bylaw No. 11777 (as amended)). 97 pp.

Fabos, J Gy and J Ahern (eds.). 1995. Greenways: the beginning of an international movement. Elsevier, New York, NY. 491 pp.

Fernandez-Juricic, E and J Jokimaki. 2001. A habitat island approach to conserving birds in urban landscapes: case studies from southern and northern Europe. Biodiversity Conservation 10 (12): 2023-2043.

Flink, C A and R M Searns. 1993. Greenways: a guide to planning, design, and development. Edited by L LaB Schwarz. Island Press, Washington, DC. 375 pp.

Forman, R T T. 1995. Land mosaics: the ecology of landscapes and regions. Cambridge Univ. Press, NY. 632 pp.

Gilbert, O L. 1991. The ecology of urban habitats. Chapman and Hall, London. 369 pp.

Godfrey, J D. 1993. Edmonton beneath our feet. Edmonton Geological Society, Edmonton, AB. 150 pp.

Gordon, D. (ed.). 1990. Green cities: ecologically sound approaches to urban space. Black Rose Books, Montreal, PQ. 299 pp.

Green, B and Vos, W. (eds.). 2001. Threatened landscapes: conserving cultural environments. London: Spon Press. 184 pp.

Grinder M I and P R Krausman. 2001. Home range, habitat use, and nocturnal activity of coyotes in an urban environment. Journal of Wildlife Management 65 (4): 887-898.

Halfpenny, J C and R D Ozanne. 1989. Winter: an ecological handbook. Johnson Publishing Company, Boulder, CO. 273 pp.

Hodge, G. 1998. Planning Canadian communities – an introduction to the principles, practice, and participants. 3rd edn. International Thomson Publishing, Toronto, ON. 470 pp.

Hough, M. 1995. Cities and natural process. Routledge, NY. 326 pp.

Kaplan, R, S Kaplan, and R L Ryan. 1998. With people in mind: design and management of everyday nature. Island Press, Washington, DC. 239 pp.

Lawton K and E B Wiken. 2000. Understanding wildlife habitats in urban areas. Forestry Chronicle 76 (2): 259-262.

Macionis, J J and V N Parillo. 2001. Cities and urban life. 2nd ed. Prentice Hall, Upper Saddle River, NJ. 474 pp.

Markham, S E. 1988. The development of parks and playgrounds in selected Canadian prairie cities: 1880-1930. Unpublished PhD Thesis. Department of Recreation and Leisure Studies. University of Alberta, Edmonton, AB.

McNeely, J A. 2001. Editorial. Cities and protected areas: an oxymoron or a partnership. Parks 11(3), 1-3.

Milholland, B. 2002. North Saskatchewan River guide: mountain to prairie a living landscape. North Saskatchewan Watershed Alliance, Edmonton, AB. Text and maps. unpaged.

Nicholas-Lord, D. 1987. The greening of cities. Routledge and Kegan Paul, London. 270 pp.

Pressman, N. 1995. Northern cityscape: linking design to climate. Livable Winter Cities Association, Yellowknife, NWT. 244 pp.

Pressman, N. 1999. Living in harmony with winter. Winter Cities Forum, Prince George, BC.

Ravetz, J. 2000. City Region 2020. Earthscan Publications, UK. 307 pp.

Roseland, M. 1998. Toward sustainable communities: resources for citizens and their governments. New Society Publishers, Gabriola Island, BC. 241 pp.

Sabloff, A. 2001. Recording the natural world: humans and animals in the city. University of Toronto Press, Toronto, ON. 252 pp.

Sgro, J. (Chair). 2002. Canada's urban strategy: a blueprint for action. Prime Minister's task force on urban issues. Ottawa, ON. 35 pp.

Sukopp, H and S Hejny (eds.). and I. Kowarik (co-editor). 1990. Urban ecology: plants and plant communities in urban environments. SPB Academic Publishing bv, The Hague, The Netherlands. 282 pp.

Tigas, L A, D H Van Vuren, and R M Sauvajot. 2002. Behavioral responses of bobcats and coyotes to habitat fragmentation and corridors in an urban environment. Biological Conservation 108(3): 299-306.

Traut, A H, and M E Hostetler. 2003. Urban lakes and waterbirds: effects of development on avian behavior. Waterbirds 26(3): 290-302.

Von Droste, B, H Plachter and M Rössler (eds.). 1995. Cultural landscapes of universal value – components of a global strategy. Gustav Fischer Verlag, New York, NY. 464 pp.

Wackernagel, M and W Rees. 1996. Our ecological footprint: reducing human impact on the earth. New Society Publishers, Gabriola Island, BC. 160 pp.

Westworth Associates Environmental Ltd. 2001. Conserving Edmonton's natural areas: a framework for conservation planning in an urban landscape. Community Services, City of Edmonton, AB. 174 pp.

Wheaton, E E. 1998. But it's a dry cold: weathering the Canadian prairies. Fifth House Ltd., Calgary, AB. 185 pp.

White, R R. 2002. Building the ecological city. Woodhead Publishing, Cambridge. 238 pp.

The City of Edmonton, located in the Province of Alberta in Western Canada, is about 700 km² in size. The region has about one million citizens. The city map shows the main access roads, the 70 km² ribbon of green along the North Saskatchewan River, the main waterways, and the location of natural areas (dots). (City map prepared by Dale Lewis, City of Edmonton.)

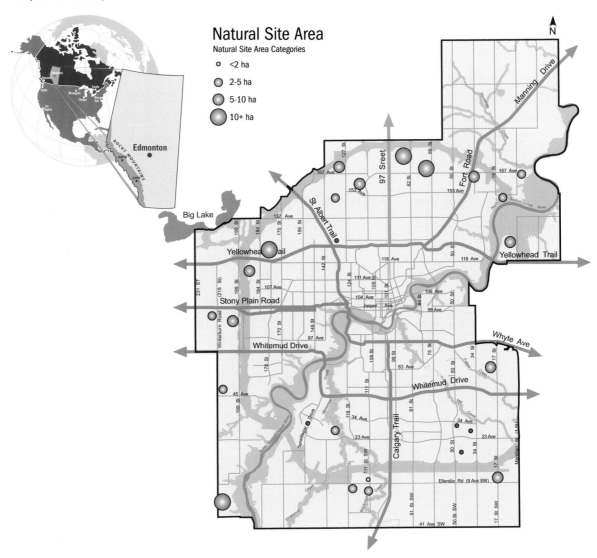

A land cover classification image developed by Jeff Truscott from satellite data (year 2000) for the City of Edmonton and surrounding landscapes. The area covered is about 22 x 32 km. Notable features include the central downtown core, the high cover of trees (spruce/aspen) in the older neighbourhoods and along the North Saskatchewan River and associated ravines, and the regional agricultural land (agriculture/grass/pasture).

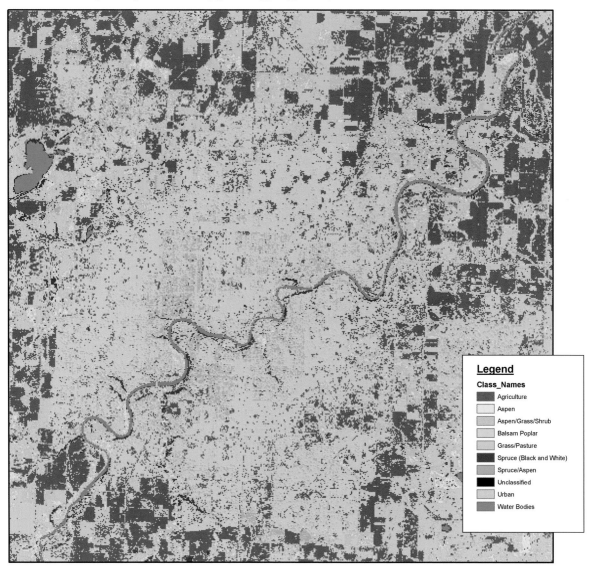

Legend

Class_Names

- Agriculture
- Aspen
- Aspen/Grass/Shrub
- Balsam Poplar
- Grass/Pasture
- Spruce (Black and White)
- Spruce/Aspen
- Unclassified
- Urban
- Water Bodies

Our Conservation Legacy in Edmonton

Ross W. Wein, University of Alberta

Prehistory

The glacial legacy around Edmonton is obvious in sand dunes, gravel and sand deposits, and glacial drainage channels (Godfrey 1993). Life did not return to our region until the one kilometre thick sheet of ice began to retreat about 12,000 BP (years Before Present). There are clues about post-glacial climatic fluctuations and what types of plants and animals first inhabited the region in the well-preserved pollen record from lakes and bogs (see review paper by Campbell and Campbell 2000). The early presence of animals and plants made it possible for humans to inhabit the region at 10,000 to 11,000 BP; hundreds of archaeological sites indicate that Aboriginal people used the resources of the North Saskatchewan River Valley (and probably modified the Valley to some extent) over thousands of years. The major ecosystems began to resemble those seen today at about 6000 years ago (Godfrey 1993, Strong and Leggat 1992). More recent and more precise analysis of sediments provide evidence for significant climate changes, including a rapidly moistening period about 2000 BP and the Medieval Warm Period at about 1000 BP (Campbell 1998).

Godfrey, J D. 1993. Edmonton beneath our feet. Edmonton Geological Society, Edmonton, AB. 150 pp.

Campbell, I D and C Campbell. 2000. Late Holocene vegetation and fire history at the southern boreal forest margin in Alberta, Canada. Paleogeography, Palaeoclimatology, Palaeoecology 164: 263-280.

Strong, W L and K R Leggat. 1992. Ecoregions of Alberta. Alberta Forest Lands and Wildlife, Edmonton, AB. 59 pp. plus map.

Campbell, C. 1998. Late Holocene lake sedimentology and climate change in southern Alberta, Canada. Quaternary Research 49: 96-101.

Although there is a tendency to picture the landscapes of Edmonton as covered by pristine forests, the reality is that landscapes of the North Saskatchewan River Valley were always dynamic. The dynamics included the impacts of droughts and fires, floods and erosion, buffalo herds and human populations.

The Early History Period

There are literary sources of information about landscapes and vegetation during the late 1700s to 1900 AD. Lake sediment records (Campbell 1998) show that the significant climate change to the cool and moist Little Ice Age at 350 to 300 years BP (Before Present) would have strongly influenced Aboriginal people. The subsequent climatic warming has continued to the present. Henday's 1754-55 journal provides insight into the landscape conditions (Burpee 1973). Generally there has been a change in the vegetation from grassland and shrubland to aspen; important forces causing vegetation changes were the extirpation of the large herds of bison (in the 1870s to 1880s) and fires in the spruce and aspen vegetation (as noted on his way through the Edmonton area on September 26, 1846 by Paul Kane 1968, pp. 93-94). With the expansion of the European fur trading industry, increasing quantities of lumber and fuel wood were required by the forts.

As human populations increased, Metis and European farmers increasingly modified the original vegetation. Trees were harvested and domestic stock grazed in the valley, while the flood plains and the tablelands were cultivated. Commercial mining for coal was begun with the first settlers. In general, there was little thought by early settlers to conservation as we know it today.

Burpee, L J (editor) 1973. The Journal of Anthony Henday, 1754-55: York Factory to the Blackfeet Country. Canadiana House, Toronto. 51 pp. Reprint of 1907 edition.

Kane, P. 1968. Wanderings of an artist among the Indians of North America. M.G. Hurtig Ltd., Edmonton, AB. 329 pp. (first published 1859 by Longman, Brown, Green, Longmans and Roberts)

Fort Edmonton, 1879: Virtually all of the landscapes along the North Saskatchewan River are young, post-fire *Populus spp.* (Source: City of Edmonton Archives, EA10-71).

Coal mining provided domestic and industrial energy well into the 1950s. Coal seams exposed on the eroded river bank were tunnel mined (Source: Provincial Archives, #B1548).

Gold fever extended to the dredging of the North Saskatchewan River gravels (Source: Provincial Archives, #B5595, dated 1898).

Jim Little's Brickyard, Victoria Park. Clay brick production for commercial buildings and some houses used local clay and wood or coal for firing (Source: Provincial Archives, #B1343, dated 1903).

Log boom on the North Saskatchewan River with a sawmill on the north facing bank terrace. Note evidence of massive soil movement on the south facing bank. Large quantities of wood were required for fuel and construction materials of the developing city (Source: Provincial Archives #B9180).

Agriculture, and particularly cereal grain production, rapidly changed the land around Edmonton in the late 1800s and early 1900s (Source: Ernest Brown, Photo #157, Provincial Archives #B9017).

Garden produce from the fertile soils of the lower North Saskatchewan River terraces was important for the rapidly growing population (Source: Provincial Archives, #A1389, dated 1917).

The Industrial Period

Our city is a young city, developing quickly from a fur trading post to an agriculture-based city, to an industrial city especially after World War II. Many of the books celebrating Edmonton emphasize the historical development (Anonymous 1976, Bedford 1976, Chan-Marples 1981, Esdale and McDermid 1914, Gilpin 1984, Hesketh and Swyripa 1995, MacGregor 1967). Even early in the century there was a great need for river valley resources to build the city. Wood, first cut locally and then progressively farther up the North Saskatchewan, was needed for fuel, wooden homes and sidewalks. Energy was mined from local coal seams for brick making and many other forms of heating. Meat, milk, and eggs came indirectly from cultivated flat land and grazed valley sides Gravel pits were common in the fragmented valley and agriculture was the dominant use of the landscapes. Photographs of this era show only a few young aspen trees in the valley (e.g. Esdale and McDermid 1914).

By the 1920s, Edmonton became an increasingly strong vacuum into which resources flowed from increasing distances. Housing, roads, railways and bridges were being built, but in contrast to many other cities, the massive earth flows in the valley restricted building on the valley slopes. Resource extraction and the building of suburbs shifted to the tablelands. Valley ecosystems began to re-establish, except in transportation corridors, gravel pits, dumps, sewage plants, golf courses and other low intensity development areas, including parks.

The North Saskatchewan River always ran wild with floods and ice-jams in the spring. Some modification occurred as the river was used for transportation, log drives and gravel dredging for gold early in the 20th century. Dams have been constructed on the river and water usage for agriculture irrigation and city water continues to increase. This is our legacy of biodiversity protection.

Anonymous. 1976. Edmonton: the way it was. The Fort Edmonton Historical Foundation, Edmonton, AB. Unpaged.

Bedford, E. 1976. An historical geography of settlement in the North Saskatchewan River Valley, Edmonton. University of Alberta Press, Edmonton, AB. 201 pp.

Chan-Marples, L. 1981. North Saskatchewan River valley communities: historical study. Edmonton Parks and Recreation, Edmonton, AB. (various paging)

Esdale, M and F G McDermid. 1914. Edmonton: Alberta's capital city. The Esdale Press Ltd., and McDermid Engraving Co. Ltd., Edmonton, AB. 180 pp.

Gilpin, J F. 1984. Edmonton: Gateway to the North: an illustrated history. Windsor Publ. Ltd., Edmonton, AB. 319 pp.

Hesketh, B and F Swyripa (eds.). 1995. Edmonton: The Life of a City. NeWest Publishers Ltd., Edmonton, AB. 336 pp.

MacGregor, J G. 1967. Edmonton: a history. M G Hurtig Publishers, Edmonton, AB. 326 pp.

In areas that were left undisturbed, the ecosystems began to recover. In 1907, protection of the river valley was proposed by Frederick C. Todd, a Montreal landscape architect and then in 1915 the Province of Alberta adopted a report prepared by Frederick C. Todd which established policy for the protection of the valley and ravines for recreation purposes. Another important year was 1933, when a zoning bylaw was prepared by the city which regulated land-use by preserving river valley lands as parkland.

From 1970s onward

It was during this period that the municipal government defined the limit of the river valley and ravine system as a protected area and a number of plans were prepared and implemented. There has been an acceleration of conservation and this is the topic of our celebrations.

Benchmark dates for conservation since 1970 in Edmonton include the following: (Note: This list was initially developed by Grant Pearsell).

1970	Edmonton City Council adopts a 'top of the bank' policy which defines the limit of the river valley and ravine system, introduces principles governing development in proximity to the valley and prescribes regulation for development permits/zoning certificates in areas adjacent to the limit of the valley and ravine system.
1970	The *Edmonton Parks Master Plan* (1970-1980) sets forth policies for long-term purchase of river valley lands for parks and environmental protection.
1971	The *General Municipal Plan* provides river valley policy objectives with respect to environmental protection and designates lands for long range acquisition for future park use.
1972	*Edmonton Regional Plan* designates large portions of the river valley as 'Metropolitan Recreation' land.

18

1975	Edmonton City Council directs the City Planning Department to prepare a *'Development Scheme Bylaw'* and adopts the main objectives identified in the *River Valley Study* (1974).
1976	The Province of Alberta begins passing Orders-in-Council applying Restricted Development Area legislation to most of the river valley from Devon to Fort Saskatchewan.
1980	The City of Edmonton's *General Municipal Plan* reaffirms principles, guidelines and policies for the preservation of the river valley.
1982	The City of Edmonton doubles in size to 700 km² by annexing surrounding lands which include a variety of naturally vegetated and relatively undisturbed sites.
1983	Edmonton City Council directs the administration to prepare a revised *North Saskatchewan River Valley Area Redevelopment Plan.*
1985	Edmonton City Council approves the *North Saskatchewan River Valley Area Redevelopment Plan Bylaw* which establishes the major portion of the system as an environmental protection area and for use as an urban and natural park. This plan initiates a process for more effective future management of the river valley and ravine system.
1986	A report entitled *Urban Natural History Interpretive Sites in and Adjacent to Edmonton* is prepared for the City of Edmonton's Parks and Recreation Department by David Ealey. This report identifies 1049 natural areas within and adjacent to Edmonton.
1992	The City of Edmonton's Planning and Development Department produces a report entitled *Environmentally Sensitive and Natural Areas Protection Within Edmonton's Table Lands: Policy and Implementation Background Study* which proposes that Edmonton's natural area sites be identified and classified as the basis for future recognition and protection.
1992	The *Ribbon of Green: North Saskatchewan River Valley and Ravine System Master Plan* is completed. This document provides the planning framework for open space development in the river valley into the year 2000.
1993	In response to the identified need for identification and classification of natural sites an *Inventory of Environmentally Sensitive and Significant Natural Areas* is prepared by Geowest Environmental Consultants and others for the City of

Westworth Associates Environmental Ltd. 2001. Conserving Edmonton's natural areas: a framework for conservation planning in an urban landscape. Community Services, City of Edmonton, AB. 174 pp.

Edmonton. This document provides an updated inventory of natural areas, identifies environmentally sensitive and significant natural areas in the North Saskatchewan River Valley and Ravine System, and classifies sites based on their relative significance.

1995   Edmonton City Council adopts *Policy C-467 Conservation of Natural Sites in Edmonton's Table Lands* which states that the City of Edmonton will encourage the conservation and integration of as many environmentally sensitive and significant natural areas into Edmonton's future urban development as are sustainable and feasible.

1998   Strategic priorities identified in *Plan Edmonton: Edmonton's Municipal Development Plan* were to preserve and enhance the river valley, natural areas, and open spaces and to recognize the importance of linkages within the urban fabric.

1999   Geowest Environmental Consultants prepares the document *Natural Areas in Edmonton: Assessment of Conservation Value and Potential* at the request of the City of Edmonton. The document assesses and prioritizes the existing natural areas within the City's municipal boundaries for future conservation action.

2001   A report entitled *Conserving Edmonton's Natural Areas: A Framework for Conservation Planning in an Urban Landscape* is prepared by Westworth Associates Environmental Ltd. and others to help develop more effective strategies for conserving natural areas and recommends a short list of sites on which to focus conservation efforts. On September 11, 2001, Council approves a number of key recommendations in the report.

2001   The City of Edmonton purchases a 20 ha piece of land containing a large portion of Significant Natural Area NW 384 using the Natural Areas Reserve Fund. This transaction represents the first purchase of land by the City for the purpose of conservation outside of the North Saskatchewan River Valley and Ravine System.

2002   The City of Edmonton appoints a Conservation Co-ordinator to facilitate implementation of Policy C-467.

2003   The Natural Areas Implementation Committee and the Natural Areas Advisory Committee are initiated.

Aboriginal Land-Use of the Greater Edmonton Area

Heinz W. Pyszczyk, Management Branch, Alberta Community Development

Ross W. Wein, Renewable Resources, University of Alberta

Elizabeth Noble, Learning Network, Faculty of Education, University of Alberta

Abstract

In this paper we review archaeological and other evidence of Aboriginal land-use of the Greater Edmonton area. Much of that evidence now lies hidden beneath the urban landscape and often evidence only emerges when we build new roads, neighborhoods or industrial facilities. Over the last 25 to 30 years archaeologists have found and documented hundreds of Aboriginal archaeological sites in the area. Those archaeological sites and their contents indicate that Aboriginal people used the area for well over 5000 years. They hunted, fished, and gathered the raw resources necessary for their livelihood – a pattern of land-use that continued with the introduction of the fur trade and establishment of the first European forts. We consider the identity of these historic Aboriginal groups and whether this long, consistent pattern of

Aboriginal land-use encouraged the first Euro-Canadian traders to build their forts in the region. Aboriginal land-use continues today and we encourage readers to visit these areas.

Otinow – "A Place Where Everyone Came"
(Wilson Gotchew, 2001 EUB Hearings, Edmonton)

No one knows when Cree people first gave the Edmonton area its name. It could have been the beginning of the fur trade when many people came to the first *Forte des Prairies* to trade; or it had its roots at a much earlier time (for the Blackfoot it was *Aakowis* or the "the big House" (Holmgren and Holmgren 1976: 87). However, the rich archaeological record of the Edmonton area suggests that there was an Aboriginal presence here for many millennia, long before Europeans realized that the world was round or that other peoples lived in distant lands.

This study summarizes what is known about Aboriginal history and land-use in the Greater Edmonton area, an area bounded by the present communities of Redwater and Morinville in the north, and Calmar and New Sarepta in the south (Figure 1). Even though that archaeological record is still incomplete and often deficient in certain types of information, it reflects where the people camped, how they used the available raw resources, and for how long they had done so. This study compares the intensity of Aboriginal land-use of the Greater Edmonton area to other areas along the North Saskatchewan River. We also consider how this pattern of Aboriginal land-use affected decisions by early Europeans to first settle here and trade with Aboriginal people.

Holmgren, E J and P M Holmgren. 1976. Over 2000 place names of Alberta. Modern Press, Saskatoon, SK. 301 pp.

Figure 1

The study area and number/distribution of archaeological sites according to Sub-Borden Block (each 11.5 km x 18.5 km).

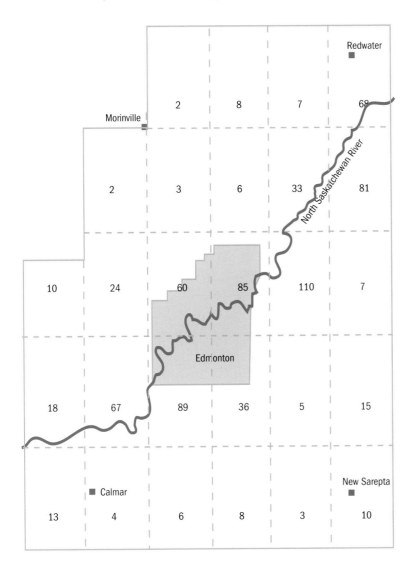

Helgason, G. 1987. The first Albertans, an archaeological search. Lone Pine Publishing, Edmonton, AB. 222 pp.

Vickers, R J. 1986. Alberta Plains prehistory: a review. Archaeological Survey of Alberta, Occasional Paper No. 27. Alberta Culture. Edmonton, AB.

Godfrey, J D. 1993. Edmonton beneath our feet. Edmonton Geological Society. Edmonton, AB. 150 pp.

A New Land Emerges

The migration of humans into the New World, and eventually to Alberta, is a complex and highly controversial issue (Helgason 1987, Vickers 1986). The earliest peoples likely came over the Bering Land Bridge that connected Asia and the Americas when sea levels had dropped. They continually moved southward as the large glaciers melted and receded from the land (beginning around 14,000 years ago). It is unknown whether these people traveled along the west coast of North America or along an ice-free corridor, running along the foothills of Alberta, between the large ice fields. Some archaeologists believe that the first Americans arrived long before the last major glaciation of the Americas, sometime before 25,000 years ago. Eventually, however, Aboriginal people would reach and settle the Edmonton region, but not before the ice melted and the land emerged from beneath it (Godfrey 1993, Vickers 1986: 20-24).

During a very short period of geological time the landscape and climate of the Greater Edmonton area underwent a remarkable transformation (Table 1). The disappearance of the almost one kilometre thick sheet of ice would influence where future Aboriginal people lived on the land and how they used the available resources. By 12,000 years, after the ice had melted, a large glacial lake covered the Edmonton area; later it would rapidly drain through a channel to the south (Godfrey 1993). By about 11,000 years ago major drainage channels (North Saskatchewan River, Whitemud, Blackmud, Mill Creek, and Sturgeon River) began to form, rapidly cutting through the unconsolidated sediments. Some drainage channels, such as the North Saskatchewan River, rapidly cut down to their present depth probably by 8,000 to 9,000 years ago.

24

Table 1

Some important natural and human events that influenced Aboriginal life in the Edmonton region. (from Campbell 1998; Godfrey 1993; Pyszczyk 1996; Helgason 1987; Vickers 1986).

13,000 BP	Glaciers of the last ice age (Wisconsin) begin to retreat.
12,000 BP	Edmonton area under water from Glacial Lake Edmonton.
11,000 BP	Edmonton is ice-free. Current landscape and vegetation begin to form.
6,800 BP	Mount Mazama in Oregon exploded leaving Edmonton covered in a layer of ash.
11,000 to 4,000 BP	Very warm climatic conditions in Alberta.
2000 BP –	Bow and arrow becomes increasingly more popular and the Atlatl and dart are used less often. Climate rapidly becoming wetter.
1800 BP	The appearance of pottery on the northern plains and parklands.
1000 BP	Medieval Warm Period
350-300 BP	Little Ice Age

BP = Calendar years before present

There are clues, other than the archaeological record, about post-glacial climatic fluctuations and what types of plants first inhabited the area. The well-preserved pollen record from lakes and bogs provides information about the vegetation on the landscapes from this time period (Campbell and Campbell 2000). Older research identifies a cool spruce period from 11,000 to 8,000 BP. Animal remains of an extinct form of bison found in the North Saskatchewan River terrace sediments (near the Alberta Legislature building) have been dated to 11,345 years ago (Godfrey 1993). The early presence of bison and other animals and plants made it possible for humans to inhabit the region 10,000 – 11,000 years ago. After this period there was a dry, warm parkland period from 10,000 to 6,000 BP. Older research suggests

Campbell, I D and C Campbell. 2000. Late Holocene vegetation and fire history at the southern boreal forest margin in Alberta, Canada. Paleogeography, Palaeoclimatology, Palaeoecology 164: 263-280.

Strong, W L and K R Leggat. 1992. Eco-regions of Alberta. Alberta Forestry, Lands and Wildlife. Edmonton, AB. 59 pp. plus map.

Campbell, C. 1998. Late Holocene lake sedimentology and climate change in southern Alberta, Canada. Quaternary Research 49: 96-101.

that there was little change in the pollen record over the past few thousand years; in other words the major ecosystems began to resemble those of today (Strong and Leggat 1992). More recent and precise analysis of sediments provide evidence for significant climate changes, including a more humid period about 2,000 BP and the Medieval Warm Period at about 1,000 BP (Campbell 1998).

These climatic and geological events influenced when early Albertans arrived and how they used the land as it was transformed from a lake bottom to a terrestrial landscape with deep river and creek valleys. The creation of this new landscape allowed new opportunities for its use by Aboriginal people, perhaps in the following ways:

- it created more diverse habitats and biomass,
- it concentrated certain food resources in specific areas during certain times of the year,
- down cutting of the river valleys exposed critical resources (e.g., rocks suitable for stone tool making) that otherwise would have been difficult to find elsewhere and,
- it created micro-environmental living conditions in the river and creek valleys, on top of the glacial hills, and on the post-glacial sand dunes.

The Archaeological Evidence and Aboriginal Land-Use

In Alberta, Aboriginal human history as described by archaeologists has been divided into three major segments of time, referred to as the Early (c. 11,500 – 7,500 years ago), Middle (c. 7,500 – 1,750 years ago) and Late (c. 1,750 – 300 years ago) Prehistoric Periods (Vickers 1986:10-11).

Whenever humans exploit the resources of an area, they leave behind a physical record known as an archaeological site (a place where people camp, hunt, gather, or make their tools). There are

Figure 2

The distribution of archaeological sites, Riverbend area, neighbourhoods 4 and 5 (adapted from Whelan and Heitzmann 1980: 20).

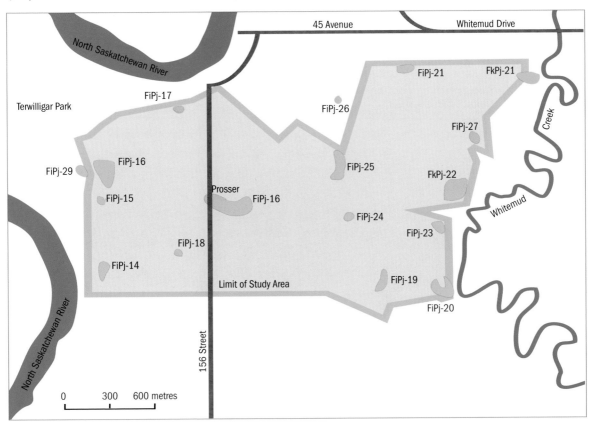

approximately 780 recorded archaeological sites in the Greater Edmonton area (Figure 1). While this large number of archaeological sites in the Greater Edmonton area seems impressive, it really is not. Only one site occurs in every 7.4 km^2. This figure will increase as we find more sites. For example, before Riverbend became a

Whelan, J P and R J Heitzmann. 1980. Historical Resources Conservation Program, Riverbend, sites FjPi-16, 20 and 22. Final Report on Permit Number 79-21, on file at the Archaeological Survey of Alberta. Edmonton, AB.

Pyszczyk, H W. 1995. Edmonton's archaeology: "History beneath the streets". Unpublished manuscript, read for Edmonton Bicentennial Conference. Edmonton, AB.

neighborhood, archaeologists (Whelan and Heitzman 1980) thoroughly searched for sites in a 3.94 square kilometer area; they found 17 archaeological sites, or one site/0.23 km² (Figure 2). Because we have not looked everywhere, many more sites likely exist but have not been found; others have already been destroyed by urban and industrial development (Pyszczyk 1995). Just to the east of the city is the 195 km² Elk Island National Park where similar surveys have identified about 225 Aboriginal sites or a density of 1.15 sites per km² (Elk Island National Park staff, 2002). Probably there are many other sites outside the city and the park in the Beaverhills-Cooking Lake moraine that have not been explored.

Unfortunately, the number of archaeological sites cannot directly measure the Aboriginal population at any given time period, for a variety of reasons (i.e. not all sites have been found, some sites have been destroyed, or used a varying number of times). However, the archaeological evidence shows that the number of dated archaeological sites in the Edmonton area increases through geologic time, as it does in other parts of Alberta. This likely means increasing population densities over 10 or 11 millennia. A comparison of archaeological site density through time of the Edmonton area to parts of southern and northern Alberta shows that the rate of increase in site density is greater than in the north but much less than in the south (Figure 3). Equally interesting is the slow, steady increase of archaeological sites over time in the Parkland, the rather abrupt increase of sites in southern Alberta at the end of the Late Prehistoric Period, and the almost imperceptible increase of archaeological sites in northern Alberta. The latter may have reached a human carrying capacity very early.

Table 2 shows that there are more archaeological sites in the Greater Edmonton area than in three other areas of equal size elsewhere along the North Saskatchewan River in Alberta. This

Figure 3

Prehistoric archaeological site density to region, Alberta (data for Bow River and Oldman River, from Ronaghan 1986: 292-293).

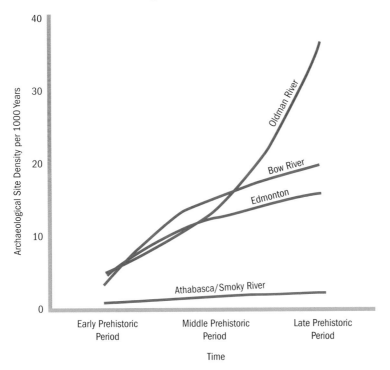

could mean that the Greater Edmonton area was more important for Aboriginal settlement than elsewhere along the river. However, it may simply mean that because of greater urban and industrial development in the Edmonton area the search has been more intensive than elsewhere along the river (the Historical Resources Act of Alberta requires that archaeologists search for archaeological sites prior to any development in an area).

Another more objective way to measure and compare regional Aboriginal land-use intensity is to look at the ratio of

Table 2

Archaeological site frequencies near and away from the North Saskatchewan River. Note: Area site frequencies are based on nine minor Borden blocks (each 11.5 km x 18.5 km), of equal size, that intersect the river.

Area	Number of Archaeological Sites	Ratio
Near River:Away from River		
1. Elk Point/Frog Lake	115	6.4:1
2. Smoky Lake Area	61	3.4:1
3. Edmonton	611	6.1:1
4. Rocky Mountain House	35	1.9:1

archaeological sites near the North Saskatchewan River as opposed to the number of sites further away in each area. This approach assumes that the number of development projects is roughly similar both close and away from the river in each area. In Table 2, we calculated the ratio of archaeological sites near to and away from the river in the same four areas. Both the Frog Lake and Edmonton areas have very high archaeological site ratios near as opposed to away from the North Saskatchewan River (Table 2). This suggests that these two areas were more important for Aboriginal land-use than other areas along the river.

The distribution of archaeological sites, and their size, is also not uniform within the Greater Edmonton area, or along other parts of the North Saskatchewan River. More archaeological sites occur near the North Saskatchewan River, or along the edges of major creeks (e.g. Whitemud and Blackmud Creeks) than in those areas away from these waterways. There are various reasons, cited earlier, for this pattern of Aboriginal land-use. The river and creek valleys attracted a diversity of animals, produced certain species of plants, and produced large concentrations of spawning fish at the mouths of creeks in the spring. Equally important to a people who relied heavily on a stone tool technology, down cutting by the rivers and creeks exposed buried glacial gravels where rocks suitable for stone tool making could be easily extracted (Pyszczyk 1985, 1996).

Elevated landforms were an important factor in Aboriginal campsite selection (good lookouts for defence and food animals, windy in the summer to avoid annoying mosquitoes). The Edmonton area contains a series of hills (kames – formed by glacial processes), strung along the south bank of the North Saskatchewan River. These are relatively high and dry, and command a good view of the surrounding area. Some of the largest, and longest occupied archaeological sites are found on these hills. Most sites on these hills contain many archaeological features (e.g. hearths) many diagnostic tools, and large quantities of fire-cracked rock; all these characteristics suggest major campsites. Today the hills blend into our urban landscape, but many are familiar to Edmontonians. The large hill near the corner of Rabbit Hill Road and Riverbend Road, Rabbit Hill, Mount Pleasant Cemetery, Calgary Trail South and Whitemud Freeway, 50th Street and Whitemud Freeway, are a few of the more familiar (Pyszczyk 1996).

The size of archaeological sites is another measure of land-use intensity by a people; large sites were formed where many people camped together, or a group of people used a site over and over for long periods of time. In the Greater Edmonton area there are a number of very large (some over 1 km long) archaeological sites. The Prosser Site (on the corner of Riverbend Road and Rabbit Hill Road) and the Strathcona Science Park site (across the river from Rundle Park) were occupied repeatedly, spanning a period of thousands of years (e.g. see Heitzmann and Priegert 1980; Newton and Pollock 1985; Ives 1985; Pyszczyk 1985). Furthermore, as Figure 4 shows, the largest and most often reoccupied

Pyszczyk, H W. 1985. Archaeological investigations at the Strathcona Science Park Site (FjPi-29). Archaeological Survey of Alberta, Manuscript Series No. 4. Alberta Culture.

Pyszczyk, H W. 1996. Archaeology guide and tour of Greater Edmonton Area. The Provincial Museum of Alberta, Edmonton, and Strathcona Archaeological Society, Edmonton, AB. 57 pp.

Figure 4

The relationship between archaeological occupation length/size and distance from the North Saskatchewan River.

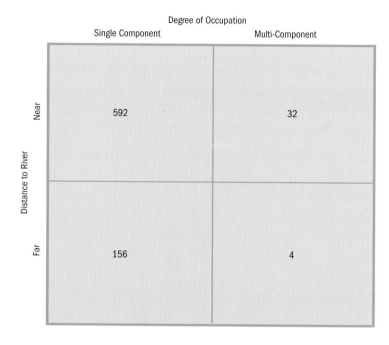

Heitzman, R J and J Priegert. 1980. The Prosser Site, FiPj-12. Archaeological Testing Program. Final Report on Permit 79-40, on file at Archaeological Survey of Alberta. Edmonton, AB.

Newton, B and J Pollock. 1985. FjPi-29, a prehistoric workshop site in the Alberta Parklands. Archaeological Survey of Alberta, Manuscript Series No. 2. Alberta Culture. Edmonton, AB.

Ives, J W. 1985. The results of mitigative excavations during the fall of 1979, Strathcona Science Park Archaeological Site (FjPi-29). Archaeological Survey of Aberta Manuscript Series 3. Alberta Culture. Edmonton, AB.

archaeological sites are more frequent near the North Saskatchewan River than further away from it in the Greater Edmonton area. Currently, we do not know whether the frequency of multi-component (reoccupied) sites is greater in the Edmonton area than elsewhere along the river.

From this archaeological evidence, a sketch of Aboriginal land-use and procurement strategies is beginning to emerge. The hunting-gathering people were very mobile exploiting resources when they became available. But, what kind of hunter-gatherers were they? Throughout the world some hunter/gathering societies used a logistical procurement strategy, as opposed to others that used a foraging strategy (Binford 1979). In a logistical procurement strategy groups moved from a relatively permanent residential camp to smaller temporary camps (occupied for more than one day) to exploit resources. Generally, in this system of land-use the people acquired rock materials (lithics) for making stone tools while carrying out their primary economic activities. Foragers on the other hand traveled from a main residential camp to exploit a specific resource and then returned to the residential camp on a daily basis; that specific resource could include lithics for stone production.

In his investigation of the Strathcona Science Park archaeological site Ives (1985: 83-88) speculated which one of these Aboriginal land-use systems might have been more prevalent in the Greater Edmonton area. We think, based on the current data, that Aboriginal people used a logistical procurement system to acquire the necessary resources because:

- many of the smaller secondary archaeological sites in the area were occupied for some time to exploit resources. This many relatively large, multicomponent (repeatedly occupied) sites would not be expected in a foraging procurement system; the latter system would have a few very large permanent residential sites and many very small specific resource extraction sites;

- many of the archaeological sites, representing temporary campsites, seem to be multi-tasking, including those where lithic raw materials were procured. In other words, if you moved to an area to hunt moose, you might when the opportunity arose, pick up some quartzite stone (the most common material for stone tool making in the area) to make stone tools. Or, simply put, stone "… quarrying locations and activities were largely expedient, and had much greater reference to other socio-economic activities" (Ives 1985: 87).

Binford, L R. 1979. Organization and formation processes: looking at curated technologies. Journal of Anthropological Research 35(3): 255-273.

It is currently not known whether this was also the procurement method used by the earliest Aboriginal people in the area. The North Saskatchewan River Valley would have been in its formative stages, supporting more biomass and biodiversity in the region than today or even 5000 years ago. However, down cutting of the river would have exposed glacial tills containing suitable materials for stone tool making very early in the process (Godfrey 1993). One simple way to examine whether early Aboriginal land-use changed over time is to compare the distribution of Early Prehistoric Period archaeological sites to those of subsequent time periods. The data in Figure 5 consists of only those sites containing diagnostic projectile points (denoting a certain time period). Such sites, for the most part, would be residential or longer occupied camps, since it is here that these articles were most often made, repaired, or discarded (Binford 1979: 263). The results indicate that the distribution of known Early Prehistoric Period archaeological sites, while fewer in numbers, is relatively similar to those of later time periods. Most sites occur near the river and on high elevations (Figure 5). The current evidence therefore suggests that there was a high degree of continuity in Aboriginal land-use over a very long period of time. Currently however, because of the poor resolution of the archaeological record, we do not know whether very earliest Aboriginal peoples also used a logistical or foraging procurement strategy (or both).

The First Europeans and the Beginning of the Fur Trade

There are more sources of independent information about landscapes, vegetation and people during this period when compared to earlier times. The archaeological record provides the human dimensions. The lake sediment and pollen record is still valid and the annual tree growth records reflect climate variation

Figure 5

The study area and distribution of known Early Prehistoric, Middle and Late Prehistoric period archaeological sites according to Sub-Borden Block.

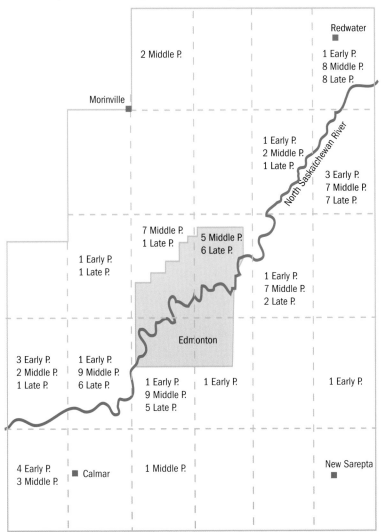

for 250 years or more. The historical records of early explorers were enhanced by Aboriginal oral history to some extent.

From lake sediment records (Campbell 1998), the significant climate change to the cool and moist Little Ice Age at 350 to 300 years BP would have strongly influenced Aboriginal people and the newly arrived Europeans. The subsequent climatic warming has continued to the present. The tree growth record over the past two hundred years could prove useful but unfortunately such work is unavailable for the Edmonton area. Fortunately there are pollen and charcoal records over the last few hundred years from ponds in Elk Island National Park (Campbell and Campbell 2000). Generally there has been a change in the vegetation from grassland and shrubland to aspen but the most important force causing vegetation change was the extirpation of the large herds of bison (in the 1870s to 1880s) and less extensive fires in the aspen vegetation.

Written records of the 1750s by early European explorers, such as Anthony Henday, allude to historic Aboriginal lifestyles (Burpee 1973). For example, throughout the winter of 1754-55 his group traveled west from the Red Deer region and then north and northeast, eventually ending up along the North Saskatchewan River very close to Edmonton in the spring (Beaudoin and Pyszczyk 1998; MacGregor 1954). By March 7, his group (consisting of three men, nine women and children) made a permanent camp near the edge of the North Saskatchewan River (Burpee 1973). For the next month more people joined them, creating a large camp along the river. The men moved out from this base camp to hunt and often returned after one or two days: "...the Young Men hunting, and not yet returned" (Burpee 1973: 42). There was also much feasting and ceremony before Henday's party finally departed by canoe on their long journey to York Factory.

Henday's camp was sizeable and where the people carried out many functions (e.g., hunting, canoe building, ceremonies, feasting);

Burpee, L J. (editor). 1973. The journal of Anthony Henday, 1754-55: York Factory to the Blackfeet Country. Canadiana House, Toronto. 51 pp. Reprint of 1907 edition.

Beaudoin, A B and H W Pyszczyk. 1998. Where was Anthony Henday and what did he see? Alberta Archaeological Review 28: 25-31.

MacGregor, J G. 1954. Behold the Shining Mountains. Applied Arts Products Ltd., Edmonton, AB. 276 pp.

small parties of people left camp to hunt and gather raw resources. This system of resource gathering resembles more a logistical procurement strategy, although there are references to the hunters going out only on a daily basis and returning at night. Henday's description also suggests that the Greater Edmonton area, at least late in its history, was an important gathering and staging place for Aboriginal groups such as the Cree at certain times of the year – and that is perhaps where its Cree name *OTINOW* originated.

The archaeological record rarely, if ever, can identify what specific Aboriginal ethnic group (i.e., Blackfoot, Cree, Assiniboine) occupied an area thousands of years ago. The exception during the Late Prehistoric Period and just prior to the arrival of Europeans is suggested by two variants of Aboriginal pottery in Alberta:

- a Plains pottery, common in southern Alberta and historic to the Plains groups (Blackfoot confederacy), that reaches as far north as the North Saskatchewan River, including the Edmonton Area; and,
- a northern forest pottery style related to forest groups (Cree) which is only found in the Lac La Biche area in Alberta, but occurs further northeast in Saskatchewan (including along the North Saskatchewan River) and Manitoba (Myer 1988: 60-63; Learn 1986).

Aboriginal pottery occurs in the Greater Edmonton area. The pieces that have been analyzed are of the Plains variety. Ives recovered a pottery neck sherd from the Strathcona Science Park archaeological site, which he believed was "… typical South Saskatchewan Basin complex pottery, perhaps a late variant estimated to be in use from AD 1000 to the 19th century" (Ives 1985: 40). This evidence suggests that at least during the Late Prehistoric Period, Plains Aboriginal peoples (likely ancestral to Blackfoot) occupied the Greater Edmonton area.

Myer, D. 1988. The Old Women's Phase on the Saskatchewan Plains: some Ideas. pp. 55-64. In: Archaeology in Alberta 1987, edited by Martin Magne, Archaeological Survey of Alberta, Occasional Paper No. 32. Alberta Culture and Multiculturalism.

Learn, K C. 1986. Pottery and prehistory of Blackfox Island: technical patterns in a cultural perspective. M.A. Thesis, Department of Anthropology, The University of Alberta, Edmonton, AB.

Other types of evidence also support this archaeological evidence. European explorers stated that the Edmonton region was Blackfoot territory. In 1754-55 Anthony Henday and his party, consisting of Cree and Assiniboine people, traveled through the area between Red Deer and the North Saskatchewan River. It was clear from his comments that they were in Archithinue (who were probably Blackfoot) territory: "I asked the Natives why they did not trap Wolves; they made Answer that the Archithinue Natives would kill them, if they trapped *in their* country..." (Burpee 1973:38, emphasis ours). Magne (1987: 220-232) has compiled a series of maps, from 1700 AD to 1850 AD, based on the observations of explorers traveling through the area, showing where various Aboriginal groups were located. The maps indicate that traditional territories were already changing before 1800. Cree and Assiniboine were traveling into areas (including the Greater Edmonton area) that were once the sole domain of the Blackfoot, and perhaps Sarsi (see Brink 1986: 57).

Arrival of the Fur Traders

By the time the North West Company and the Hudson's Bay Company arrived in 1795, to construct their fur trade posts across from the present-day Fort Saskatchewan (Kidd 1987), there was already a well-established Aboriginal land-use system of hunting, gathering, trapping and trading in place. Hunting and trapping were already deeply embedded in traditional Plains and Forest Aboriginal societies. The Cree and Assiniboine women in Henday's party were making winter clothes from local furs: "Clear frosty weather. It snowed a little last night. Travelled none. The Indian men a Beaver hunting: the Women dressing skins for cloathing" (Burpee 1973: 36). During this time period, the people may have increased their trapping and hunting activities to acquire European goods. However, not all Aboriginal groups may have trapped/hunted and traded on a

Magne, M and Contributors. 1987. Distributions of native groups in western Canada, A.D. 1700 to A.D. 1850. In: Archaeology in Alberta 1986, edited by Martin Magne pp. 220-232. Archaeological Survey of Alberta, Occasional Paper No. 31. Alberta Culture and Multiculturalism. Edmonton, AB.

Brink, J. 1986. Dog Days in Southern Alberta. Occasional Papers No. 28. Alberta Culture. Edmonton, AB.

Kidd, R S. 1987. Archaeological excavations at the Probable Site of the First Fort Edmonton or Fort Augustus, 1795 to Early 1800s. Provincial Museum of Alberta, Human History, Occasional Paper No. 3. Alberta Culture and Multiculturalism. Edmonton, AB.

Aboriginal encampment of canvas teepees below the Hudson Bay Co. Big House (Source: Ernest Brown, 1900, Provincial Archives #B883).

consistent basis even when Europeans had established permanent forts in the region (Pyszczyk 1997). This inconsistency may explain why the North West Company brought Iroquois trappers with them; many would remain in Alberta including the Edmonton area (Nicks 1980).

The first fur traders were attracted to the Edmonton region to gain an advantage over their opponents, and to harvest the abundant fur resources. In the words of North West Company clerk Duncan McGillivray in 1795, the Edmonton Area was a "… rich and plentiful Country, abounding with all kinds of animals, especially Beavers and Otters, which are said to be so numerous that the Women and children kill them with Sticks and hatchets" (Morton 1929: 77). Sophisticated Aboriginal trapping methods may have been unnecessary during the initial part of the fur trade. However, fur resources were depleted rapidly in the region leading to the movement of forts, and eventually into the Fort Edmonton in 1801 (Pyszczyk 1996). Earlier in 1795, further downriver Duncan McGillivray noted that the "Country around Fort George is now entirely ruined" (Morton 1929: 77); this happened in only three to

Pyszczyk, H W. 1997. The use of fur trade goods by the Plains Indians, Central and Southern Alberta, Canada. Canadian Journal of Archaeology 21: 45-84.

Nicks, G C. 1980. Demographic anthropology of native populations in western Canada, 1800 – 1975. Ph.D. Thesis, Department of Anthropology, The University of Alberta. Edmonton, AB.

Morton, A S. (editor). 1929. The journal of Duncan M'Gillivray of the North West Company at Fort George on the Saskatchewan, 1794-5. MacMillan, Toronto, ON.

Hunting, trapping and fishing were the first Aboriginal/European industries that were celebrated in the area (Source: Ernest Brown, 1897, Provincial Archives #B1521).

Johnson, A M. (editor). 1967. Saskatchewan journals and correspondence: Edmonton House 1795-1800, Chesterfield House 1800-1802. Hudson's Bay Record Society, London.

four years. At Fort Edmonton I, "made beaver" furs brought to the fort rapidly declined in only a seven-year period (Kidd 1987: 107; Johnson 1967: Appendix A).

The attractions of untapped, abundant fur resources, along with the rapid depletion of furs in other regions downriver were some, but not the only, reasons the fur traders moved into the Edmonton area. Certainly the historic journals cited earlier suggest that Edmonton was a key rendezvous point and staging area in the annual travel patterns of Aboriginal groups by the 1750s and it may have been so for thousands of years. The fact that the Cree named it as a key meeting place, and that feasting and ceremonies were conducted in Edmonton during the spring, suggests that large groups of Aboriginal people gathered. The gatherings would have attracted European traders, who were to a large extent dependent on Aboriginal people for furs and meat provisions. This model of Aboriginal settlement is based on one that Myer and Thistle (1995) have described along the lower reaches of the Saskatchewan River. In their extensive study of this phenomenon they cite historic references to groups of Cree meeting repeatedly in the spring at certain areas to feast, conduct ceremonies and, "…to cut Birch trees and make their Canoes of the bark" (Dobbs 1744: 37). Many of these places along the river, where large groups met to socialize and conduct ceremonies in the spring, also had Cree names. This activity attracted the traders to build their forts nearby because in the words of Samuel Hearne, "…each Different Tribe are desirous of having goods brought as near their own doors as Possible…" (Tyrrell 1934: 117). Myer and Thistle (1995: 431) point out that the construction of a post at any of these Cree sites would then , "… have served to increase the importance of the location to the members of the regional band(s) attached to it." The authors conclude that Aboriginal hunter-gatherer social geography "… exerted a major influence on the introduction and the organization of the fur trade throughout the forest region of northern North America" (Myer and Thistle: 433).

The Greater Edmonton area, at least by the early 1700s, may very well have become such a place, first serving as a focal point for European settlement, and then remaining as a focal point for both Europeans and Aboriginal peoples throughout the 19th and 20th centuries (Pyszczyk 1995, 1996). Whenever there is discussion of why the traders chose Edmonton to build the first forts, the reasons are always given from a purely Euro-Canadian perspective – the area had good local resources, was close to the Athabasca drainage system, etc. While that may be true, what is often overlooked is the strong influence that Aboriginal groups probably had in the selection and then the settlement of Edmonton by the first

Myer, D and P C Thistle. 1995. Saskatchewan River rendezvous centers and trading posts: continuity in a Cree social geography. Ethnohistory 42: 403-443.

Dobbs, A. 1744. An account of the countries adjoining to Hudson's Bay in the northwest part of America. London: J. Robinson, at the Golden Lion in Ludgate.

Tyrell, J B. (editor). 1934. Journals of Samuel Hearne and Philip Turnor. Champlain Society, Vol. 21. Toronto, ON.

Nicks, G C. 1969. The archaeology of two Hudson's Bay Company posts: Buckingham House (1792-1800) and Edmonton House III (1810-1813). M.A. Thesis, Department of Anthropology, The University of Alberta. Edmonton, AB.

Foster, J. 1979. Indian-White relations in the Prairie West during the Fur Trade Period – a compact. In: The spirit of Alberta Indian treaties, edited by Richard Price. Institute for Research on Public Policy and Indian Association of Alberta. 202 pp.

Europeans. As Foster (1979: 185) so aptly put it, for trade between people to work, it has to be satisfactory to both parties, including where trade is to take place. We need only to look downriver in 1813 to find an example of this. James Bird, chief trader of the Hudson's Bay Company Fort Edmonton III closed the post in three short years because of very poor trade (Nicks 1969: 30; HBCA B.60/a/10, IM49).

Whether this pattern of Aboriginal land-use in the Greater Edmonton area has an even longer antiquity is still uncertain although some evidence points that way. There are large concentrations of archaeological sites and/or very large archaeological sites, denoting long continuity of land-use by large groups of people – a pattern that is certainly similar to that of the Greater Edmonton area later during the fur trade period.

The End of a Way of Life?

"…we do not mean to ask for food every day but only when we commence and in case of famine or calamity. What we speak of and do now will last as long as the sun shines and the river runs."

(Mistahwahsis, speaking when negotiating Treaty Six; PMA 970.41233 Sa49)

The signing of major treaties in the 1870s to early 1880s by Aboriginal people in Alberta was followed by the introduction of the reserve system and the depletion of the bison. These factors curtailed many aspects of Aboriginal life in central Alberta – in particular the high degree of mobility and a traditional subsistence base. There is no need to retell this story here, which is best told by Aboriginal people themselves. What needs to be done is to complete the circle – of how current Aboriginal land-use and the reserve system in the Greater Edmonton area came to be and how it relates

Table 3

Aboriginal reserves in the immediate vicinity of Edmonton.

http://www.aand.gov.ab.ca/images/graphics/maps/range_indian_reserves_b.jpg

Number	Name	Location	Other Details
	Papaschase	S. Edmonton	Cree; reserve disbanded
133	Alexis Reserve	N. of Lac Ste. Anne	Sioux Nation ancestry
133A	Paul First Nation	E. of Lake Wabamun	Sioux Nation ancestry
133B	Paul First Nation	N.E. of Lake Wabamun	
134	Alexander Reserve	N. of Calahoo	Plains Cree
135	Enoch Reserve	S.W. of Edmonton	Woodland Cree
138	Erminskin Reserve	Hobbema	Cree

to the peoples' history. In particular, how do the present day Aboriginal bands and the distribution of their populations relate to that past? If you look at a map of the distribution of Aboriginal people in central Alberta, there is a cluster of reserves in and around Edmonton and another cluster of reserves in the Elk Point-Frog Lake area (Figure 6). The major reserves near Edmonton are listed in Table 3.

These two clusters were the first two localities where fur trade posts were established along the North Saskatchewan River on the Alberta side (1792 in the Frog Lake area and 1795 in the Edmonton area). While the construction of these posts certainly attracted Aboriginal people to come and trade, the fact that the people already had strong ties to the land before Europeans arrived may in fact have attracted the fur trade to their residential areas. Furthermore, when asked to choose land for reserves various Aboriginal bands chose the lands in their traditional hunting grounds (Dempsey 1986, Foster 1995). The historic references

Dempsey, H A. 1986. Indian tribes of Alberta. Glenbow-Alberta Institute. Calgary, AB. 100 pp.

Figure 6

The distribution of Aboriginal reserves in Treaty 6 Area, Alberta.

Foster, J. 1995. Personal communication.

certainly support the movement of Cree into the Greater Edmonton area long before the permanent establishment of fur trade posts. Today, around Edmonton, most reserves are Cree, or have ties to the Sarsi (Siouan peoples), while the Blackfoot chose their reserves further south. Thus, it is entirely possible that both the high population of Cree people and reserves is directly connected to a very long land-use history of the Edmonton area.

Significant Current Cultural Sites and Activities in the Edmonton Area

There are many depositories of cultural artifacts and documents available to the public (Table 4). The Royal Alberta Museum in Edmonton has displays and much more information stored for reference. Outside of the Edmonton region there are valuable collections and displays that assist in understanding Aboriginal use of the region. The present living cultural history is now found where Aboriginal people live. Cultural events celebrating the Plains and Parkland Peoples are common in Edmonton because many Aboriginal people are urbanites. Others live on reserves close to

A sweat lodge: descendants of Aboriginal peoples can still connect with their heritage in the North Saskatchewan River Valley (photo by Ross W. Wein, 2001).

Table 4

Current Aboriginal cultural displays and other resources that would assist visitors to understand the early peoples in the vicinity of Edmonton.

Cultural sites	Location	Special features
Royal Alberta Museum	Edmonton	Displays, Collections
Jasper Yellowhead Museum and Archives	Jasper	Feature Aboriginal peoples in the foothills and mountains
Glenbow Museum	Calgary	Features displays of Aboriginal life, Collections
Head-Smashed-In Buffalo Jump	Fort Macleod	Displays and landscape trails, 5000 years of Plains People and buffalo, UNESCO World Heritage Site
Writing-On-Stone	Milk River	Archaeological Preserve to protect rock art of the Plains People
Wanuskewin Heritage Park	Saskatoon	Displays under cover, landscape features with cultural remnants (medicine wheels, buffalo jumps)

Edmonton (see Figure 6 and Table 3) and, just to the south in the Hobbema area, cultural events are common and widely advertised.

Conclusions

The way people are distributed over the landscape today has roots that are deep in their history. Edmonton was an important place to many generations of Aboriginal people long before and during the fur trade, and remains so today. The archaeological record marks that land-use and gives us glimpses of lifestyles. Eventual exchange and trade between Euro-Canadian society and Aboriginal peoples during the fur trade era may have influenced not only where Aboriginal people traded but where Europeans first decided to build their forts. The land, and the lives of the two peoples were inextricably intertwined resulting in what we have today.

46

Many Aboriginal heritage sites have been lost during the extensive urban modification of the river valley by Edmontonians before and just after the turn of the 20th century. Over decades, the tablelands became the suburbs and the valley was increasingly dedicated to conservation and recreation. Since the ribbon of green has some level of protection, there is some assurance that Aboriginal heritage sites in the valley are protected. Significant numbers of archaeological sites have been found, excavated or protected, largely due to recent government legislation. The Alberta Historic Resources Act, introduced in 1975, protects all heritage resources, including archaeological sites, in the province. The evidence that these sites contain has led to understanding Prehistoric and Historic Aboriginal land-use a little better.

Dedication

This paper is dedicated to the descendants of the pre-European and the first Euro-Canadian inhabitants of the Edmonton area. Today there are over 40,000 Aboriginal people (21% of Alberta's Aboriginal population) living in Edmonton (Statistics Canada, 2001 Census of Canada).

Useful Websites

http://www.gov.edmonton.ab.ca/fort/
http://www.pma.edmonton.ab.ca/human/archaeo/research/fort.htm
http://www.gov.ab.ca/aboutalberta/history_firstnations.cfm

Edmonton's river valley and ravines still provide a link to natural ecosystems and Aboriginal heritage (photo by Ross W. Wein, 2001).

The North Saskatchewan River and Watershed

Adele M. Mandryk, University of Alberta

Abstract

The North Saskatchewan River Valley is a major ecological corridor across western Canada that links natural ecosystems and supports a largely urban human population. The watershed provides a wide array of food, fiber, minerals, power, and recreation resources. From a conservation perspective, the headwaters of the river in Banff National Park are the major protected areas. The portion of the river from the Saskatchewan Glacier to the Banff National Park Boundary was designated a Canadian Heritage River in 1989. Although the cumulative human impacts on the river and watershed are just being quantified at present, the watershed seems to provide for species movement through hydrologic connectivity. Scientific predictions over decades are needed to understand how present and future rates of change in the watershed will affect changes in biodiversity sustainability and therefore quality of life of our citizens.

Introduction

While some human communities rely on ground water, many more rely on clean, safe water that is collected by watersheds and flows through streams and rivers. Many of the world's great cities have developed beside rivers and over time these urban areas have expanded their infrastructure, enveloping both sides of the river. Rivers have always been valued for their ecological goods and services. As an immediate supply of drinking water and a ready site for waste disposal rivers have been essential to economic development. In addition, rivers provide irrigation and food, transportation, hydroelectricity, and recreation. Increasingly, rivers are valued as sites of biological diversity and natural corridors that link ecosystems. Riparian ecosystems support some of the highest levels of plant, mammal, bird, fish, and insect diversity. In cities, the concepts of 'greenways' (Fabos and Ahern 1996), biological corridors and heritage river status (Government of Canada 2004) to protect the natural and cultural heritage of local rivers is gaining popular support among the Canadian public, ecologists and urban planners (Henry *et al.* 1999).

The citizens of the communities in the North Saskatchewan River watershed have a natural and cultural heritage linked with the North Saskatchewan River (Milholland 2002, North Saskatchewan Watershed Alliance 2005). The North Saskatchewan River corridor is a major east-west link across Canada and was the means by which explorers, traders and settlers arrived to found Fort Edmonton. The biggest city in the watershed, Edmonton, was incorporated in 1904 and has grown in size from 8.7 km² to about 700 km² in 100 years (City of Edmonton 2004). With a Greater Edmonton population of just under one million, the majority of the people of the watershed are concentrated along the river. By numbers alone, this urban area acts like a huge plug,

Fabos, J G and J Ahern. 1996. Greenways: the beginning of an international movement. Elsevier, New York, NY, 491 pp.

Government of Canada. 2004. Canadian Heritage Rivers System. Web Page. URL: http://www.chrs.ca. 17 May 2004.

Henry, Jr, A C, D H Hosack, C W Johnson, D Ro, and G Bentrup. 1999. Conservation corridors in the United States: benefits and planning guidelines. J. Soil Water Conservation 54: 645-50.

Milholland, B. 2002. The North Saskatchewan River Guide. North Saskatchewan Watershed Alliance, Edmonton, AB. Unpaged.

North Saskatchewan Watershed Alliance. 2005. Canadian Heritage Rivers System: North Saskatchewan River Background Study. (in press).

City of Edmonton. 2004. Web Page. URL: http://www.gov.edmonton.ab.ca. 18 May 2004.

contaminating air, modifying water flow, fragmenting forest and wetland ecosystems, and limiting biodiversity protection and movement. Awareness of the impact of urbanization on the natural environment and subsequently on human quality of life is raised in the popular media almost daily.

North Saskatchewan River

The North Saskatchewan River is 1,287 km long (Figure 1). Elevation ranges from 3,389 m at the summit of Mount Saskatchewan with a steep gradient to 1,100 m in the foothills, to 500 m at the Alberta/Saskatchewan border. This interprovincial waterway flows through the province of Alberta, joins the South Saskatchewan River in Saskatchewan, enters into Manitoba's lakes, and finally empties into Hudson Bay through the Nelson River. The source of the river is the Saskatchewan Glacier in the Columbia Icefields of the Rocky Mountains. Glacial melt water accounts for 5% of the winter flow and 50% of the summer flow of the river (Alberta Environment 2004). Climate change models predict warmer climates and reduced water flows in the North Saskatchewan River as rapidly melting glaciers disappear (Environment Canada 2004).

The Alberta portion of the river is 640 km long and together with its many tributaries connects the biodiversity of the sub-alpine, montane, upper and lower foothills, dry mixed wood and central parkland natural subregions (Alberta Community Development 2004, Anonymous 1994). After Glacial Lake Edmonton drained, about 12,000 years ago, the flow of water draining from the Rocky Mountains cut through the sedimentary rock forming the North Saskatchewan River Valley (Godfrey 1993) exposing resources such as coal, sand, gravel, and clay. Today, the watershed supports the industries of agriculture, petroleum,

Alberta Environment. 2004. Alberta river basins. Web Page. URL: http://www3.gov.ab.ca/env/water/basins/BasinForm.cfm. 18 May 2004.

Environment Canada. 2004. Threats to Canada's water supply. Web Page. URL: http://www.ec.gc.ca/EnviroZine/english/issues/42/feature2_e.cfm. 18 May 2004.

Alberta Community Development. 2004. Alberta Natural Heritage Information Centre. Web Page. URL: http://www.cd.gov.ab.ca/preserving/parks/anhic/flashindex.asp. 18 May 2004.

Anonymous. 1994. Natural Regions and Subregions of Alberta, Alberta Environment. Map.

Godfrey, J D (ed.) 1993. Edmonton beneath our feet. Edmonton Geological Society. Edmonton, AB. 150 pp.

Figure 1

The Alberta portion of the North Saskatchewan River watershed (sub watersheds are given) begins at the Saskatchewan Glacier in the Columbia Ice Fields of the Rocky Mountains. The river valley cuts across Alberta, through Edmonton, and then across Saskatchewan and Manitoba to Hudson Bay (Source: North Saskatchewan Watershed Alliance, 2004).

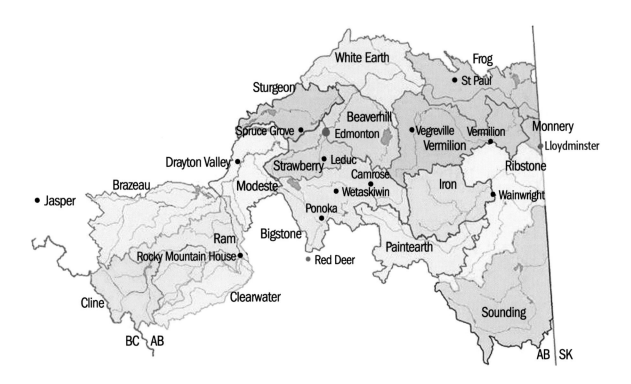

Winter (pan ice shown here) can arrive as early as October to the North Saskatchewan River and dominate conservation and management for almost six months (photo by John R. Wood).

Alberta Geological Survey. 2004. Geoscape Edmonton. Web Page. URL: http://www.ags.gov.ab.ca. 18 May 2004.

Scott, G A J. 1995. Canada's vegetation: a world perspective. McGill-Queen's University Press, Montreal, PQ. 361 pp.

Strong, W L. 1992. Ecoregions and ecodistricts of Alberta. Edmonton: W. L. Strong Ecological Survey Ltd. prepared for Alberta Forestry, Lands and Wildlife, Edmonton, AB.

forestry, and mining (e.g. gravel, coal, and salt); some speculate that diamonds are the new economic frontier (Alberta Geological Survey 2004).

North Saskatchewan River Watershed

The North Saskatchewan River watershed has a total area of 432,000 km². In Alberta, the watershed is 80,000 km² or approximately 12.5% of Alberta's landmass (Alberta Environment 2004, Figure 1). The watershed has 18 sub-basins drained by the North Saskatchewan River and the Battle River. The steep elevational gradient from the mountains to the foothills brings a corresponding increase in temperature and decrease in moisture. The lower elevation is characterized by a boreal climate of low precipitation, short, warm summers and long, cold winters with continuous snow cover (Scott 1995). The annual mean temperature of the watershed ranges from 2.5 to 10°C. Annual precipitation ranges from 400-800 mm, with moister conditions at upper elevations and to the north, and drier conditions at lower elevations and to the south (Strong 1992).

The North Saskatchewan River Valley dominates the City of Edmonton landscape (photo by Ross W. Wein).

River, Valley and Watershed Contributions to Conservation

Many ecologists believe that natural, complex patterns across the landscape are the most likely arrangements to protect biodiversity and are critical to ecosystem stability (Bennett 1999, Forman 1995). In addition, others believe that hydrologic connectivity is an overlooked aspect of biodiversity conservation (Honnay *et al.* 2001, Pringle 2001, Strange *et al.* 1999). Theoretically, this points to river systems as key components in the creation of bioregional conservation networks. Bioregional conservation networks are systems of interlinking ecosystems, buffers and corridors at the watershed or regional level that are intended to protect and

Bennett, A F. 1999. Linkages in the landscape: the role of corridors and connectivity in wildlife conservation. International Union for Conservation of Nature and Natural Resources, Cambridge, UK. 254 pp.

Forman, R T T. 1995. Land mosaics: the ecology of landscapes and regions. Cambridge University Press, New York, NY. 632 pp.

Honnay, O, W Verhaeghe, and M Hermy. 2001. Plant community assembly along dendritic networks of small forest streams. Ecology 82: 1691-1702.

Pringle, C M. 2001. Hydrologic connectivity and the management of biological reserves: a global perspective. Ecological Applications 11: 981-998.

Strange, E, K D Fausch, and A P Covich. 1999. Sustaining ecosystem services in human-dominated watersheds: biohydrology and ecosystem processes in the South Platte River Basin. Environmental Management 24: 39-54.

Poiani, K A, B D Richter, M G Anderson, and H E Richter. 2000. Biodiversity conservation at multiple scales: functional sites, landscapes, and networks. BioScience 50: 133-146.

Soulé, M E and J Ternorgh (eds.). 1999. Continental conservation: scientific foundations of regional reserve networks. Island Press, Washington, DC. 227 pp.

The ravines, such as the Whitemud Ravine shown here, are little studied, but very important for biodiversity protection (photo by Ross W. Wein, 1999).

United Nations Environment Program. 2004. Convention on biological diversity. Web Page. URL: http://www.biodiv.org/default.aspx. 18 May 2004.

Kirchner, F J, B Ferdy, C Andalo, B Colas, and J Moret. 2003. Role of corridors in plant dispersal: an example with endangered *Ranunculus nodiflorus*. Conservation Biology 17: 401-410.

Naiman, R G, H Decamps, and M Pollock. 1993. The role of riparian corridors in maintaining regional biodiversity. Ecological Applications 3: 209-212.

Schaefer, J M. 1992. Designing and protecting river corridors for wildlife. Rivers 3: 14-26.

conserve biological diversity (Poiani *et al*. 2000, Soulé and Ternorgh 1999). The parties to the Convention on Biological Diversity in Jakarta ratified this concept in 1993 as the framework for global biodiversity protection (United Nations Environment Program 2004). Canada is a party to this convention.

Riverine systems may be critical to protecting and conserving biological diversity over the long-term. The close proximity of water and land provides a rich matrix of habitat types that provide resources for survivorship, reproduction and short- and long-distance movement of terrestrial and aquatic animals and plants (Kirchner *et al*. 2003, Naiman, *et al*. 1993). The way in which river corridors facilitate plant movement is under investigation (Honnay *et al*. 2001) and animal movement along these corridors has been well documented (Schaefer 1992). Corridors may also have an important conservation role considering warming trends caused by climate change. It is thought that corridors that maintain large contiguous habitats or the continuity of reserves along an environmental gradient are likely to be the most valuable in maintaining the continuity of species populations (Bennett 1999). The North Saskatchewan River system is a biogeographic linkage that connects altitudinal and latitudinal ecological zones. These east-west and north-south corridors maintain contiguous habitat over biogeophysical gradients of temperature and moisture. The potential for long-term biodiversity conservation in these corridors is high.

The Ecological Condition of the North Saskatchewan River Valley

Human disturbance is a legacy of the North Saskatchewan River watershed, as humans have benefited from the resources of the North Saskatchewan River and watershed for at least 5,000 years (Huck and Whiteway 1998). Over the past century, upland ecosystems have been converted by resource extraction and urban infrastructure development. On the rivers, two large dams (Big Horn and Brazeau) regulate water levels and velocities.

Attempts are being made to protect environmentally significant natural areas, many of which are located on the North Saskatchewan River or in close proximity (Anonymous 1997). The headwaters of the river are in Banff National Park; the portion of the river from the Saskatchewan Glacier to the Banff National Park Boundary has been designated a Canadian Heritage River. The cumulative human impacts on the watershed are currently being documented in the State of the North Saskatchewan River Watershed Report (North Saskatchewan Watershed Alliance 2005).

Landscape ecologists and conservation biologists generally agree that ecosystem stability is a function of natural biodiversity

Huck, B and D Whiteway. 1998. In search of ancient Alberta. Heartland Publications, Winnipeg, MB. 287 pp.

Anonymous. 1997. Environmentally significant areas of Alberta. 1 and 2. Edmonton: Sweetgrass Consultants Ltd. prepared for Alberta Environmental Protection.

North Saskatchewan Watershed Alliance. 2005. State of the North Saskatchewan River Watershed.

fluctuations over time and space. While human disturbance such as land conversion and toxic pollution are major threats, the North Saskatchewan River system continues to contribute to natural diversity and long-term sustainability of species through a watershed that has retained a considerable degree of connectivity. Scientific predictions over decades are needed to understand how present and future rates of change in the watershed will affect changes in biodiversity sustainabilty and therefore quality of life of our citizens.

Acknowledgements

Thanks to Sharon Willianen, Manager of the North Saskatchewan Watershed Alliance, for permission to use the watershed map and resource materials and to Dr. Ross Wein and Dr. John Wood for many hours of discussion and their support in pursuing these ideas.

Terrestrial Ecosystems of Edmonton and Surrounding Landscapes

J. Derek Johnson, Canadian Forest Service, Edmonton

Abstract

Edmonton lies in the Central Parkland Natural Subregion, which is an ecotone between the Boreal Forest Natural Region to the west and north, and the Grassland Natural Region to the south. This paper introduces some of the native plants and animals of the Central Parkland ecosystem remnants found within a 100 km radius of the city. While the region still supports considerable natural diversity and islands of what is considered to be natural, much of the landscape has been converted to agriculture or is under increasing threat from continued urbanization.

Introduction

Edmonton was built in the Central Parkland Natural Subregion of Alberta, which originally covered about 64,200 km^2 or 10% of Alberta's land area (Alberta Environmental Protection 1995, Anonymous 1997, Van Tighem 1993). In Alberta, this subregion extends in a broad arc up to 200 km wide between the grasslands,

Alberta Environmental Protection. 1995. A framework for Alberta's Special Places. Report No. 1. Natural Regions. Alberta Environmental Protection. Edmonton, AB. 23 pp.

Anonymous. 1997. The grassland natural region of Alberta. Alberta Environmental Protection. Edmonton, AB. 229 pp. plus maps.

Van Tighem, K. 1993. Alberta's endangered species: keeping the wild in the West. Borealis 4(12): 1-16.

from around Olds in the south, and the boreal forest north of Edmonton in the north (Figure 1). Surficial deposits include hummocky and ground moraines, glacial lake-beds, kame moraines and dune fields. Elevations range from about 500 m above sea level at the Saskatchewan border to over 1,100 m in the lower foothills of the Rocky Mountains. Shallow lakes and permanent wetlands were once common in the area.

To the south the Grassland Natural Region (Bird 1961, Strong and Leggat 1992) is characterized by flat to gently rolling terrain with few major hill systems (Alberta Environmental Protection 1995, Van Tighem 1993). Most of the sedimentary bedrock is covered with glacial till deposits. Some areas are blanketed by glacial lake sediments, sand dune fields, and outwash plains. Badlands have developed where river valleys and their associated coulees and ravines are carved deeply into bedrock, especially along the Red Deer, South Saskatchewan and Milk Rivers.

The North Saskatchewan River Valley in Edmonton has remnant grasslands on steep slopes with south and southwest exposures (photo by John R. Wood, 2004).

Bird, R D. 1961. Ecology of the Aspen Parkland of Western Canada in relation to land-use. Canada Department of Agriculture, Research Branch Publication No. 1066. 155 pp.

Strong, W L and K R Leggat. 1992. Ecoregions of Alberta. Publication No. T:245. Alberta Forestry, Lands and Wildlife. Edmonton, AB. 59 pp.

Figure 1

The natural regions of Alberta showing Edmonton on the North Saskatchewan River. Edmonton lies in the Central Parkland which has vegetation characteristics of the Grassland to the south and of the Boreal Forest to the north (from Alberta Environment).

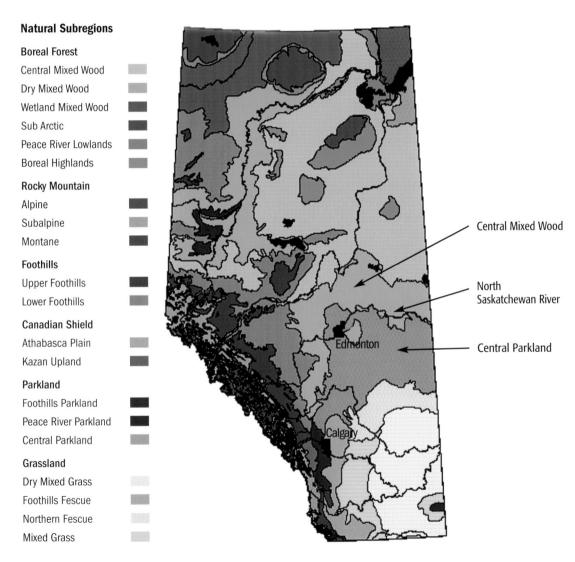

Natural Subregions

Boreal Forest
Central Mixed Wood
Dry Mixed Wood
Wetland Mixed Wood
Sub Arctic
Peace River Lowlands
Boreal Highlands

Rocky Mountain
Alpine
Subalpine
Montane

Foothills
Upper Foothills
Lower Foothills

Canadian Shield
Athabasca Plain
Kazan Upland

Parkland
Foothills Parkland
Peace River Parkland
Central Parkland

Grassland
Dry Mixed Grass
Foothills Fescue
Northern Fescue
Mixed Grass

Central Mixed Wood

North
Saskatchewan River

Central Parkland

Edmonton

Calgary

To the north, the Boreal Forest Natural Region (Strong and Leggat 1992) is Alberta's largest natural region, occupying some 52% of Alberta's land area (Alberta Environmental Protection 1995, Anonymous 1998, Van Tighem 1993). It consists of broad lowland plains and discontinuous hill systems. The bedrock is buried beneath deep glacial deposits. Outcrops occur only rarely along major river valleys. The presence of extensive wetlands is a major characteristic of this natural region. Bogs, fens, marshes and swamps are common.

Biology of the Central Parkland Natural Subregion

Within the subregion there is a gradual transition in the vegetation from northern rough fescue (*Festuca hallii* (Vasey) Piper) grassland, with scattered groves of aspen (*Populus tremuloides* Michx.), in the south, to closed groves of aspen, with a lush, species-rich understory, in the Edmonton area. Shrub communities of western snowberry (*Symphoricarpos occidentalis* Hook.), prickly rose (*Rosa acicularis* Lindl.), choke cherry (*Prunus virginiana* L.), and saskatoon (*Amelanchier alnifolia* Nutt.) are extensive in the northern portion of this subregion. Black and Dark Brown Chernozem soils occur under the grasslands in the south, with Dark Gray Chenozems and Luvisols being found under the moist, closed deciduous forests in the north. Gleysols occur in wet depressions. Prairie fires, periodic droughts and the grazing activity of millions of plains bison (*Bison bison*) shaped the vegetation patterns of this subregion in the past. Today, native vegetation and wetlands are becoming scarce because most of the land has been cultivated to grow agricultural crops. The majority of the remaining natural land is on rougher terrain or poorer soils.

At the southern edge of this subregion typical grassland bird species occur, such as upland sandpiper (*Bartramia longicauda*), Sprague's pipit (*Anthus spragueii*), and Baird's sparrow

Anonymous. 1998. The boreal forest natural region of Alberta. Alberta Environmental Protection. Edmonton, AB. 312 pp. plus maps.

On north-facing slopes and in ravines, white spruce have matured since harvesting declined in the Edmonton region. Dying and dead spruce trees provide habitat for insects, mammals and birds (photo by Ross W. Wein, 2000).

Packer, J. 1983. Moss's Flora of Alberta. 2nd ed. University of Toronto Press, Toronto, ON. 687 pp.

Kershaw, L, J Gould, D Johnson, and J Lancaster (eds.). 2001. Rare vascular plants of Alberta. Alberta Native Plant Council, The University of Alberta Press, Edmonton, AB. 484 pp.

Johnson, D, L Kershaw, A MacKinnon, and J Pojar. 1995. Plants of the western boreal forest and aspen parkland. Lone Pine Publishing, Edmonton, AB. 392 pp.

Fisher, C and J Acorn. 1998. Birds of Alberta. Lone Pine Publishing, Edmonton, AB. 384 pp.

Bovey, R B and E Pluciennik (illus.). 1990. Birds of Edmonton. Lone Pine Publishing, Edmonton, AB. 128 pp.

Stelfox, H and C Fisher. 1998. A winter birding guide for the Edmonton region. Edmonton Natural History Club, Edmonton, AB. 56 pp.

(*Ammodramus bairdii*), which become less common farther north. Along the northern fringe, boreal forest species such as woodchuck (*Marmota monax*), broad-winged hawk (*Buteo platypterus*), and rose-breasted grosbeak (*Pheucticus ludovicianus*) are more common. Franklin's ground squirrel (*Spermophilus franklinii*) and piping plover (*Charadrius melodus*) occur primarily in the Central Parkland Natural Subregion of Alberta.

Plants and Animals of Edmonton and Region

The biota of the province is reasonably well known: vascular plants (Packer 1983, Kershaw *et al.* 2001, Johnson *et al.* 1995), birds (Fisher and Acorn 1998, Bovey and Pluciennik 1990, Stelfox

Pattie, D L and C Fisher. 1999. Mammals of Alberta. Lone Pine Publishing, Edmonton, AB. 240 pp.

Russell, A P and A M Bauer. 1993. The amphibians and reptiles of Alberta: a field guide and primer of boreal herpetology. The University of Calgary Press and The University of Alberta Press, Calgary and Edmonton, AB. 264 pp.

Nelson, J S and M J Paetz. 1992. The fishes of Alberta. The University of Alberta Press/The University of Calgary Press, Edmonton/Calgary, AB. 437 pp.

Joynt, A and M G Sullivan. 2003. Fish of Alberta. Lone Pine Publishing, Edmonton, AB. 176 pp.

Anonymous. 2001. The general status of Alberta wild species 2000. Alberta Environment/Alberta Sustainable Resources Development, Edmonton, AB. 46 pp.

and Fisher 1998), mammals (Pattie and Fisher 1999), amphibians and reptiles (Russell and Bauer 1993), and fishes (Nelson and Paetz 1992, Joynt and Sullivan 2003). Rare species have been identified (Anonymous 2001).

The core of Edmonton with transport facilities and buildings is sterile and unnatural from a native species diversity point of view. Despite the city's attempts at planting trees and installing flower boxes, some naturalists emphasize that there is not much alive in the city's core other than people and pigeons.

Much more natural conditions are found along the North Saskatchewan River Valley, one of Edmonton's greatest assets. Many cities have built right up to their riverbanks, not so for Edmonton. Edmonton is fortunate to have a relatively green corridor along much of the river valley because most of the slopes are too steep to build on. Particularly on the moist, north-facing banks of the river, thick woods of aspen (*Populus tremuloides* Michx.), balsam poplar (*Populus balsamifera* L.), white birch (*Betula papyrifera* Marsh.) and white spruce (*Picea glauca* (Moench) Voss) develop. The south-facing banks, because of their steepness and exposure, offer a totally different appearance. Because of the exposure and dryness, many plant species more characteristic of the prairies to the south can be found on these banks; however, invasion by non-native species has become a problem on some of these slopes.

The number of animals in the city always delights our naturalists. White-tailed jackrabbits (*Lepus townsendii*) are surprisingly common in many areas of the city, including the university farm. They can hold their own against cats, but are no match for most dogs, the main predator in the city. White-tailed jackrabbits have expanded their range in the Edmonton area, at the expense of their smaller cousins, the snowshoe hare (*Lepus americanus*), as more wooded land was cleared for agriculture.

While many natural areas on the uplands have succumbed to expanded agriculture and urban sprawl, the Whitemud Creek valley, feeding into the North Saskatchewan River, has remained much the same over the past two or three decades, except for the presence of more people and trails. A major management problem along the creek relates to beaver (*Castor canadensis*) activity. The wildlife choice is between balsam poplar trees or beaver. You cannot have both. Many of the largest balsam poplar trees along the creek have had wire cages placed around them to protect them from the beaver. While white-tailed deer (*Odocoileus virginianus*) and other large mammals are occasionally seen along the creek, the red squirrel (*Tamiasciurus hudsonicus*) is by far the most commonly seen mammal. Canadian tiger swallowtail butterflies (*Papilio canadensis* Rothschild and Jordan) are commonly seen along the creek in June and early July. Insects are one of the greatest voids in our knowledge of natural areas.

Patsy Cotterill and Bob Priebe in young forest that characterize many of the forests in the North Saskatchewan River Valley in the Edmonton region (photo by John R. Wood).

Environment Canada. 1986. Wetlands in Canada: a valuable resource. Lands Directorate, Environment Canada. Fact Sheet 86-4. Ottawa, ON. 8 pp.

Allen, L. 2004. Alberta Natural Heritage Information Centre preliminary plant community tracking list. Alberta Community Development, Edmonton, AB.

Remnants of Native Ecosystems in the Region

East of Edmonton lies the Cooking Lake moraine, an area of irregular topography, potholes, and nutrient-poor, coarse-textured soils that are inhospitable to agriculture. The water bodies on the moraine are important to many forms of wildlife. The area is popular for acreage developments; however, there are still many areas that are relatively natural, such as the Sherwood Park natural area. Most of these are dominated by aspen communities with highly variable understories of beaked hazelnut (*Corylus cornuta* Marsh.), rose (*Rosa* spp.), and low bush cranberry (*Viburnum edule* (Michx.) Raf.). In still others there are few shrubs and the understory is primarily wild sarsaparilla (*Aralia nudicaulis* L.). It has been estimated that 80% of the wetlands surrounding Edmonton have been lost to agriculture and urban expansion since the time of settlement (Environment Canada 1986). Farther east, Beaverhill Lake, near Tofield, is an important nesting and staging area for many species of waterfowl and shorebirds.

Elk Island National Park is an island of dry mixed-wood boreal forest at the northern edge of the central parkland natural subregion. Historically, the land has been highly modified by fires, grazing animals, beaver and clearing by farmers. Today, the area is primarily covered by deciduous tree species; however, in areas that have been undisturbed for a long time, such as the islands in Astotin Lake, white spruce, the characteristic climax species of the dry mixed-wood boreal forest, flourishes. The park supports many diverse aquatic communities, some of them rare, such as the water arum (*Calla palustris* L.) and Cyprus-like sedge (*Carex pseudocyperus* L.) community (Allen 2004).

Moving from the very wet to the very dry, the sand dunes in the Bruderheim–Redwater area support stands of jack pine (*Pinus banksiana* Lamb.), often with an understory of reindeer lichens

(*Cladina* spp.). This is a community type more characteristic of northeastern Alberta, although there are small areas southwest of Edmonton, around the Devonian Botanic Garden and the Clifford E. Lee Nature Sanctuary. Porcupines (*Erethizon dorsatum*) are often found in these areas and they can do considerable damage or kill trees due to their feeding activities on the bark.

Just west of the city, along Highway 16, is the Wagner Natural Area; an area of spring-fed fens that is uncommon in Alberta. These springs flow year round, even on the coldest days of winter. Interspersed among stands of coniferous trees are marl (calcium carbonate) ponds. These wetlands are unique habitat supporting specialized species such as 16 of the 26 species of orchid known to occur in Alberta. Sparrow's-egg lady's slipper (*Cypripedium passerinum* Richardson) is one of the more common and showy species. Six of the 10 insectivorous plant species occurring in the province can also be found in this natural area. Western (Boreal) toads (*Bufo boreas*) are common, but Canadian toads (*Bufo hemiophrys*) do not occur here. This is one of a number of unusual quirks of distribution that occur in the natural area. Great horned owls (*Bubo virginianus*), and owls in general, are less abundant than a number of years ago.

Protecting Natural Area Remnants

Some of our natural areas have less than natural parts to them. Agriculture has had a strong impact in most areas. Patches of agricultural land in and around natural areas can reduce the amount of fuel build-up and therefore fire no longer plays a natural role. Management could maintain natural features of the area and also provide some economic benefit. In grassland or parkland areas there may be a need to cut the grass, either to reduce the thatch and consequent fire hazard or to control shrub incursion into the grassland; in addition, the mown hay could be sold for revenue to help pay for the maintenance of the natural area. In forested natural areas there may come a time when it is felt necessary for management purposes to cut some of the trees to maintain the desired forest structure of the natural area, with the cut trees again providing revenue for area maintenance.

Some natural areas are suitable for educational activities such as walks along formal trails and educational products such as guidebooks. On the other hand, some natural areas are quite sensitive to human activities and should not be disturbed. When establishing natural areas and developing use guidelines for them, we must think of more than just the summer. While summer may be the season when peak activity takes place, other times of the year can be important to both people and wildlife and this must be taken into account when developing management plans for the area.

Volunteers, partnerships and societies are essential for both the establishment and maintenance of natural areas. Some people would say that volunteers are doing the work the government has abdicated; others would say it is work over and above what the government does; still others would say it is work entirely different from what the government does. Regardless of opinions, volunteers provide expertise and energy to help educate the public and those in the halls of power.

Acknowledgements

I would like to thank Lorna Allen with Parks and Protected Areas of Alberta Community Development, Terry Thormin from the Royal Alberta Museum, and Edgar T. Jones.

Can People and Wildlife Coexist? Planning Guidelines for Urban Wildlife

David A. Westworth, Westworth Associates Environmental Ltd.

Abstract

Wildlife are a valued component of urban parks and natural areas. Despite renewed interest by planners and resource managers in conserving our natural biodiversity, loss and fragmentation of habitat remains a major obstacle to the goal of maintaining viable wildlife populations in urban areas. Sustaining the diversity of wildlife species in our natural areas and green spaces requires a fundamental shift in the way that we have traditionally planned and built communities. Planning for wildlife should be carried out with clear and realistic objectives, together with an understanding of the fundamental ecological principles that govern the survival of wildlife populations. This paper provides a review of these ecological principles and offers guidelines to assist planners, developers and resource managers concerned with maintaining the ecological richness and quality of our urban environment.

Introduction

Because of the intrinsic aesthetic appeal of wildlife, there is broad public support for policies that promote wildlife conservation in urban areas. However, the goal of maintaining viable wildlife communities in densely-populated urban areas poses unique problems for planners and resource managers. Urban development remains a major cause of wildlife habitat loss in North America, and despite a more enlightened approach to urban planning and conservation generally, our track record in sharing our living spaces with other species has been very spotty.

The topic of this discussion, urban wildlife, and particularly the question of whether or not wildlife and humans can successfully coexist in urban areas, is a very broad issue. Current efforts to manage wildlife in urban areas focus primarily on two issues – maintaining the diversity of wildlife species in urban parks and natural areas and resolving conflicts between people and wildlife. The present discussion considers only the first of these issues and is intended to offer some insights and approaches that might be helpful to planners, developers, and resource managers concerned with maintaining the ecological richness and quality of our urban environment.

Urban Wildlife

Although we frequently use the term urban wildlife, we are of course talking about many of the same species and communities of organisms that inhabit rural areas (Figure 1). Whether they live within urban or rural landscapes, all wildlife species share basic requirements for food, water, cover and space. They are also subject to the same demographic processes and governed by the same principles that influence the survival of species or populations in less-developed areas.

Wildlife are common backyard visitors along Edmonton's river valley and ravine system. (photo by David A. Westworth).

Urban wildlife species are, however, subject to a number of major stressors including habitat loss and fragmentation, competition with non-native species, increased mortality from collisions with vehicles, overhead wires and windows, predation by domestic cats and dogs, and exposure to pollutants (Adams 1994). They are also exposed to potential physiological stresses associated with noise, human disturbance and urban climate change.

A number of urban-adaptable wildlife species will survive in urban areas with little or no conservation effort, and sometimes at densities substantially higher than in rural areas. For other species, a goal of maintaining communities of organisms or preserving natural biodiversity within urban landscapes requires careful planning and management.

Ecological Principles Relevant to Urban Planning

An understanding of some basic ecological principles related to conservation biology and landscape ecology is essential in designing plans or strategies for sustaining wildlife populations in urban areas. Conservation biology refers to the scientific study of factors and processes affecting the survival of species. Landscape ecology is the study of the structure, function and dynamics of ecosystems over large areas.

Habitat fragmentation and small patch effects: Although there is general consensus that habitat loss is the primary factor responsible for the decline of wildlife populations (Fahrig 1999), another feature of habitat loss is fragmentation. In relation to forest management, habitat fragmentation has been defined as reducing the size and connectivity of stands in a forest. McGarigal and McComb (1999) describe habitat fragmentation as a landscape-level process in which a specific habitat is progressively sub-divided into smaller and more isolated fragments.

Adams, L W. 1994. Urban Wildlife Habitats: A Landscape Perspective. University of Minnesota Press, Minneapolis, MN. 186 pp.

Fahrig, L. 1999. Forest loss and fragmentation: which has the greater effect on persistence of forest-dwelling animals? pp. 87-95 in: J A Rochelle, L A Lehmann, and J Wisniewski (eds.). Forest Fragmentation: Wildlife and Management Implications. Koninklijke Brill, Leiden, The Netherlands.

McGarigal, K and W C McComb. 1999. Forest fragmentation effects on breeding bird communities in the Oregon Coast Range. pp. 223-246 In: J.A. Rochelle, L.A. Lehmann, and J. Wisniewski (eds.). Forest Fragmentation: Wildlife and Management Implications. Koninklijke Brill, Leiden, The Netherlands. 301 pp.

Kareiva, P and U Wennergren. 1995. Connecting landscape patterns to ecosystem and population processes. Nature 373: 299-302.

Bunnell, F L. 1999. What habitat is an island? pp. 1-31 in: J A Rochelle, L A Lehmann, and J Wisniewski (eds.). Forest Fragmentation: Wildlife and Management Implications. Koninklijke Brill, Leiden, The Netherlands.

Galli, A E, D F Leck, and R T Forman. 1976. Avian distribution patterns in forest islands of different sizes in central New Jersey. Auk 93: 356-364.

Freemark, K E and G Merriam. 1986. Importance of area and habitat heterogeneity to bird assemblages in temperate forest fragments. Biological Conservation 36: 115-141.

MacArthur, R H and E O Wilson. 1967. The Theory of Island Biogeography. Princeton University Press, Princeton, NJ.

Concern that has been focussed on fragmentation by conservation biologists primarily relates to the potential effects of habitat fragmentation on population processes, particularly population extinction (Kareiva and Wennergren 1995, Bunnell 1999, McGarigal and McComb 1999). This notion is based on the well-established premise that as a habitat fragment becomes smaller it is able to support both fewer species and fewer individual organisms (Galli *et al.* 1976, Freemark and Merriam 1986, Adams 1994).

Increased isolation of fragments reduces the likelihood that organisms are able to move between habitat fragments. The population processes that operate within habitat fragments (or patches) have been compared to those that occur on oceanic islands, as described by MacArthur and Wilson's (1967) equilibrium theory of island biogeography. This theory postulates that smaller islands will support fewer species and experience more extinctions than large islands (primarily because of the vulnerability of small populations to stochastic events) and that more isolated islands will support fewer species because of the lower likelihood of immigration.

Although these ideas have been confirmed by subsequent empirical research, considerable discussion continues to occur around the issue of whether and to what extent habitat patches function in the same manner as oceanic islands. The central issue in this discussion involves the question of isolation and the extent to which species can move between habitat patches across a fragmented landscape.

Effects of patch size and shape: The size of a habitat patch influences wildlife abundance and diversity in several ways. In addition to the possibility that small patches will support an insufficient breeding population to avoid local extinction, differences in the characteristics and quality of habitat have been noted between smaller and larger patches. Large patches are more likely to support a greater diversity of habitat types and vegetation structural stages than small patches, thereby providing more niches for animals. As well, smaller patches are more likely to experience the edge-related effects of microclimatic change, disturbance, invasive species, increased predation and nest parasitism (Hobbs and Huenneke 1992, Paton 1994, Kremsater and Bunnell 1999, Herkert *et al.* 2003).

Both the size and shape of a habitat patch affect the amount of habitat available for edge species and for interior species (Bender *et al.* 1998, Barnes and Adams 1999). Although some studies report that edge effects may extend several hundred metres into a stand, most effects are concentrated within about 50 m of the patch edge (Barnes and Adams 1999). As illustrated in Figure 1, the proportion of interior habitat is rapidly reduced as the area of a patch is reduced or the shape of the patch becomes more linear. At some point, a patch consists entirely of edge habitat and does not provide suitable habitat for certain warblers, ovenbirds or other species that rely on interior habitat.

The conclusion that smaller habitat patches support fewer species than larger patches has been verified by many studies. Adams (1996) reviews a number of studies that pertain specifically to urban areas (Figure 2). These studies indicate that the relationship between patch size and species richness occurs at many taxonomic levels, including birds and invertebrates. More recently, Crooks (2002) studied the use of urban habitat fragments by nine native species of mammalian carnivores. He reported that six of these species were sensitive to fragmentation, generally disappearing as habitat patches became smaller and more isolated.

Landscape connectivity and the role of corridors: From the perspective of landscape ecology, a landscape consists of three main components: a matrix, habitat patches, and corridors connecting the habitat patches (Barnes and Adams 1999). In a

Hobbs, R J and L F Huenneke. 1992. Disturbance, diversity and invasion: implications for conservation. Conservation Biology 6: 324-337.

Paton, W C. 1994. The effect of edge on avian nesting success: how strong is the evidence? Conservation Biology 8: 17-26.

Kremsater, L and F L Bunnell. 1999. Edge effects: theory, evidence and implications to management of western North American forests. pp. 117-153 *in*: J.A. Rochelle, L.A. Lehmann, and J. Wisniewski (eds.). Forest fragmentation: wildlife and management implications. Koninklijke Brill, Leiden, The Netherlands. 301 pp.

Herkert, J R, D L Reinking, D A Wiedenfeld, M Winter, J L Zimmerman, W E Jensen, E J Finck, R R Koford, D H Wolfe, S K Sherrod, M A Jenkins, J Faaborg, and S K Robinson. 2003. Effects of prairie fragmentation on the nest success of breeding birds in the midcontinental United States. The Journal of the Society for Conservation Biology 17: 587-594.

Bender, D J, T A Contreras and L Fahrig. 1998. Habitat loss and population decline: A meta-analysis of the patch size effect. Ecology 79: 517-533.

Barnes, T G and L Adams. 1999. A Guide to urban conservation planning. Publ. FOR-74. College of Extensive Service, University of Kentucky. 8 pp.

Crooks, K R. 2002. Relative sensitivities of mammalian carnivores to habitat fragmentation. Conservation Biology 16: 488-502.

Figure 1.

Effects of patch size and shape on habitat availability for interior species.
Interior habitat decreases as the patch becomes smaller and more linear.

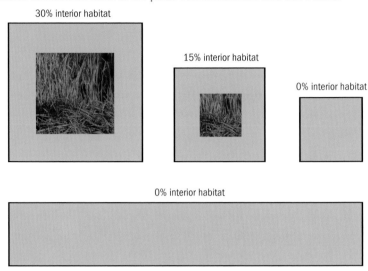

30% interior habitat

15% interior habitat

0% interior habitat

0% interior habitat

Figure 2

Effects of patch size on faunal species diversity (adapted from Adams 1994).
Small patches can have very low diversity.

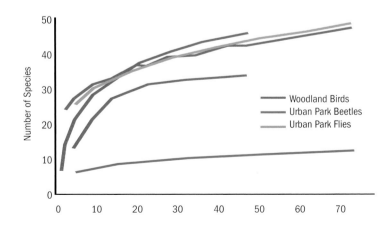

fragmented landscape, the matrix becomes the dominant component of the landscape and corridors become increasingly important in linking habitat patches. The importance of corridors depends on both the types of species that exist there and the nature of the surrounding matrix.

Research on the effects on wildlife of habitat fragmentation resulting from timber harvesting has shown that effects are species specific. Because of inherent differences in gap-crossing abilities, wildlife species respond to landscape patchiness differently, with some species appearing relatively resilient to the effects of fragmentation (Bunnell 1999, With 1999). This has led some authors to use percolation theory and other analytical approaches to explain the response of species to the various degrees of patchiness that might exist on a landscape (With 1999).

Although some species, notably birds, are able to move relatively easily across patchy landscapes, others are not. Small mammals, such as mice, voles and chipmunks, have been shown to have limited gap-crossing ability, and depend on vegetative corridors to avoid predation and move safely between habitat patches (Wegner and Merriam 1979, Henderson *et al.* 1985, La Polla and Barrett 1993). The role of corridors in minimizing the effects of isolation on small mammals in fragmented habitats is illustrated in a study conducted by Mech and Hallett (2001), which compared the genetic distances between populations of red-backed voles and deer mice within three types of landscapes: landscapes with a contiguous forest cover, isolated or fragmented landscapes, and landscapes in which uncut forest patches were connected by a corridor of closed-canopy forest. In the case of the red-backed vole, a closed-canopy forest specialist, forest fragmentation increased the genetic distance between sampled populations; however, genetic differences were less pronounced between populations linked by corridors. In the case of

With, K A. 1999. Is landscape connectivity necessary and sufficient for wildlife management? 97-115 pp. In: J.A. Rochelle, L.A. Lehmann, and J. Wisniewski (eds.). Forest fragmentation: wildlife and management implications. Koninklijke Brill, Leiden, The Netherlands. 301 pp.

Wegner, J F and F Merriam. 1979. Movement by birds and small mammals between a wood and surrounding farmland habitat. Journal of Applied Ecology 16: 349-358.

Henderson, M T, G Merriam, and J Wegner. 1985. Patchy environments and species survival: chipmunks in an agricultural mosaic. Biological Conservation 31: 95-105.

LaPolla, V N and G W Barrett. 1993. Effects of corridor width and presence on the population dynamics of the meadow vole (*Microtus pennsylvanicus*). Landscape Ecology 8: 25-37.

Mech, S G and J G Hallett. 2001. Evaluating the effectiveness of corridors: a genetic approach. Conservation Biology 15(2): 467-474.

the deer mouse, a habitat generalist, genetic distances were not significantly different among the various landscape configurations.

Despite their greater mobility, birds have also been shown to use corridors to move between patches of suitable habitat (Machtans *et al.* 1996). There is even evidence that wooded streets that connect urban parks may function as corridors for certain bird species, allowing these species to extend foraging and nesting activities into the urban matrix (Fernandez-Junicic 2000).

The importance of corridors to wildlife in fragmented landscapes is likely influenced by the characteristics of the landscape matrix. Many species are adapted to natural landscape heterogeneity and are able to move through areas of suboptimal habitat in search of resources (food, breeding sites) associated with patches of preferred habitat. As the landscape matrix becomes less hospitable, this movement is expected to decrease. In urban areas, where the landscape matrix is dominated by residential, commercial and industrial development, the landscape matrix becomes particularly hostile and impermeable to many wildlife species. For these species, movement between habitat patches will not occur in the absence of wildlife corridors. In this sense, it might be argued that habitat patches within an urban landscape are more likely to function like oceanic islands than they would if the surrounding matrix consisted of managed forest or even agricultural land.

Metapopulations and source-sink theory: Because the number of breeding individuals within habitat patches decreases with reductions in patch size, a population of a particular species may rely on access to a number of patches of suitable habitat to maintain minimum viable population size and avoid local extinction (Shaffer 1987, 1990). The term metapopulation was introduced to describe populations that are actually comprised of smaller sub-populations distributed between disjunct habitat patches (Levins 1970 cited in

Machtans, C S, M-A Villard, and S J Hannon. 1996. Use of riparian buffer strips as movement corridors by forest birds. Conservation Biology 10: 1366-1379.

Fernandez-Juricic, E. 2000. Avifaunal use of wooded streets in an urban landscape. Conservation Biology 14(2): 513-521.

Shaffer, M L. 1987. Minimum viable populations: coping with uncertainty. In: M.E. Soulé (ed.) Viable populations for conservation. Cambridge University Press, Cambridge, UK. 189 pp.

Shaffer, M L. 1990. Population viability analysis. Conservation Biology 4: 39-40.

Bunnell 1999). Because of the small population sizes, each patch faces the risk of local extinction and relies on recolonization from other patches. Connectivity between habitat patches is essential to maintain the metapopulation.

Within a fragmented landscape some habitat patches may be large enough to sustain local populations, whereas others are not. From a population perspective the larger patches may serve as sources, while the smaller patches act as sinks (With 1999). In fragmented landscapes some populations are only likely to survive if core source habitats produce enough surplus young to compensate for the increased mortality rates experienced in sink habitats (Perkins *et al.* 2003). This type of metapopulation arrangement is illustrated in Figure 3. Habitat corridors are necessary to facilitate dispersal between patches and prevent the disappearance of species from patches functioning as population sinks.

An Approach to Planning for Wildlife in an Urban Landscape

Planning for wildlife in urban areas involves applying these ecological principles to the urban planning and landscape design process. Although we have much to learn about how to apply these principles in ways that will effectively preserve biodiversity in urban areas, various authors have suggested guidelines that can be incorporated into a planning framework to promote urban habitat conservation (Adams 1994, Barnes and Adams 1999, Hansen *et al.* 1993). The following approach, which is described as a series of steps, incorporates many of these ideas.

Step 1: Set Clear Goals or Objectives

Most municipalities now have a broad conservation strategy or have policies in place that govern natural area conservation. Since habitat

Levins, R. 1970. Extinction. pp. 77-107 In: M. Gerstenhaber (ed.). Lectures on mathematics in the life sciences. Vol. 2. American Mathematical Society. Providence, RI.

Perkins, D W, P D Vickery, and W G Shriver. 2003. Spatial dynamics of source-sink habitats: effects on rare grassland birds. J. Wildl. Manage. 67(3): 588-599.

Hansen, A J, S L Garman, B Marks, and D L Urban. 1993. An approach for managing vertebrate diversity across multiple-use landscapes. Ecological Applications 3: 481-496.

Figure 3

Arrangement of habitat patches in a metapopulation.

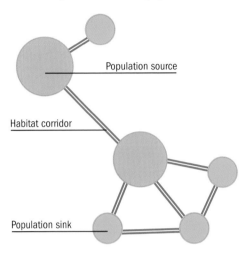

Population source

Habitat corridor

Population sink

conservation goals must be balanced with other community goals, the process of establishing conservation goals and priorities normally involves community consultation and input from planners, developers, landscape architects and conservation organizations. What most municipalities are lacking are detailed plans or procedures for implementing these broad policies.

Unambiguous goals that clearly set out the conservation priorities help to guide the planning process. Broad goals related to maintaining biodiversity, ecological integrity, or ecosystem health are often too general to base specific planning and management actions on. A need exists to focus these objectives. For example, in terms of biodiversity conservation, an effort should be made to identify which components of biodiversity can realistically be maintained within a particular urban landscape. We know that it is possible to implement strategies to conserve biodiversity at a number of organizational levels (Hansen *et al.* 1993). Because we cannot maintain populations of all species in an urban landscape does not make efforts to conserve portions of our biodiversity any less relevant.

Tools are available to assist planners and resource managers in establishing biodiversity objectives. Published lists that provide information on home range sizes, sensitivity to landscape change and gap-crossing abilities by many vertebrate wildlife species are helpful for identifying species that can be expected to survive in fragmented, urban landscapes. Selection of umbrella species or a suite of indicator species may be helpful in focusing conservation efforts (Roberge and Angelstam 2004).

Step 2: Conduct Inventories

How can we realistically develop plans or programs to conserve wildlife in an urban landscape if we don't know what we have to work with? An inventory of remaining habitat and biodiversity is an essential requirement for effective planning. Because of cost considerations, however, many cities are reluctant to initiate city wide inventories of their ecological resources.

Inventories should be conducted at both the stand and patch scale and at the landscape scale. Detailed inventories of the plant and animal species associated with specific habitat types is needed to establish biodiversity benchmarks and to identify any rare or unique species or habitats that require special management provisions. At the landscape scale the inventory should include an analysis of the size and distribution of habitat patches and the degree of connectivity between remaining habitat areas.

Step 3: Develop Habitat Conservation Plans

Once inventories are completed, planners can move on to the difficult tasks of determining which habitat patches should be protected and developing landscape designs that will meet their

Roberge, J and P Angelstam. 2004. Usefulness of the umbrella species concept as a conservation tool. Conservation Biology 18 (1): 76-83.

conservation goals. This is where the "rubber meets the road" and likely represents the point at which urban habitat conservation programs either succeed or fail. Land values in cities like Edmonton make the cost of securing natural areas at least an order of magnitude higher than they would be in rural areas. Determining fiscal priorities can be a long and difficult process involving policy makers, the civic administration, stakeholders and the public at large. This aspect of urban habitat conservation is addressed by other authors in this volume. My objective is to attempt to relate the ecological principles described above to planning guidelines that may be helpful to planners in implementing urban habitat conservation programs once funding is in place and conservation priorities are determined.

Planning for Wildlife at the Landscape Scale

Planning for wildlife should occur at a number of scales; however, it is unlikely that a goal of conserving a substantial portion of the region's natural biodiversity can be achieved unless habitat conservation strategies are first put in place at the landscape scale. This entails conserving habitat patches that are representative of regional vegetation communities and connecting them in ways that will facilitate movement or dispersal of wildlife between patches. This should include efforts to retain some larger patches to provide habitat for interior species, as well as any rare or unique habitats that may be important for endemic species.

Habitat conservation planning would benefit from an analysis of patch dynamics, including the identification of potential sources, sinks, and corridors. Although population viability analysis for a wide range of species is impractical, a more detailed analysis of habitat requirements for a suite of indicator species would be helpful in identifying landscape-scale conservation requirements.

Hansen *et al.* (1993) point out that there is a strong theoretical basis as well as empirical evidence for using habitat as an indicator of demography. Geographic information systems (GIS) are a valuable tool for evaluating habitat conservation opportunities at the landscape scale.

Planning for Wildlife at the Patch Scale

A number of tools are available for conserving natural habitats within urban areas (Westworth Associates Environmental Ltd. 2001). In addition to acquiring these sites, however, planners should also develop landscape designs that will continue to sustain wildlife populations within these natural areas. These should include provisions to protect core habitat areas from excessive human disturbance and to design buffers that will reduce the adverse effects of adjacent land-uses.

A number of authors (Adams 1994, Barnes and Adams 1999, Noss and Cooperrider 1994) have suggested a possible design for urban wildlife reserves that address some of these concerns (Figure 4). Based on earlier work by Harris (1984) and Noss and Harris (1986), this approach incorporates a form of conservation zoning and buffering to protect the natural values of conserved sites and connecting corridors to link core habitat areas.

It is important that urban habitat designs also consider human needs and preferences. Access to our green spaces is important to maintain public support for conservation programs. Although there is a need to protect core habitats to achieve biodiversity objectives, there is also a need to provide sufficient opportunities for people to interact with nature. Children, for example, are more interested in "creepy-crawly" forms of wildlife and make extensive use of smaller ponds, woodlots or open spaces located within neighbourhoods. Several years ago I was conducting an

Westworth Associates Environmental Ltd. 2001. Conserving Edmonton's Natural Areas: a framework for conservation planning in an urban landscape. Community Services, City of Edmonton. Edmonton, AB. 174 pp.

Noss, R F and A Y Cooperrider. 1994. Saving nature's legacy: protecting and restoring biodiversity. Island Press, Washington, DC. 416 pp.

Harris, L D. 1984. The fragmented forest: island biogeography theory and the preservation of biotic diversity. University of Chicago Press, Chicago, ILL.

Noss, R F and D Harris. 1986. Nodes, networks, and MUMs: preserving diversity at all scales. Environmental Management 10: 299-309.

Figure 4

A possible design for urban habitat reserves (adapted from Noss and Harris 1986).

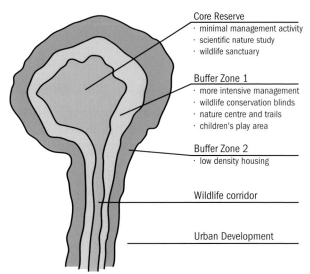

Core Reserve
· minimal management activity
· scientific nature study
· wildlife sanctuary

Buffer Zone 1
· more intensive management
· wildlife conservation blinds
· nature centre and trails
· children's play area

Buffer Zone 2
· low density housing

Wildlife corridor

Urban Development

environmental assessment of a proposed development in Hermitage Park in Edmonton. While conducting a baseline field survey I stopped to talk to two young boys on bicycles. When I asked them what wildlife they had seen, they listed several species and then rode off, returning momentarily with a young red-sided garter snake in hand. They then led me to a pond that was serving as a rearing habitat for hundreds of young snakes.

Designing Corridors for Wildlife

If, as suggested earlier, an urban landscape consists of habitat patches scattered across an inhospitable and relatively impermeable matrix, then corridors linking these habitat patches are essential for maintaining wildlife populations and conserving biodiversity. The need for corridors is not restricted to wildlife. Isolated vegetation communities that face the loss of pollinating insects or corridors for seed dispersal may also lose genetic diversity (Kirchner *et al.* 2003).

The concept of designing habitat corridors to link isolated habitat fragments into a regional reserve network has been explored by Noss (1993) and others. Landscape ecologists and planners have incorporated many of these ideas into the concept of greenways (Smith and Hellmund 1993). Greenways have evolved into a major planning approach in North America, providing multiple-use corridors that, properly designed, can help to offset the effects of fragmentation on wildlife while providing a range of recreation benefits to people. Within the City of Edmonton, the North Saskatchewan River Valley and ravine system, which is protected as part of Edmonton's ribbon of green, provides a greenway corridor that extends across the city. Recent planning studies have recommended the conversion of utility corridors to greenways as a means of linking isolated habitat patches in the city's tablelands with the river valley and ravine system (Westworth Associates Environmental Ltd. 2000).

From an urban planning and design standpoint, there are two issues that need to be considered – designing effective corridors between habitat patches and protecting these corridors from subsequent fragmentation by road construction or other development. Presently, well established guidelines for corridor design are lacking, although this issue is receiving increased

Kirchner, F, J Ferdy, C Andalo, B Colas, and J Moret. 2003. Role of corridors in plant dispersal: an example with the endangered *Ranunculus nodiflorus*. Conservation Biology 17 (2), 401-410.

Noss, R F. 1993. Wildlife corridors. pp. 43-68. In: D.S. Smith and P.C. Hellmund (eds.). Ecology of Greenways. University of Minnesota Press, Minneapolis, MN.

Smith, D S and P C Hellmund (eds.). 1993. Ecology of greenways. University of Minnesota Press, Minneapolis, MN. 222 pp.

Westworth Associates Environmental Ltd. 2000. A conservation-based approach to urban development in the Heritage Valley Area. Report prepared for Planning and Development, City of Edmonton. Edmonton, AB. 180 pp.

Henein, K and G Merriam. 1990. The elements of connectivity where corridor quality is variable. Landscape Ecology, 4(2/3): 157-170.

Etter, D R, K A M Hollis, T R Van Deelen, D R Ludwig, J E Chelsvig, C L Anchor, and R E Warner. 2002. Survival and movements of white-tailed deer in suburban Chicago, IL. J. Wildl. Manage. 66(2): 500-510.

attention by conservation biologists and landscape ecologists. Clearly wildlife species differ widely in terms of their gap-crossing ability and corridor requirements. A general guideline would be to design corridors to meet the requirements of the most sensitive species that the urban habitat conservation program is intended to protect. Alternatively, corridors can be designed to address the needs of an umbrella species, a species whose protection would be expected to benefit the largest number of other species. Corridor requirements are likely to vary across an urban landscape. Small habitat patches that are being retained as habitat for certain birds, small mammals and amphibians, and reptiles have different corridor requirements than larger patches designed to accommodate carnivores or ungulates.

The width of corridors and other specific design criteria should be established in consultation with biologists familiar with the species in the region. Generally, corridors should be wide enough to minimize edge effects, including exposure to excessive levels of predation (Noss 1993). Low quality corridors could act as population sinks, adversely affecting the size of a metapopulation (Heinein and Merriam 1990). Corridors that include the full range of habitats found in habitat conservation areas are more likely to meet the needs of a diversity of wildlife species. Promoting the retention and planting of native species within corridors also promotes biodiversity conservation by reducing the flow of invasive plant and animal species into conservation areas.

Roads are a major cause of habitat fragmentation and a significant cause of wildlife mortality. Although hunting and predation are the leading causes of deer mortality in rural areas, vehicle collisions have been shown to be the principal mortality factor in suburban deer populations (Etter *et al.* 2002). These concerns have led planners and resource managers to examine a variety of approaches for allowing wildlife to cross roads. These vary from dry or wet culverts to facilitate roadway crossings by amphibians or small mammals (Clevenger and Waltho 1999) to extensive fencing programs and construction of large underpasses or overpasses to permit crossing by ungulates and large carnivores (Clevenger *et al.* 2002).

What many of these roadway-crossing solutions have in common is their high cost relative to the least expensive construction alternatives. Cost factors frequently result in the construction of roads across stream valleys and other natural landscape corridors that effectively block wildlife movement or force animals to cross road surfaces, resulting in wildlife mortality. In some instances, major roadways become mortality sinks and may threaten the survival of a wildlife population. Roads that inhibit dispersal of animals promote isolation of populations and seriously compromise the conservation function of a wildlife corridor (Noss 1993).

In the City of Edmonton, we have examples of both well designed crossings and poorly designed crossings. Recent examples such as the bridge crossings that were approved at Ellerslie Road and Blackmud Creek and at the crossing of Wedgewood Ravine by the Anthony Henday Freeway incorporate provisions for wildlife movement corridors (Figure 5). Because of the comparatively high construction costs, these solutions were only agreed upon after lengthy and sometimes heated discussions among project engineers, biologists, landscape architects and administrators. Unfortunately these battles are being fought on a case-by-case basis and the outcomes are not always acceptable from a conservation perspective. This is a case where a need exists for leadership by government authorities to ensure that infrastructure development proceeds in a manner that is consistent with the municipality's conservation objectives.

Clevenger, A P and N Waltho. 1999. Dry drainage culvert use and design considerations for small- and medium-sized mammal movement across a major transportation corridor. pp. 263-277 In: Proceedings of the Third International Conference on Wildlife Ecology and Transportation. G. Evink, P. Garrett, and D. Ziegler (eds.)

Clevenger, A P, B Chruszcz, K Gunson, and J Wierzchowski. 2002. Roads and wildlife in the Canadian Rocky Mountain Parks – Movements, mortality and mitigation. Final Report (October 2002). Report prepared for Parks Canada. Banff, AB.

Figure 5

An example of a bridge design that incorporates provisions for movement of wildlife.

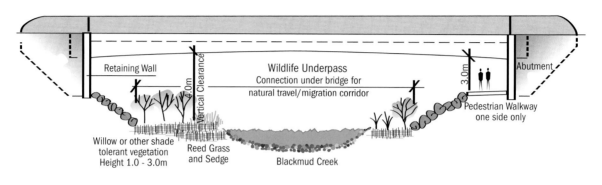

Retaining Wall

Vertical Clearance 3.0m

Wildlife Underpass
Connection under bridge for
natural travel/migration corridor

3.0m

Abutment

Pedestrian Walkway
one side only

Willow or other shade
tolerant vegetation
Height 1.0 - 3.0m

Reed Grass
and Sedge

Blackmud Creek

Wildlife Corridor Design
Ellerslie Road/Blackmud Creek Bridge
South Elevation

Developing Urban Stormwater Ponds as Wildlife Habitat

Natural wetlands are among our most diverse and productive wildlife habitats. They are also habitats that face high threat from urban development. Faced with the dilemma of wetland loss, biologists and landscape architects have, in recent years, advocated the retention of natural wetlands as components of municipal drainage plans and construction of wet stormwater detention ponds that include provisions for wildlife.

Many such ponds have now been constructed in Edmonton and other communities. Virtually all of these ponds attract some wetland wildlife, notably Canada geese, although they differ widely in their suitability as wildlife habitat. Most fail to address all of the habitat requirements of the species they are designed to attract. For example, some ponds include islands or unmowed vegetation along shorelines as nesting habitat for waterfowl but the steep shorelines fail to allow

'Naturalized' stormwater detention ponds attract many species of wetland wildlife, but do they pose a risk to wildlife? (photo by David A. Westworth).

the establishment of adequate brood-rearing cover. In cases where adequate cover is not provided, wildlife attracted to these ponds may face high predation rates by gulls, corvids or domestic pets.

There is a need for municipal authorities to develop guidelines that will assist planners and developers in designing stormwater ponds that better meet the needs of wildlife. Provincial and federal wildlife agencies and conservation organizations such as Ducks Unlimited can provide assistance in developing these guidelines. Organizations such as the National Institute for Urban Wildlife in the United States have also published guidelines specifically related to the design of urban stormwater ponds as wildlife habitat.

There is also a need to monitor wildlife use of these ponds to determine their habitat effectiveness and to assess potential wildlife health risks. Stormwater runoff is not the same as rainwater. As stormwater drains across roads, residential lots, construction sites, golf courses and other surfaces in urban areas, it accumulates a wide-range of toxic substances including oil and grease, pesticide residues, polychlorinated biphenyls (PCBs), polycyclic aromatic hydrocarbons (PAHs) and heavy metals such as lead, zinc, copper and mercury. Recent studies have raised concern that the chemical pollutants in stormwater may be hazardous to aquatic life.

Environment Canada reports that a recent survey of stormwater detention ponds in southern Ontario municipalities found that levels of one or more of these organic and inorganic contaminants in the sediments exceeded provincial guideline levels in 14 of the 15 ponds sampled (Bishop *et al.* 1999). Concentrations of some compounds in the water exceeded the Canadian Water Quality Guidelines for the Protection of Aquatic Life (CCME 1999). With respect to wildlife, these researchers detected elevated levels of PCBs and DDE in red-winged blackbird eggs at two sites where they nested and reduced survival of leopard frog eggs and tadpoles at one of four sites selected for amphibian bioassays. On the basis of these initial findings the researchers concluded that stormwater ponds do not provide good quality habitat for fish and wildlife and recommended that natural wetlands not be used to treat stormwater (Bishop *et al.* 1999).

Conclusion

In conclusion, while wildlife and people can coexist in urban areas, sustaining the diversity of wildlife species in our natural areas and green spaces requires a fundamental shift in the way that we have traditionally planned and built communities. Urban landscapes need to be designed for wildlife as well as for people. Planning for wildlife should be carried out with clear and realistic objectives, together with an understanding of the fundamental ecological principles that govern the survival of wildlife populations. Exposure to wildlife increases our enjoyment of our open spaces and backyards, and the presence of a diverse wildlife community serves as an indicator of a diverse and healthy urban environment.

Bishop, C A, J Stuger, L Dunn, D Forder, and S Kok. 1999. Stormwater detention ponds of Southern Ontario: Are they a risk to wildlife? Great Lakes Fact Sheet. Canadian Wildlife Service, Environment Canada. Downsview, ON.

Urban Wildlife Issues in Northern Cities: A Case Study for Edmonton

Ross W. Wein and Anish Neupane, University of Alberta

Abstract

Protected areas in urban settings have high value and will become increasingly valuable over time for plant and animal biodiversity protection, recreation, relaxation and other health reasons. The most heavily modified landscapes of urban areas retain some measure of biodiversity protection and our young, northern cities have retained more than most cities. This review for the City of Edmonton introduces the state of our knowledge about plant and animal wildlife and both the positive and negative aspects of human-wildlife interactions. We recognize that the city has lost many large mammal species such as bison, grizzly bears and wolves, but citizens can still be thrilled with the range of plant and animal species in the river valley. The most common negative interactions include collisions of large mammals with motor vehicles and wildlife entering human habitations that result in property devaluation. It is hoped that upland protected areas in Edmonton can be linked to the valley so that wild plants and animals can maintain viable populations.

Forman, R T T. 1995. Land mosaics: the ecology of landscapes and regions. Cambridge Univ. Press, NY. 632 pp.

Flink, C A and R M Searns. 1993. Greenways: a guide to planning, design and development. Edited by L.LaB. Schwarz. Island Press, Washington, DC. 375 pp.

Fabos, J Gy and J Ahern (eds.). 1996. Greenways: the beginning of an international movement. Elsevier, Amsterdam. 491 pp.

Murphy, D D. 1988. Challenges to biological diversity in urban areas. Pages 71-76 In E. O. Wilson, (ed.). Biodiversity. National Academy Press, Washington, DC. 521 pp.

Soulé, M E. 1991. Land use planning and wildlife maintenance: guidelines for conserving wildlife in an urban landscape. APA Journal, Summer: 313-323.

White, R R. 1994. Urban environmental management. Wiley, New York, NY. 233 pp.

Adams, L W. 1994. Urban wildlife habitats: a landscape perspective. University of Minnesota Press, Minneapolis, MN. 186 pp.

Introduction

The theory and practice of rural landscape conservation has received much attention in recent decades (Forman 1995) and at the same time conservation in urban areas has undergone a renaissance as evidenced by the greenways concept (Flink and Searns 1993, Fabos and Ahern 1996). Increasingly, there is interest in the protection of biodiversity within greenways of urban landscapes (Murphy 1988, Soulé 1991, White 1994) and establishment of an interconnected network of functional conservation units, which we term a conservation net.

There are many visions and practical approaches to the study and management of urban wildlife. Adams (1994) classified urban areas into three zones based on the intensity of land-use. The first, metro centre, is the city core where there is little vegetation suitable for wildlife habitat and there are few wildlife species except avian residents that nest around buildings: Edmonton has a small percentage of this zone. The second zone, suburbia, has landscaped spaces and remnants of former natural areas where wildlife find suitable habitat. Here, wildlife has become dependant on intentional or unintentional food and shelter resources provided by humans. This zone is represented in Edmonton by a circle of older neighborhoods, built before the 1970s, around the city core. The third zone, urban-rural interface, is where opportunities to conserve more of the natural landscape still exists. In Edmonton this represents the more recently developing suburbs. Adams (1994 p.73) also recognizes the value of corridors as "strips of habitat that serve as travel lanes for the seasonal movement of wildlife and as interconnecting links between or among habitat reserves" that cross these zones. These seasonal travel corridors in Edmonton are represented by the North Saskatchewan River Valley and ravines.

In northern climates, there are strong seasonal changes in wildlife populations. Best known are the migratory birds, which return in the spring and then are widely distributed through the city. In the autumn and winter, migratory species travel south and winter residents move into the valley for thermal shelter and food resources. These seasonal patterns are modified by humans who provide additional thermal, food and shelter resources for wildlife.

The general objective of this study was to review the present state of some urban wildlife and some of the interactions between humans and wildlife in the North Saskatchewan River Valley and uplands of the City of Edmonton.

City of Edmonton Characteristics

The natural ecosystems of the City of Edmonton are similar to those described for the Aspen Parkland Ecoregion (Strong and Leggat 1992) of which 95% has been heavily modified by agriculture (Van Tighem 1993). The history of industrial resource use in the Edmonton region can be traced back to the mid- to late-1800s when river valley forests were harvested for fuel, construction materials, and farms. Photographs of this era show only a few stands of young aspen trees (e.g. Esdale and McDermid 1914). By 1900, agricultural cropland developed quickly on most of the tableland while the river valley was pastured. Later, as suburban development replaced farming, the ecosystems of the valley began to develop into young forests.

The northern city of Edmonton is located at 53° 33'N latitude and is about 700 km^2 in size. The North Saskatchewan River has cut to a depth of 100 to 150 m into the sedimentary geological formations. The highly unstable and erodable slopes of the valley are not conducive to construction (Godfrey 1993) and legislation prevents building on the slopes. The 74 km^2 ribbon of green

Strong, W L, and K R Leggat. 1992. Eco-regions of Alberta. Alberta Forestry, Lands and Wildlife, Edmonton, AB. 59 pp.

Van Tighem, K. 1993. Alberta's endangered species: keeping the wild in the West. Borealis 4(12): 1-16.

Esdale, M and F G McDermid. 1914. Edmonton: Alberta's capital city. The Esdale Press Ltd., and McDermid Engraving Co. Ltd., Edmonton, AB. 180 pp.

Godfrey, J D. 1993. Edmonton beneath our feet. Edmonton Geological Society, Edmonton, AB. 150 pp.

Anonymous. 1992. Ribbon of green: North Saskatchewan River Valley and Ravine System Master Plan. Edmonton Parks and Recreation, City of Edmonton. Edmonton, AB. 112 pp.

Anonymous. 1980. Environmental inventory and analysis of the North Saskatchewan River Valley and Ravine System – vegetation pp. 104-144, wildlife pp. 145-202. In North Saskatchewan River Valley and Ravine System Biophysical Study. Submitted to City of Edmonton. Edmonton, AB. 391 pp.

O'Leary, D, J Bentz, D Ealey and A Schwabenbauer. 1993. Inventory of environmentally sensitive and significant natural areas – City of Edmonton. Prepared for Planning and Development, City of Edmonton by Geowest Environmental Consultants. Edmonton, AB. 303 pp. plus map.

Westworth Associates Environmental Ltd. 2001. Conserving Edmonton's Natural Areas; a framework for conservation planning in an urban landscape. Community Services, City of Edmonton. Edmonton, AB. 174 pp.

City of Edmonton. 1995. Conservation of natural sites in Edmonton's table lands. Policy No. C467. Edmonton, AB. 15 pp.

City of Edmonton. 1996. Parks and Recreation Bylaw No. 2202. Edmonton, AB. 21 pp.

(Anonymous 1992) protected area consisting of the North Saskatchewan River Valley, and its 14 associated ravines, is the backbone of conservation areas within the city boundaries and is viewed as a natural conservation corridor. Protected areas studies include Anonymous (1980), O'Leary *et al.* (1993) and Westworth Associates Environmental Ltd. (2001); policies that relate to these areas are included in several bylaws (City of Edmonton 1995, 1996).

People and Wildlife

Edmonton is a small city (about 750,000 people) when viewed in the international context. Human use surveys show that interviewees visited the trail system an average of 26 times and the river valley parks an average of 10 times over the past year. Translating these estimates to the population of Edmonton, there are millions of visits to the valley annually; the city planners expect the number of users to increase over time.

All of this activity represents the invasion of the wildlife habitat by humans. Much of the human activity occurs during the day and early evening, so the nights are for the wildlife. There is also much more human activity during the long days of summer, so the winter remains the domain of the non-migratory wildlife species.

Even though the biodiversity of the valley attracts thousands of people each month, we have a weak understanding of the wildlife inventory over time. How many native and introduced species of wildlife do we have in the valley? This is not well known, although available synthesis lists from secondary sources suggest the following: vascular plants (325), mosses (about 50), lichens (about 40), mammals (50), birds (total 150, summer breeding 60, winter 60, birds along river 30), amphibians/reptiles (7), fishes (27) (Anonymous 1980, O'Leary *et al.* 1993). A useful comparison can

Walkers enjoy wildlife in the city, but some dogs are attracted to porcupines – to the dog's detriment (photo by Ross W. Wein, 1996).

be made with the Elk Island National Park where the numbers are vascular plants (430), mammals (47), birds (230), and amphibians/reptiles (6) (Chapman 1991). Probably most of the plant and animal species of the Aspen Parkland are represented in Edmonton but population estimates of animals are few. Information on such topics as rare species is scarce or dated and few detailed surveys or repeated monitoring studies are available. There have been winter surveys of deer in the valley (Folinsbee 1993) and there is a data set of road kills for the years 1996 and 1997. The Annual Christmas Bird Count attracts hundreds of observers.

There are also records of conflicts between people and groups of wild species that include insects, birds and mammals. Mammals that receive more notice in the popular media are skunk, beaver, coyote, porcupine, deer, and moose. Nuisance species of birds and

Chapman, R. 1991. The discoverer's guide to Elk Island National Park. Lone Pine Publishing and The Friends of Elk Island Society, Edmonton, AB. 96 pp.

Folinsbee, J. 1993. City of Edmonton deer survey 15 January 1993. Unpublished report. Department of Environmental Protection, Edmonton, AB. 11 pp.

mammals (as identified under the Agriculture Pests Act, Pests and Nuisance Control Regulation) include the following: English sparrow, pigeon, European starling, magpie, bushy-tailed wood rat, coyote, skunk, ground squirrel (Richardson's, Franklin's, thirteen-lined, Columbian), northern pocket gopher, deer mouse, meadow vole, and house mouse (City of Edmonton, Community Services, Wildlife Management Guidelines, draft report).

Administrative responsibility for recording these conflicts has changed over time. At present, on City property, Pest Management Services deals with species such as beaver, skunk and squirrel. For private property, the City Pound issues traps to property owners. The River Valley Park Rangers of the City of Edmonton investigates complaints related to wildlife and deal with them in appropriate manners; the Rangers co-ordinate their activities with other government agencies. Government of Alberta, Fish and Wildlife primarily deals with large animals that include deer and moose. Alberta Transport, Driver Safety, Research and Traffic Safety keep data on the motor vehicle collisions involving wild and domestic animals, as reported by the Edmonton Police Service.

Wildlife Populations

Wild plants and vegetation in the valley have changed dramatically over time. Before city development there were only native plant species and most landscapes were dominated by spruce and aspen forests while riverside landscapes were dominated by balsam poplar, alder and willows (Strong and Leggat 1992). Forests were almost completely harvested and now stands of trees are mostly less than 80 years of age. During the early days of city development there were probably more extensive areas of agricultural weeds in the valley than today, as the forest returns. Gardening enthusiasts introduced many non-native tree, shrub, vegetable and fruit species, which have become part of our river valley flora.

Urbanization has eliminated the grizzly bear, wolf and bison; infrequently, species moving into the city along corridors include black bear and cougar. Other species were heavily hunted and trapped during the early development of the city and are now recovering as forests mature. There is little documentation of the recent changes of wild species and population changes over years. When examining the populations of wildlife it is important to recognize the overwhelming numbers of domestic cats and dogs that strongly influence wild animal populations in parts of the city. Almost 60,000 people have registered about 50,000 dogs and over 32,000 cats in the year 2000 (City of Edmonton, Bylaw Services); many people use the valley parks and trails for dog walking daily.

While emphasizing the few wildlife studies, there is much general knowledge and some population estimates for some species. Some species can vary widely in number from year to year; for example, many deer died as a result of deep snow and then warm air temperatures that caused crusting of the snow in 1996. As deer congregate for shelter in the river valley and ravines in the winter, they can be more easily counted. Records from a 1993 winter aerial survey (Table 1) provide estimated densities as low as 0.7 deer/ km² in the city core and as high as 2.8 deer/ km² in the Whitemud/Blackmud Creek areas. Coyotes recorded at the same time had a mean density for all areas studied of 0.12/km². Beaver have been identified by citizens as a problem species and there has been a continuing program of monitoring populations, which tend to be quite stable. A 2001 survey estimated a city beaver population of about 2000, with a population of about 1000 in the Whitemud and Blackmud Creeks (Glyn Williams 2002). A 2003 survey estimated the city beaver population to be about 1700, with

City of Edmonton, Bylaw Services. Personal communication.

Williams, G. 2002. Community Services, City of Edmonton. Personal communication.

Table 1.

Estimated numbers and densities (#/km²) of white-tailed deer, mule deer and coyotes during a river valley aerial survey on January 15, 1993 (adapted from Folinsbee 1993). Densities are recorded in brackets. Six unidentified deer in the Southwest River Valley were not included in the density calculations.

Location	Area (km²)	Whitetailed Deer	Mule Deer	Coyotes
Southwest River Valley	42	50 (1.2)	35 (0.8)	1 (0.02)
Whitemud-Blackmud	19	51 (2.6)	4 (0.2)	1 (0.05)
City Core	14	6 (0.4)	4 (0.3)	4 (0.28)
Northwest	43	68 (1.6)	0	8 (0.18)
Total	119	175(1.5)	43 (0.4)	14 (0.12)

Williams, G. 2004. Community Services, City of Edmonton. Personal communication.

Argument, D. 2002. Elk Island National Park staff. Personal communication.

a population of about 700 in the Whitemud and Blackmud Creeks and about 1000 in the North Saskatchewan River (Williams 2004). Wildlife managers recognize that the County of Strathcona has between 300 and 400 moose; a survey in December, 2001 provided an estimated density of 0.35 moose/km². Another useful comparison of animal populations is with the 195 km² Elk Island National Park, where densities are bison (almost 4/km²), elk (5/km²), moose (2/km²), coyote (0.5/km²) and beaver (5/km²) (Argument 2002).

More quantitative data are available for birds in the City. The Edmonton Christmas bird counts have been conducted in late December for many years with the strong support from many naturalists. Over the past decade there were between 50 and 60 species of winter residents (Table 2). The five most abundant bird species were house sparrow, black-capped chickadee, rock dove, Bohemian waxwing and black-billed magpie. Common waterfowl

Coyotes Still Sing in My Valley

Table 2

The City of Edmonton Christmas Bird Counts for the years 1997-2003 (adapted from http://birdsource.tc.cornell.edu/cbcdata/: access date: February, 2004). Groupings follow Fisher and Acorn (1998)

Groupings	Year							Mean	Std Dev
	1997	1998	1999	2000	2001	2002	2003		
Waterfowl	978	336	668	669	488	3156	212	930	1013
Birds of prey	43	16	38	42	21	26	33	31	11
Grouse-like birds	34	143	153	153	72	26	4	84	65
Doves, cuckoos	2709	1814	4456	4456	2161	6032	3188	3545	1505
Owls	35	19	42	44	55	57	36	41	13
Woodpeckers	275	397	454	454	503	559	616	465	111
Jays, crows	3502	3075	3674	3676	3035	3520	3351	3405	264
Chickadees	3622	4395	4974	4974	5753	5830	5731	5040	821
Nuthatches,creepers	399	406	508	508	421	820	1417	640	372
Kinglet, thrushes	41	18	21	23	67	28	96	42	29
Starlings, waxwings	3934	9509	1342	1342	6981	2844	1582	3933	3176
Shrikes	5	2	6	6	8	5	12	6	3
Sparrows, grosbeaks, buntings	277	459	380	10	7	343	648	303	233
Finch-like birds	320	1863	1809	2214	1095	927	3981	1744	1180
House sparrows	6392	7149	6434	6434	4398	3984	426	5031	2344
No. of species	59	54	61	60	61	63	57	59	3

included mallard and common goldeneye and common raptors included merlin and northern goshawk. There is considerable variability in counts from year to year because of many factors. Weather immediately before and during the count is important. For example, the 100th bird count in 1999 was conducted when the temperatures ranged from a low of –13°C to a high of 7°C; this did not deter observers. Longer-term weather also has effects

Hikers in the valley and ravines might be fortunate to see beaver in the evening. Most of us see trees harvested by beaver (photo by Ross W. Wein, 2001).

on bird counts. With high autumn temperatures water birds will find more than usual open water on the North Saskatchewan River and even more open water will be found below thermal-electric and sewage treatment plants, prompting waterfowl to remain longer.

Wildlife – Human Interactions

In most urban areas the recorded complaints against wildlife are few; wildlife managers believe many more people have positive and unrecorded interactions. Although some people view wildlife as a nuisance (beaver kill trees, coyotes threaten pets), most people would like to see more wildlife. Even while considering this view, humans have impacted wildlife to such an extent that some management of wildlife is necessary in urban settings where competition for space is critical (Adams 1994). Any instituted control program is invariably opposed by segments of society. The discussion below attempts to place some boundaries on the dimensions of the wildlife-human interactions.

Plant life in the city has many positive aspects that range from summer shading to animal habitat. Of course there are negative effects and one of the most negative is pollen allergies that begin with the spring opening of flowers and that end with the frosts of autumn. Some urban designers have suggested that urbanites have compounded the problem by planting horticultural varieties that have high densities of flowers and therefore have high pollen production. People who walk in the valley are well aware of the thistles, bristles and thorns that can catch in clothing and skin. Poison ivy is rare but is found in the valley. These annoyances can be avoided readily if one recognizes the species.

The City of Edmonton, Community Services Department is responsible for the maintenance of all developed and naturalized green space including the natural areas in the river valley. Presently, the Forestry Section is undertaking a program to replace trees and shrubs that died as a result of the severe drought conditions in the winter and summer of 2000 to 2002. The City's turf management program involves the mowing and maintenance of developed turf including environmental and conservation issues such as treatments of fertilizer and herbicide. The annual turf maintenance budget of $4.2 million dedicates $221,000 to broadleaf weed herbicide spraying and $127,000 to fertilizing. The remaining $3.8 million is dedicated to mowing, trimming and turf enhancement tasks. In 2003, for the developed turf area of 4,494 ha, a total of 373 ha (8.2%) was sprayed with herbicides for broadleaf weeds. For the

Increasing numbers of Canada Geese are attracted to parks and are being considered as a nuisance (photo by John R. Wood, 2004).

Chan, E. 2004. Personal communication.

naturalized areas (areas no longer mowed), of the 385 ha, there is only spot herbicide spraying for noxious weeds. As for the vegetation control in the river valley, only the occasional use of herbicide is necessary to control noxious invasive weeds on the edge of native tree stands (Chan 2004).

Generally it is specific wild mammal species that receive the most negative press, but specific birds and insects also receive their share of criticism for responding to human-caused changes to habitat. For example, wildlife are attracted to human-changed vegetation (grass for Canada geese on golf courses and picnic areas) and to structures (nesting sites on bridges, buildings); the feeding of wildlife, especially birds, is common in winter. In northern climates, heat release from buildings and industrial complexes encourages migratory animals to delay departure times or even become winter residents.

Although there are complaints against wildlife each year, there are few serious problems (Table 3). The list of ten problem species on private land is headed by skunks and squirrels while on city property the complaints are against squirrels and beaver because they fell trees and/or remove the bark for food. Due to absence of natural predators, beaver numbers are kept in check by the City of Edmonton through control programs designed to bring the population down to ecologically sustainable levels (Pest Management Services, City of Edmonton). About 200 were removed from city parks annually. Coyotes are viewed as a threat to pets, mainly by home-owners at the edge of the valley and those who walk their pets in the valley (River Valley Park Rangers, City of Edmonton). Geese are not recorded in Table 3, but people see them as a problem because of their high numbers and their feces in city parks and golf courses. About 300 eggs were oiled in 2003 and small numbers of flightless geese were rounded up and relocated in

Table 3

Number of complaints regarding wildlife in public and private lands for the period January to October, 2000 (adapted from data provided by Pest Management Services, City of Edmonton). To keep these data in perspective, there are 200-300 dog bites per year that require medical attention and of those about 10 dogs are quarantined (City of Edmonton 2002).

Species	City land	Private land	Total
Beaver	19	0	19
Bat	2	0	2
Coyote	7	0	7
Fox	1	0	1
N. Pocket Gopher	4	0	4
Porcupine	2	21	23
Rabbit	3	1	4
Skunk	1	182	183
Squirrel	26	127	153
Woodchuck	1	0	1
Totals	66	331	397

City of Edmonton, Bylaw Services. 2002. Personal communication.

Zazulak, E. 2004. Zoonotics Officer, Capital Health, Environmental Section. Personal communication.

Edmonton Police Services. Personal communication.

the summer. To keep in perspective the number of complaints presented in Table 3, reported animal bites (mostly dogs) were 286, 273, 230, 329, 265, and 408 for the years 1998 to 2003, respectively (Zazulak 2004). Another problem relates to deer and moose as road hazards because of collisions with motor vehicles. Table 4 presents data from 1996 and 1997 when just over 100 animals were killed annually. Additional data, presented in Table 5, for the 1995 to 2000 period estimate that between 127 and 201 collisions with animals (most with property damage of $1000 or more) injured between three and nine persons annually (Edmonton Police Services).

Table 4

Numbers of deer and moose (almost all are deer) killed in transportation corridors in the City of Edmonton for the years 1996 and 1997 (adapted from data provided by River Valley Park Rangers, City of Edmonton).

	Year	
Transportation Corridors	1996	1997
Major	57	60
Minor	46	42
Totals	103	102

Another concern is animals invading lawns and family dwellings. Pest control companies are well aware that there are differences that are strongly related to older neighbourhoods near ravines and other natural areas. Pest control companies are called continuously throughout the year about problem bats, mice, pigeons and squirrels. Other species exhibit a seasonal cycle of invasions and some species are most active during the change of seasons. In the spring, females seek locations to raise young. In the spring and summer, young and inexperienced animals are exploring and wandering onto and into properties. Examples include young skunks and gophers. In the autumn, most animal populations are highest and people see them more often. Examples include wasps, bees and ants. In late autumn, animals seeking winter shelter become a problem for some homeowners. In the winter, the loss of snow cover can lead to invasions of family homes by rodents that are seeking shelter.

Insects are the subject of complaints because they cause humans discomfort, they can spread disease, and some people are allergic to stings and bites. The number one insect pest is probably the mosquito; there are about 30 species in the Edmonton region.

Table 5

Number of collisions involving wild and domestic animals as reported by Edmonton Police Services 1995-2000 (adapted from data provided by Alberta Transportation, Driver Safety, Research and Traffic Safety Initiative, January 2, 2002). Note there were no human fatalities during these years.

Severity of Collision	1995	1996	1997	1998	1999	2000
Total Collisions	127	146	160	190	201	183
No. with Property Damage ($1000+)	125	140	153	187	196	175
No. of People Injured	3	7	8	4	5	9

Edmonton and surrounding counties (1,400 km²) have an extensive program ($800,000 annually) of insecticide application from the ground and from helicopters during the months of July and August. The first insecticide application is on open water that results from snowmelt and then additional applications are made after each rainfall of about 50 mm. About 2,600 km of roadsides and about 36,000 ha are aerial treated annually. The number of insect stings from bees and wasps are not well documented but pest control companies are busy removing nests especially in August and September.

Pybus , MJ. 2004. Wildlife Disease Specialist, Alberta Fish and Wildlife. Personal communication. See http://www.gov.ab.ca/srd/fw/diseases

A few potential wildlife–human health issues in Alberta have been studied (Pybus 2004). Fortunately, these issues are not serious in the Edmonton area. Hantavirus infections from rodents, especially deer mice, have caused sickness and several deaths in Alberta. Rabies, which is locally present in southern Alberta, is of minor concern in the skunks, foxes and bats of Edmonton. Citizens should be careful if handling any wildlife that appears to be sick. The tapeworm, *Echinococcus granulosis*, of coyotes can be transmitted to humans but only those who handle the animals, such as trappers and researchers, might become infected. Campers contracting *Girardia* during July and August have usually been infected near the mountains (Edmonton Capital Health). Of more widespread concern at present is the mosquito-borne West Nile virus, which was important in 2003 but not in 2004 (http://www.health.gov.ab.ca/public/diseases).

The Future

Recognizing the considerable support for maintaining wildlife in the Edmonton region, how can the ecological integrity of the valley and wildlife populations be improved? There are a number of current and positive actions by the City of Edmonton. One is the development of an Integrated Pest Management strategy that will evaluate the use of all pesticides. A second is the development of Wildlife Management Guidelines, which emphasizes conservation while recognizing the realities of problem wildlife. Having recognized these initiatives, it is important to point out that there is a need for stronger wildlife inventories and research into solving management issues.

One major issue is the continuing fragmentation of habitats by city development because more fragmented habitats support fewer species (Soulé 1991). Fragmentation forces species such as deer to increasingly use transportation corridors to move in and out of the River Valley. City managers recognize that some transportation corridors are used more commonly by wildlife. In the northeastern part of the city (east of 100 Street and north of 100 Avenue) there is the Fort Road/Manning Freeway, the LRT and CN tracks as well as the Yellowhead Highway. In the northwest (west of 101 Street and north of 100 Avenue) are the Yellowhead Highway, the CN tracks (heading west and north) and the St. Albert Trail Highway.

Edmonton Capital Health. Personal communication.

In the southeast (east of 100 Street and south of 101 Avenue) there are the Sherwood Park Freeway, Wayne Gretzky Drive, rail tracks and Whitemud Drive. In the southwest (west of 101 Street and south of 101 Avenue) there are the Whitemud Drive, Fox Drive and Calgary Trail. Animal movement in these areas presents a significant hazard for humans and animals alike. While there is no long-term program to monitor the use of these corridors by wildlife, data on road kills suggest that wildlife, particularly deer, are blocked by these transportation corridors. Solutions are needed and those solutions should involve more effective multiple corridors.

Protection of the ribbon of green is important as both habitat and corridors to other conservation areas, including areas outside of the City of Edmonton boundaries. It is hoped that additional valley and tableland protected areas such as those recommended by O'Leary *et al.* (1992) and Westworth Associates Environmental Ltd. (2001) will be linked to this valley system. Unique areas such as archaeological sites are being lost each year. In this case the protection of such sites will also provide biodiversity protection. In addition, there is also much room for habitat enhancement that would protect rare species and those species particularly enjoyed by our citizens.

Most conservationists encourage city managers to continue to emphasize biodiversity protection and ecological integrity maintenance in our valley. As Dennis Murphy (1988, quoted in Adams 1994. p. 139) pointed out, "Our urban centres can be viewed as bellwethers of our global environmental fate ... If we cannot act as responsible stewards in our own backyards, the long-term prospects for biological diversity in the rest of this planet are grim indeed."

Acknowledgements

This work arose from university class field trips into the North Saskatchewan River Valley and recent studies of plant diversity in the North Saskatchewan River Valley of the Edmonton region. We acknowledge the many individuals from pest control companies who provided perspectives on wildlife control issues. Provincial and city resource managers who assisted in locating information and discussing our use of data and our conclusions include, in alphabetical order: George Diduck (River Valley Park Rangers, City of Edmonton), John Folinsbee and Margo Pybus (Alberta Fish and Wildlife) Al Gibson (Conservation Officer, Alberta Fish and Wildlife) and Glyn Williams and Gary Chan (Community Services, City of Edmonton).

Wildlife in the Midnight Urban Wilderness

Jim Butler, University of Alberta

Abstract

The presence of wildlife, such as beaver or coyotes, and an expectation of encountering them are seen as important parts of a wildland experience. This paper presents a naturalist's insight into the night life and wild side of Edmonton that is a departure from the marketing themes of nightlife we typically encounter. Many species of wildlife are most active at night when the majority of humans are indoors. While urban wilderness is an oxymoron, eight factors are presented that create a perception of a wilderness experience for many within the city limits. Midnight walks, combined with quiet sitting on park benches near the city's river valley, are explored for their remarkable opportunities for meeting coyotes, owls, and porcupines, and even long-distance migrants from South America. Many of these encounters are more subtle than most might expect, involving more of the auditory senses than most of us utilize. The paper concludes that wildlife is an understated contributor to our quality of life and our sense of place – at night.

Year-round resident great horned owl nesting in old magpie nest in the North Saskatchewan River Valley (photo by Edgar T. Jones).

Wildlife After Dark

The photograph was frustrating to attempt, an act of madness, but I simply had to try. It was midnight. I pressed the camera lens, fully open, against the kitchen window and tried to hold it still for a full minute exposure. In the view finder were two porcupines, each at separate bird feeders filled with apple chunks and German pretzels. Two striped skunks were also feeding beneath the backyard bird-feeding table, amicably sharing what the birds had not finished.

One winter a saw-whet owl came nightly, hunting the deer mice drawn to the bird seed. White-tailed jack rabbits and snowshoe hares are regular nightly visitors. A friend up the street has flying squirrels coming to the bird feeder at his kitchen window, and I have sipped tea in his kitchen at midnight as we watched them. Rarely observed, a population of these nocturnal squirrels lives in the mature spruce and hardwoods beside Emily Murphy Park, which is nearby.

During a walk along Saskatchewan Drive at night, it is common to meet a group of white-tailed deer, usually behind the Faculty Club on the University of Alberta campus. A great horned owl frequently sits on top of the Windsor Car Park. The great-horned owl is one of seventy-eight different bird species I have seen in my own yard (just west of the south end of the University of Alberta campus); these include five types of woodpeckers, 14 wood warblers, bald eagles, white-fronted geese, western tanagers, northern shrikes and rose-breasted grosbeaks. It was well after midnight when I finally encountered my first lynx as it stepped in front of my headlights as I left a drive-in theater on the southeast side of the city. None of this sounds like it takes place in the heart of an urban region of one million people.

The Concept of Urban Wilderness

If you wondered about the title of this paper, I will admit that urban wilderness probably is an oxymoron. Wilderness and urban are at opposite ends of the landscape spectrum. Wilderness exists out of reach of the managed forests of conservation lands, let alone the built landscape of a city. Wilderness is roadless, molded by the natural forces of nature, on a large enough scale that it cannot be traveled on foot in a single day, and those who hike there are temporary visitors. For all of our ability we cannot create wilderness. We can only protect it.

Wilderness is also a refugia for wildlife. With the exception of Alberta's Willmore Wilderness where hunting and mining are permitted, wild animals find sanctuary in wilderness from pursuit by human beings and from their economic activities. On the other hand, social scientists also see wilderness as a 'state of mind' or perception. Wall-size murals of wilderness scenes have replaced the sterile white institutional walls of many hospital emergency rooms, trauma centers and dental offices in North America because they have a proven calming effect. Better than the colour pink, I suspect, which is used in psychiatric wards. Urban children who camp out on park land within sight of the New York City skyline are having a wilderness experience. Canoeists running the North Saskatchewan River from Devon into Edmonton speak of wilderness values.

From my personal observation and studies over the years concerning people and nature experiences, the perception of an urban wilderness landscape and experience can be described by these eight attributes.

1. Extensive wild green space that has not been excessively cleared is present.

2. There is a framing or containment of your visual horizon. The river valley excludes most else when you are on or near the river. Nightfall blankets out all but the most illuminated areas.

3. A withdrawal from the hectic pace of industrial, media, computer and automotive technology. To enter anything, you must first leave something else behind.

4. A suspension of time set by clocks, freedom from rigid schedules, and entering into a new flow of time set by nature.

5. Reduction or absence of traffic and other industrial sound intrusion. Litter, garbage, habitat damage and pollution register as human presence and must be absent.

6. Discovery of a sense of the primitive. A primal connection to exploration and physical skills is needed. The campfire experience is very memorable.

7. An absence of humans. Small numbers of human encounters are not a distraction and are reported as a comfort, especially when they are sharing similar activities.

8. An expectation of seeing wildlife and the presence of wildlife. Seeing beaver was the most frequently reported highlight of wilderness canoeing experiences on the river.

Wildlife and the Night Lecture

For twenty years, from January to April, I taught a university course on wildlife biodiversity and ecology, with a three-hour evening lecture in buildings overlooking the Saskatchewan River Valley. This offered a unique opportunity to step outdoors with 200 students when my lecture reached the subject of the saw-whet owl. We would exit together into the night, stand beside Saskatchewan Drive facing the river valley and listen for the 'whip-whip-whip-whip' calls of the owls.

Even more unusual was that we almost always heard them, sometimes three at a time. Their song is easy to imitate and one or more would occasionally be persuaded to fly into the spruce trees in front of us in response to our imitations of their calls, or into one of the bare elm trees near the street light where the entire class would see them. When the class formally ended, some would linger as long as the owls co-operated, and some would accept an invitation to see the nocturnal flying squirrels at a nearby biologist's bird feeder. Hearing or seeing your first saw-whet owl is a memorable event, and the conversation reflected this. Most had no idea that you could meet saw-whet owls within the city, nor would they ever have thought to pause and listen for them. We are not an outdoor nocturnal species – evening hockey games, casinos, street walkers, and nightclubs notwithstanding. Only poachers and naturalists search for wildlife after dark.

Infrequent visitors to Edmonton through the North Saskatchewan River Valley are elk, lynx, black bear, moose, and mountain lion (photo by Ross W. Wein, 2001).

Habitat, Food and Movement Corridors

Urban wildlife require adequate habitat, which includes shelter of old hollow trees, windbreaks or spaces beneath people's porches, like the skunks and porcupines who winter under my own front porch. Homes and neighborhoods near the river valley, and its complementary series of forested ravines, are favoured and these natural watersheds offer movement corridors into the very heart of the city. They are effective enough to allow infrequent visitors such as lynx, black bear, mule deer, moose, elk, and even the occasional mountain lion. Mature white spruce, on the north-facing slopes of the river valley, are southern fragments of the boreal forest. Balsam poplar and trembling aspen develop hollow boles at the young age of fifty years or so and when made accessible by woodpeckers, are ideal nesting and roosting holes for the saw-whet owls.

The back alleys of older neighborhoods have trees and shrubs that provide habitat for many wild species (photo by Ross W. Wein, 2004).

Ambient temperatures are warmer in winter within the city because of our collective energy output. Food availability is more favourable because of the horticultural diversity, including hawthorne, mountain ash, oaks, privet hedges and other plantings that invite wildlife to our yards. The profusion of mountain ash trees in Edmonton has caused a concentration of wintering Bohemian waxwings in world record numbers. Snowshoe hares are more comfortable in the thick shrub cover of our yards. White-tailed jackrabbits, whose advantage lies more in speed than stealth, prefer open sports fields and the hard packed snow of neighborhood streets. They feel safer in our neighborhoods since coyotes are less likely to pursue them into the labyrinth of human habitat.

In contrast, some wild animals prefer a routine that takes place in the absence of humans. Porcupines would have little or no chance to cross city roads safely during daylight hours. Behavioral shifts in wildlife movements favour the low contact hours. At least one wildlife example in Edmonton has demonstrated to me how quickly such nocturnal shifts can occur.

Coyotes Still Sing in My Valley

Gulls are typically active by daylight. The Franklin's gull is a common summer-breeding gull in agricultural areas around Edmonton. I noticed several years ago that a local population of Franklin's gulls moved in at night to feed on popcorn and food scraps between the cars parked at the drive-in theater on the Northeast side of the city. They shifted to become nocturnal to favour an available food supply in a lighted area after midnight.

Night hawks are a night-flying member of the whippoorwill and nightjar family, and are a regular feature of cities where they incubate their pair of eggs on the gravel and tar roofs of downtown buildings. Their nasal calls of "peent" and booming dives are a common night sound as they hunt the midnight sky for insects. When I hear them outside a movie theatre or downtown restaurant, I feel it is worth sharing the event with others nearby by pointing out how the nighthawks hunt the midnight sky for insects. I note that, with their long graceful wings, they travel to their wintering grounds as far away as the Pampas of Argentina and back again, migrating over the Bahaman Islands, the Greater Antilles and Central America. Completing this journey twice a year, they are far more traveled than most Edmontonians. If one of us ever walked that far we would be greeted by the media, flowers and praise at our City of Champions welcome sign. Downtown visitors often seem bewildered when so much is unexpectedly placed before them.

Midnight Walks and Late Night Bench Watches

Midnight excursions are a long tradition for naturalists. I have led night walks with park visitors into forests throughout my career. In recent years, while an advisor to the National Parks of Thailand, I convinced them to offer night naturalist talks and walks which featured an incredible mixed symphony of insect sounds, rarely seen night animals and the possibility of having the thrill of seeing first hand the giant atlas moth, the world's largest, which is not uncommon near the lights of the park buildings. These sightings were dismissed by the staff as commonplace while visitors thrilled to the opportunity. Now it is a regular feature of the campground program. We forget the magic of midnight and the wonders of what might seem commonplace because we see it frequently. This is called *parochial perception* and is demonstrated in the attitudes toward coyotes and magpies. Eastern visitors excitedly ask, "What was that magnificent blue, black and white bird with a very long tail?" and unfortunately receive a reply of, "Oh that, that's only a magpie." Can you imagine the interpretive guide in an art museum saying, "Oh, that, that's only a Rembrandt"?

Night excursions meet nature at its finest: howling with timber wolves in Alberta's Caribou Mountains; listening to bugling elk in the mountain national parks; entering the deafening chorus of great plains toads in the grasslands. Coming across the night movements of tiger salamanders on rainy, dark highways in the Bow Valley west of Calgary is a mixed blessing when large trucks are racing by. Compassion demands that you sprint for the salamanders, conscious of their innocence, and rescue those you can from their inevitable fate. Few drivers even see them, let alone slow down for them. I used to display a bumper sticker that expressed my philosophy. It read, "I brake for turtles, frogs and large leaves."

Midnight walks are a long tradition for me and my Labrador Retriever. We meet jackrabbits every night and showshoe hares less frequently. Neither the midnight skunks nor porcupines expect to meet dogs and people, so we try to keep the encounter to the lowest level of anxiety possible for all, giving them a wide berth. There are many benefits to post-midnight walks. These include the absence of people, low levels of ambient traffic sounds, wonderful views of the aurora borealis, and starry skies, much enhanced by the reduced glare of the modern, energy efficient, blue street lights the city had the wisdom to adopt. I love the park benches overlooking the river valley, especially when sheltered from traffic sounds. From there I savour the harmonics of the coyote howls and cup my ears to better hear the whistled notes of the saw-whet owls or the groupings of four to six hoots of the great horned owls.

There is a fine patch of old-growth spruce along the Keillor bike path. A barred owl recently moved into this old forest. Barred owls are fussy about where they call home, as are the pair of goshawks who nest nearby, and the three-toed woodpeckers who can be found there in winter. On several occasions I have heard the distinctive hoot of this barred owl, matching the phrase "who cooks for you; who cooks for you," and each time it was savoured as a special reward. I give a pretty good barred owl imitation, but I never chose to call to this one. I feared he might sense some anxiety in believing another barred owl was near, posing some threat to his territory or mate. On a midnight walk through Mahogany Hammock in the Florida Everglades, I called to a perched barred owl. The male attacked us from behind in a silent aerial assault in defence of this competition for its mate. The person next to me sank to his knees as it raked his head with its talons as it flew by. Then the pair of owls stood side by side, each calling aloud in their wild courtship voices to reinforce their pair bond. They gazed defiantly down on us as I worked to stop the bleeding. Now I prefer to simply listen unobtrusively and with more tranquility.

My dog grows restless at my tendency to linger on my favourite night benches, but I find that these are excellent spaces for reflection, centering and escape. Reflection comes easiest after midnight. The curtain of nightfall, the same moon, and the same constellations seem to unite years as well as geography. A sense of place and time is less precise, more universal. A midnight tarry on a bench for quiet introspection is as important as the walk itself. Finding my favourite benches empty is also more likely after midnight, as is the opportunity to have memorable nature encounters. Some refer to it as "Seton sitting," after the Canadian pioneer nature writer, Ernest Thompson Seton. His counterpart in New York's Catskill Mountains, John Burroughs, also maintained that if you sit still in the woods long enough, the best of nature will come to you.

Spring Nights and Long-Distance Migrants

Below my favourite bench, along the riverside walking trail south of Hawrelak Park, is a small woodland pool. In spring a mixed chorus of wood frogs and boreal chorus frogs, the latter sounding like a finger nail running along the teeth of a comb, can be heard at night, and this announcement strips the pool of its vernal privacy. Both frogs are harbingers of spring, as are the Canada geese honking overhead. Birds migrate at night, mostly unseen. As tundra swans pass, their ghostly white apparitions can sometimes be seen dipping low to the street lights the way an albatross skims the ocean waves. When you listen during spring and fall, you'll hear them. Each year I await the midnight bird migration, never visible, only audible. Now the peeps of sandpipers and slurred notes of songbirds punctuate the darkness: short notes, at a pitch close to two kilocycles, very audible to our ears, about three octaves above middle C. This incredible migratory event involves one-third of the continent's songbird population, perhaps three billion songbirds, most weighing about the weight of a ball-point pen, all travelling to somewhere in the boreal forest. About two-thirds of these neo-tropical migrants are returning from

Mexico, Central America, or South America.

About 140 of the 288 species of migratory birds that breed in the North American boreal forest pass over Edmonton through the night. Three-fourths of North America's waterfowl numbers rely on the boreal for a portion of their lives. Ruby-crowned kinglets seem to lead the parade here, in mid-April with a particular rush in late May.

One cannot help but be concerned about these invisible small birds – for their vulnerability, the great expenditure of energy, the risks of navigation, and the prospect of sudden death when they crash into tall buildings. Ovenbirds are a declining ground-nesting wood warbler. This is a bird of the night in more ways than its migration. Its familiar territorial song from the hardwood forests where it nests increases in volume with a phrase which sounds like "teacher, teacher, TEACHER." But the real mystery happens at night. It gives a completely different song in a night flight in the manner of a skylark. Few naturalists have ever heard it, and I have heard it less than a dozen times. No other warbler seems to do this. Henry David Thoreau, while living on Walden Pond, knew the ovenbird and its daytime "teacher" song, but he was haunted by a night song that was mentioned frequently in his diary as belonging to a "mysterious midnight warbler," whose identity he never discovered. His friend Ralph Waldo Emerson cautioned him that he should never learn the source of this mystery or he might lose all passion for living.

Thousands of sandhill cranes fly over day and night, very audible from high elevations due to tracheas convoluted like a French horn, heading to the Mackenzie Delta and other regions of the Arctic; they return south about the third week of September. The voices of the songbirds; thrushes, vireo's and wood warblers are more subtle, far more difficult to recognize from their flight calls than when they sing in their breeding territories. However, migration biologists, concerned with the decline of songbirds in winter in the tropics (neotropical migrants), now digitally record these calls and submit them to sound spectrographic analysis for "fingerprints" and identification. This technique was pioneered by professors at Cornell and Ohio State universities in the 60's. If the Wright brothers and their fellow pioneers of flight stole the magic of the birds and their domain of the sky as has been claimed; then it might also be said that the audiospectrogram stole away a bit of the mystery of these passing midnight visitors over our cities. In fact, this migratory phenomenon is so complex that the answers only raise a multitude of new questions. I still listen in wonder as I hear them pass over. There are nights when I set my spotting scope on a tri-pod and focus it on the full moon. Sitting on one of the overlook benches, staring at the moon's reflective light you can see the birds streak by. The night sky is far from empty of life. Their magic is greater than ever.

Coyotes in the City

Both of my Labrador Retrievers often came across evidence of their wild cousins and occasionally met them face to face, each intently fixed upon the other. There was always excitement when they met another dog, any dog, of any breed, but coyote encounters were like none other. Something passed between them, holding them transfixed, that was not visible to me. It was penetrating, captivating, intense. My dog's mane would rise, his posture stiffen, the shoulder sometimes trembling. It didn't pass when the coyote would turn and fade into the bush. Not right away. It was primal. Such channels linger once opened. Coyotes are one of the wildlife treasures of the city. My best reward, on a par with watching a rippling display of aurora borealis, is hearing the yips and howls of the coyotes. A passing siren of an ambulance, fire truck or police vehicle is often enough to trigger them into a howling party. I watch the reactions of people who stop and listen; people are always invigorated by the sounds.

The coyote's voice is the signature sound of the prairie, along with the western meadowlark. In a similar way the howl of a timber wolf and the wail of a loon are signatures of the boreal forest – the two voices most desired to be heard by tourists visiting Canada's northern lakes and tourism destinations. Wolves are no longer a regular resident close to Edmonton. At least we still have coyotes, but we need to cease hostilities in our relationship with them. As many heard in the opening narrative of the 2003 adventure film *X2: XMEN UNITED*, "sharing the world has never been humanity's finest attribute." Coyotes slide among the shadows and are called the "trickster" by indigenous people, untamed and untameable by their nature, here in a landscape that is orderly, civilized, occupied and hostile to invaders. It is they who still lay claim to the wild parcels of the city after the midnight hour. And for those of us who take time to pause on a park bench at night their harmonies define the "urban wilderness."

Wildlife is under the radar for most citizens who live, work in or visit our city. There is much more to the wild side of Edmonton than most ever imagine. In summer most neighborhoods with reasonable tree cover will have at least twenty-five nesting bird species, and a stroll into the river valley could reveal an additional 28 or so. In winter the Christmas bird count is one of the largest in the world, often with over 1000 people participating in pursuit of about sixty over-wintering species in Edmonton. About 54 species of mammals (not including human beings) occur within Edmonton's city limits when we count the shrews, pocket gopher and the two species of bats that spend the winter in our attics. Nearly all of these, except four species of squirrels, are more typically active at night.

The presence of wildlife is an asset and, like city parks and treed wild green space, an indicator of our quality of life. And each and every night excursion into the outdoors offers its own unique reward. A cricket song you never before noticed; a glimpse of a low-flying silver-haired bat, the perfume of the flowering May tree or hawthornes; the glitter of fairy-like fireflies; the luminescence of forest fungi; the faint trace of a sound that reveals the presence of an invisible northern flying squirrel; a large polyphemous moth attracted to the light behind a window. There is always something you have not experienced, thought about or expected. We marvel at the new wildlife encounter and celebrate the familiar like a return visit from an old friend, such as when a lone white-throated sparrow seems to awaken in the night to announce himself, unprovoked by any rival, with the richness of his "Oh, dear sweet Canada, Canada, Canada." It is best that we remember the words of Henry David Thoreau, who reminds us that "A man is rich in proportion to the number of things he can afford to let alone."

Further Reading

Grinder, M I and P R Krausman. 2001. Home range, habitat use, and nocturnal activity of coyotes in an urban environment. Journal of Wildlife Management 65 (4): 887-898.

Guynup, S. 2003. Light pollution taking toll on wildlife, eco-groups say. National Geographic Today (April 17, 2003) (news.nationalgeographic.com)

Harde, B. 2002. Deprived of darkness: the unnatural ecology of artificial light at night. Science News 161(16): 248.

Hill, S B and D H Clayton. 1985. Wildlife after dark: a review of nocturnal observation techniques. Bell Museum of Natural History Occasional Paper 17: 1-23. University of Minnesota. Minneapolis, MN.

Matthews, A. 2001. Wild nights: nature returns to the city. North Point Press, New York, NY. 224 pp.

Further information about artificial-light ecology is available at www.urbanwildlands.org, www.darksky.org, and www.towerkill.com.

Urban White-Tailed Jackrabbits of the Edmonton Region (1992-2002)

John R. Wood, **Jonathan Krenz**, and **Terry Boyd-Zhang**
The King's University College

Abstract

The white-tailed jackrabbit (*Lepus townsendii*) is a familiar species in and around the City of Edmonton. In Alberta it has expanded its range northward with the development of urban areas and agriculture in the aspen parkland. These hares were considered a significant pest in some parts of Alberta in the early part of the 20th century, but now they are seldom more than a local nuisance to gardeners, and many urbanites enjoy their presence in the backyard. In winters of 1992, 1995, 2001, and 2002 synoptic surveys of the hare were conducted in four land-use categories within the city (river valley parks, upland parks, residential neighbourhoods and industrial areas). In 1993, 1994, and 2001 similar synoptic surveys were conducted in the rural areas adjacent to the east and southeast of the city. The mean population densities in the city ranged from 4.2 hares/km^2 (1992) to 3.1 hares/km^2 in 1994. The exurban density of hares range from a low of 0.026 hares/km² in 1994, to 0.26 and 0.27 hares/km² in 1993 and 2001, respectively. The urban-rural fringe numbers are lower than typical rural densities reported in the literature, while the urban densities fall within the range of values found for the hare in the more southern parts of its range. This suggests advantages for the mammal in northern urban areas and it is hypothesized that it will continue to expand its range wherever aspen parkland forest is cleared for urban development.

Introduction

The rapid expansion of our cities has been transforming rural or wild landscapes into urban and suburban communities for over a century (Gilbert 1989). In the process wild species are displaced from their natural habitat and faced with adapting to new conditions and coexisting with humans. It may seem surprising, but urban spaces can be high-value environments for biodiversity conservation (McKinney 2002). Many species of plants, insects, birds, and mammals are thriving in human-altered habitats. It is not unusual to see mammals such as white-tailed deer *(Odocoileus virginianus)*, foxes *(Vulpes vulpes)* and even coyotes *(Canis latrans)* in the river valley or on open land at the urban margins. Nearer the city core squirrels *(Tamiasciurus hudsonicus)*, skunks *(Mephituis mephitis)*, and the occasional porcupine *(Erethizon dorsatum)* are seen.

Not all respond alike to human presence. The ability of these organisms to adapt has been classified into three categories by degree of tolerance – Urban Avoiders, Urban Adapters, and Urban Exploiters (McKinney 2002). Species that are highly sensitive to human disturbance are called urban avoiders, or in the Old World scheme *Kulturmeider*, literally, culture avoiders (Rosenzweig 2003). Many endangered species, but not all, fall into this category

Gilbert, O L. 1989. The ecology of urban habitats. Chapman and Hall, London, UK. 369 pp.

McKinney, M L. 2002. Urbanization, biodiversity, and conservation. BioScience 52 (10): 883 – 891.

and are harmed by urban growth. Plants and animals that adjust to humans are sometimes called by the German term *Kulturfolger*, literally, culture followers. But they form two distinct categories, the urban adapters and the urban exploiters. The urban adapters are often medium-sized carnivores that have been released from competition with large predators or the small mammal and bird species that were released from this same predator pressure. The urban exploiters form the tightest bonds with us. They are mostly omnivores that exploit the shelter and rich food supply of our houses (Adams 1994). The urban exploiters are the familiar pest species – cockroaches, mice, rats, and pigeons.

The most common lagamorph in urban areas of central and southern Alberta is a displaced prairie species, the white-tailed jackrabbit (*Lepus townsendii* Bachman, 1893, Figure 1, Table 1). Alberta has two other native rabbit species. Nuttall's cottontail rabbit (*Sylvilagus nuttallii*) is restricted to the south-east corner of the province. The snowshoe hare *(Lepus americanus)* is found in the forested areas of central and northern Alberta, and is common in intact wooded portions of our ravines and river valley. The white-tailed jackrabbit (*L. townsendii*) is a grassland species. Europeans were quick to take notice of this largest of all North American

White-tailed jackrabbits are a familiar species in open spaces of urban areas (photo by John R. Wood).

Rosenzweig, M L. 2003. Win-win ecology: how the earth's species can survive in the midst of human enterprise. Oxford University Press, Oxford, UK. 211 pp.

Adams, L W. 1994. Urban Wildlife Habitats: A Landscape Perspective. University of Minnesota Press, Minneapolis, MN. 186 pp.

Table 1

Identifying "rabbits" in our neighbourhoods

(Figures courtesy of the Alberta Environment website)

White-tailed Jack Rabbits (*Lepus townsendii*)	Snowshoe Hare (*Lepus americanus*)

Larger, longer, more slender body. Long ears Coat is all white in winter, except for black-tipped ears Tail – all white Summer coat is lighter brown-grey colour	A shorter, more compact body. Much smaller ears Coat is white in winter, with black-tipped ears Tail – brown and white Summer coat is darker brown

Moulton, G E and T W Dunlay. (eds.) 1987. The Journals of the Lewis and Clark expedition. August 25, 1804 – April 6, 1805. Volume 3. University of Nebraska Press, Lincoln, NE and London, UK. 544 pp.

lagomorphs. In their 1804 Journal Lewis and Clark called it simply the "Hare of the Prairies" (Moulton and Dunlay 1987). Their apt description (complete with quaint spellings) still resonates today, covering the most salient biological features of this species:

"the tale is white round and blounty pointed the furr on it is long and extreemly fine and soft when it runs it carry's it's tale strait behind the direction of the body –"

"it resorts the open plains, is extremely fleet and never burrows or takes shelter in the ground when pursued"

"they appear to run with more ease and to bound with greater

122

agility than any anamall I ever saw."

"this anamal is usually single seldom associating in any considerable numbers."

[Lewis] Sept. 14th 1804

White-tailed jackrabbits have been studied on the prairie, but have received little attention from urban ecologists. The general public is well aware of these bunnies and is intrigued by them. Every spring pictures of wild and domestic rabbits appear in the media, and sometimes full-length articles are written about them (i.e. Rubinstein 2003). But this interest has not been translated into a deeper level of understanding of their biology; animal shelters report that citizens no longer try to rescue deer fawns but they commonly pick up abandoned bunnies. So much work remains simply to educate the public. As McKinney (2002) says, "knowledge of the species composition of urban biodiversity can be very useful as an educational tool to better understand the natural world." For some citizens in Edmonton, urban hares, squirrels, and birds are their first encounter with a wildlife species. Nation-wide there are biological surveys soliciting input from the general public. Databases exist for the Breeding Bird Survey, Butterfly Survey, Amphibian Survey, and even for Earthworms (Brown *et al.* 1996). These citizen science efforts provide valuable scientific information for decision-makers and for testing ecological theory on a large scale. However, there are no comparable data available for the majority of prairie species, especially mammals.

The biogeographical study of the range of organisms has developed with modern techniques into a science that can answer fundamental ecological questions about biodiversity. The white-tailed jackrabbit presents a number of interesting questions and opportunities. For example, in the west its numbers are declining.

Rubinstein, D. 2003. One mellow rabbit. VueWeekly 391 (April 17-23): 8 – 10.

Brown, J H, G C Stevens and D M Kaufman. 1996. The geographic range: size, shape, boundaries, and internal structure. Annual Review of Ecology Systematics 27: 597 – 623.

Carter, D, A Harestade, and F L Bunnell. 1991. Status of White-tailed Jackrabbit (*Lepus townsendii*) in British Columbia. Wildlife Branch, BC Ministry of Environment, Victoria. BC.

Lim, B K. 1987. *Lepus townsendii*. Mammal species, No. 288. American Society of Mammologists.

Mohr, W P and C O Mohr. 1936. Recent Jack Rabbit populations at Rapidan, Minnesota. Journal of Mammalogy 17:112-114.

Soper, J D. 1964. The mammals of Alberta. Queen's Printer, Edmonton, AB. 402 pp.

Harris, W C. 2001. Saskatchewan's grassland mammals: a century of change. Native Plant Society of Saskatchewan, Native Plants and You. URL: http://www.npss.sk.ca/np-and-you.html #Mammal (accessed August 16, 2004).

Scott, G A J. 1995. Canada's vegetation: a world perspective. McGill-Queens University Press, Montreal, PQ. 361 pp.

It is reported as extirpated in the Okanagan Valley of British Columbia (Carter *et al.* 1991). In Washington State its numbers are also reduced, and it has retreated from valley floors due to competition from the related species, the black-tailed jackrabbit (*Lepus californicus*) (Lim 1987). Habitat alteration by agricultural development, which appears to be a common disturbance agent, has resulted in a differential response in the range of this species – retraction in the west and expansion in the east and in the north, as we detail below. Is this the result of interspecific competition, climate alteration, or some other as yet unidentified factor? Empirical studies of many species are valuable for testing theoretical models in the synthesis between biogeography and basic and applied sciences (Brown *et al.* 1996).

Finally, until quite recently white-tailed jackrabbits exhibited the periodic, even cyclic population pattern that is common among small herbivorous mammals. In the early part of the last century populations irrupted and large numbers were destroyed to prevent crop damage (Mohr and Mohr 1936, Soper 1964). The prairie cycle has been suppressed for several decades but the mechanism is not well understood (Harris 2001). One goal of this study was to see if these animals exhibit population cycles when they invade urban habitats.

Distribution

When explorers Lewis and Clark emerged from the eastern deciduous forest onto the tall grass prairies in South Dakota the *Hare of the Prairies* was there. Its eastward distribution limit coincided with the western edge of this mixture of oak-hickory and tall grass prairie (see map, Figure 7.3 in Scott 1995). Bachman, four decades later, formally described the white-tailed jackrabbit for science with specimens collected near Carlton, Saskatchewan (Lim 1987).

Historically it ranged throughout the northern great plains, south to the middle of Kansas and east to the edge of the tall grass prairie, roughly in a line extending south from the Manitoba/Ontario borders along the Mississippi River. The range extended west through the intermountain grasslands to the east slope of the Sierra Nevada and Cascade Mountains, and from the Okanagan Valley of British Columbia in the north, to the California/Nevada borders in the south (Lim 1987). The white-tailed jackrabbit reaches higher elevations in the Rocky Mountains than the snowshoe hare. Braun and Streeter (1968) note that white-tailed jackrabbits are "permanent residents of the alpine zone" in Colorado.

This historic range has shifted under the influence of a variety of environmental factors. Over the past 100 years native grasslands, wetlands, and their bordering forested ecosystems have been greatly modified by agriculture and urban development (Bird 1961). Species that depend upon forested habitat have disappeared from farming and urban districts. Among the lagomorphs, snowshoe hares have not fared well in the agricultural zones across Minnesota, Wisconsin, Michigan and Ontario (deVos 1964); they have also declined in Alberta. White-tailed jackrabbits, on the other hand, have extended their range eastward over the past century (deVos 1964) through Minnesota, Wisconsin, and into Illinois. This surge appears to be due to expanding habitat as tall grass prairies were cultivated, rather than from deliberate human introductions as suggested earlier (Hoffmeister 1989). Long-term climate change has caused the northward range extensions of many species. These tend to be the highly mobile species such as butterflies (Crozier 2004) and birds (Parmesan and Yohe 2003). But the ecological response to climate change is also attributed to small mammals, such as the red fox (*Vulpes vulpes*) and arctic fox (*Alopex lagopus*) (Walther *et al.* 2002).

Braun, C E and R G Streeter. 1968. Observations on the occurrence of White-tailed Jackrabbits in the alpine zone. Journal of Mammalogy 49: 160-161.

Bird, R D. 1961. Ecology of aspen parkland of western Canada in relations to use. Canada Department of Agriculture, Research Branch Publication No. 1066. 155 pp.

deVos, A. 1964. Range changes of mammals in the Great Lakes region. American Midland Naturalist 71: 210-231.

Hoffmeister, D F. 1989. Mammals of Illinois. University of Illinois Press, Urbana, IL.

Crozier, L. 2004. Warmer winters drive butterfly range expansion by increasing survivorship. Ecology 85: 231 – 241.

Parmesan, C and G Yohe. 2003. A globally coherent fingerprint of climate change impacts across natural systems. Nature 421: 37 – 42.

Walther, G-R, E Post, P Convey, A Menzel, C Parmesan, T J C Beebee, J-M Fromentin, D Hoegh-Guldberg, and F Bairlein. 2002. Ecological responses to recent climate change. Nature 416 (28 March): 389-395.

Keith, L B. 1965. Early notes on wildlife from New Sarepta, AB. Can. Field Nat. 79:29-34.

Smith, H C. 1993. Alberta mammals: an atlas and guide. The Royal Alberta Museum. Edmonton, AB. 238 pp. plus map.

Soper, J D. 1961. The mammals of Manitoba. Canadian Field-Naturalist 75: 171–87.

Rogowitz, G L. 1992. Reproduction of White-tailed Jackrabbits on semi-arid range. Journal of Wildlife Management 56: 676-684.

Wooding, F H. 1982. Wild mammals of Canada. McGraw-Hill Ryerson Ltd., Toronto, ON. 272 pp.

Rogowitz, G L. and M L. Wolfe 1991. Intraspecific variation in life-history traits of the white-tailed jackrabbit. Journal of Mammalogy 72(4):796-806.

Many people report seeing "rabbits" in our city. They see them on our streets, in our yards, neighbourhood parks and even at our industrial workplaces. These sightings might include domestic rabbits that either escape or are deliberately released in our parks, but most are wild species. Historically, aspen parkland forests dominated the landscape and excluded the grass-loving *L. townsendii*. As the land has been cleared for agriculture the hares have spread northward into the newly created habitat. The first recorded sighting in the Edmonton region was made in 1922 near New Sarepta (Keith 1965). Since then they have been sighted 100 km north of Edmonton near the small town of Dapp (Soper 1964). The range in Alberta was estimated four decades ago (see figure in Soper 1964, Smith 1993); there is no evidence from provincial wildlife officers or taxidermists that they have moved further north. In Saskatchewan they are found now as far north as Prince Albert National Park and in Manitoba they are found as far north as Riding Mountain, Lake Manitoba and Dauphin Lake (Soper 1961).

Hare Ecology

The white-tailed jackrabbit is actually a hare, not a rabbit. The main difference between hares and rabbits is evident in their offspring. Hares have precocial young that are born fully furred, with open eyes, and are mobile within an hour of birth (Rogowitz 1992). Adult hares tend to be slightly larger, slimmer and have larger ears than rabbits (Table 1).

The white-tailed jackrabbit weighs between 3 and 5.4 kg and measures between 55 and 66 cm in length (Wooding 1982, Lim 1987). The females tend to be slightly larger than the males, which is unusual in mammals (Lim 1987, Rogowitz and Wolfe 1991). This is one reason, some researchers suggest, why the females are more aggressive than males during the mating. The coats of both sexes turn a thick, pure white in October. In the spring they molt to a pale grey or light brown on their backs, neck and head while the underparts and the hind feet remain more lightly coloured (Zeveloff and Collet 1988). Two distinguishing morphological features of *L. townsendii* are black-tipped ears, and a relatively long white tail. These features remain constant in both the summer and winter pelage. Taken together these distinctive characteristics make it relatively easy to distinguish snowshoe hares from white-tailed jackrabbits (Table 1).

White-tailed jackrabbits are among the athletic elites of North American wildlife. In full flight, an adult may reach speeds of over 70 km/h (Wooding 1982); average running speed is between 50-60 km/h (Lim 1987). Speed is the primary defence against predation and it can easily outpace any of its predators including, as most urbanites have seen, urban dogs. In addition to being the undisputed champion of the sprints, this mammal is a respectable swimmer and will use the 'bunny-paddle' to avoid a predator if the need arises (Wooding 1982, Zeveloff and Collet 1988).

The white-tailed jackrabbit is the most solitary of all the hares (Lim 1987). Only small groups of 4 to 20 individuals are common during the breeding season from January to March (Rogowitz 1992). However, occasionally they will congregate into groups of one hundred or more, especially when food is abundant (Lahrman 1980, Brunton 1981). We have seen males following females in January, with active courting beginning in February. Courting behaviour includes high leaps and bounds as the male (or several males) chase the female (Blackburn 1973). Males will fight viciously by biting and clawing, and kicking with their hind feet. Gestation is about 42 days, and an average of four (1-8) young, called leverets, are born in late April or May (Rogowitz 1992). The mother provides milk for the young, which are otherwise left to fend for themselves.

Zeveloff, S I and F R Collet. 1988. Mammals of the Intermountain West. University of Utah Press, Salt Lake City, UT. 365 pp.

Lahrman, F W. 1980. A concentration of white-tailed jackrabbits. Blue Jay 38(June): 130.

Brunton, D F. 1981. Nocturnal aggregations of white-tailed jackrabbits at Rimbey, Alberta. Blue Jay 39: 121-122.

Blackburn, D F. 1973. Courtship behavior among white-tailed and black-tailed jackrabbits. Great Basin Naturalist 33: 203-204.

Urban Hare Ecology

Open prairie grasslands are the favoured habitats of white-tailed jackrabbits. In these areas their speed, used for escape, is unhindered by dense vegetation. Preference studies indicate that the hare favours wide-open spaces with virtually no vegetative cover (Flinders and Hanson 1973). Open fields intersected with dense hedgerows or windbreaks seem to be the most suitable habitat (Carter *et al.* 1991). Naturalists note that they are virtually never observed in closed canopy aspen stands (Hordoof *et al.* 1988). Hares spend the day resting in a slight depression called a form, which is just large enough for the hare to crouch and may be in the open or covered (Hoffmeister and Mohr 1972). Although the form may be located in a concealed area it must be one with good sight lines. We have observed white-tailed jackrabbits in the city resting under shrubs or constructed objects, such as trailers and porches with escape routes to the front and sides.

Urban/Rural Hare Density Estimates

Methods

Winter densities of the hares in Edmonton were estimated by sampling in four land-use types – residential, industrial, river valley parks and other city parks. The densities in the representative areas were subsequently scaled to the entire city. Since the major annexation in 1982 the Edmonton city boundary now encloses 700 km². Of that total, 279 km² has been classified as agricultural land, and 111 km² as unclassified, leaving 310 km² of developed land in the city (City of Edmonton, Facts Office, 2001). The areas are as follows: residential – 109 km² (18.5%), industrial – 86.6 km² (14.7%), river valley parks – 25.6 km² (4.35%), other city parks – 17.1 km² (2.9%), and other land-uses – 72.4 km² (12.3%).

Flinders, J T and R M Hansen. 1973. Abundance and dispersion of leporids within a shortgrass ecosystem. Journal of Mammalogy 54: 287-291.

Hordoof, R A, C H Sieg and R L Linder 1988. Wildlife response to stand structure of deciduous woodlands. Journal of Wildlife Management 52(4): 667-673.

Hoffmeister, D F and C O Mohr. 1972. Fieldbook of Illinois mammals. Dover Publications, New York, NY. pp. 188-197.

Table 2
White-tailed jackrabbit sampling areas in Edmonton.

Representative Area	Location	Dimensions
Residential	Londonderry Riverbend	• 132 Avenue to 144 Ave and 66 Street to 82 Street • 66 Avenue to Rabbit Hill Road and Riverbend Road to North Saskatchewan River.
Industrial	Southside (Strathcona)	• Gateway Boulevard to 91 Street and 34 Avenue to Whitemud Drive
	Eastgate Business Park and Lambton Industrial Area	• Intersection of 50 Street and railway tracks to 101 Avenue and 50 Street to 47 Street (Eastgate Business Park) and 50 Street to railway tracks (Lambton)
River Parks	Rundle Park and Golf Course Hawrelak Park	• Northeast zone of city • Central zone of city
City Parks	Borden Park Castledowns Park Coronation Park Millwoods Park	• East-central zone of city • North-central zone of city • West-central zone of city • South-east zone of city
Rural Route A	South of Sherwood Park, Strathcona County	• RR 232 and TWP 514 South to TWP 510 • TWP 510 West – RR 232 to RR240 • TWP 510 and RR 240 South to TWP 500 • TWP 500 and RR 240 to TWP 502 and RR 240 • RR 240 to RR 233 and TWP 500 to 510
Rural Route B	South of Sherwood Park, Strathcona County	• RR 232 to 233 and TWP 520 to 522
Rural Route C	North of Highway 16, Strathcona County	• RR 223 North of Highway 16 to TWP 544 • TWP 544 East to RR 222 • RR 222 South to Highway 16

Anonymous. 1989. Inventory methods for hares and cottontails. Standards for components of British Columbia's Biodiversity No. 23. Ministry of Environment, Lands and Parks, Government of British Columbia, Victoria, BC.

Smith, G W and N C Nydegger. 1985. A spotlight, line-transect method for surveying jack rabbit. Journal of Wildlife Management 49: 699-702.

Dolbeer, R A and W R Clark. 1973. Spring population response of cottontails and jackrabbits to cattle grazing on shortgrass prairie. Journal of Rangeland Management 28: 290-293.

Dolbeer, R A and W R Clark. 1975. Population ecology of Snowshoe Hares in the central Rocky Mountains. Journal of Wildlife Management 39: 535-49.

The rural road census was conducted by following two primary routes east of the city, with the addition in 2002 of a new route north of Highway 16 (Table 2). All surveys were done at night, since *L. townsendii* is a nocturnal species. We used methods similar to those for eastern cottontail and black-tail jackrabbits (Anonymous 1989, Smith and Nydegger 1985) for the roadside surveys. Two observers made the census from a vehicle beginning at about 2000 hours and ending before 0300 hours. In urban areas the observers drove, and/or walked, routes so that they could view the study areas. The rural routes covered approximately 170 km of road, with an average visibility of 0.25 km on each side. This resulted in a survey of approximately 85 km² of rural habitat in each census. Moonlight, flashlights and binoculars were used to enhance scanning on both sides of rural roads. Counting of hares was repeated on each route, in each sample area, until the maximum number was obtained from counts on at least three nights.

Results and Discussion

Synoptic surveys were made of the city and the rural (near-urban) surroundings for 6 of the past 11 years, 1992 to 2002 (Table 3). The density of *L. townsendii* in Edmonton during these years ranged from 3.1–4.2 hares/km². This is much higher than the estimated density of 0.27–0.01 hares/ km² for rural areas over the same period (Table 3). Historically, hare densities have been higher, especially in the eastern and central portions of the range. In Minnesota, for example, Mohr and Mohr (1936) reported 107–135 hares/ km². These numbers are almost as large as those for snowshoe hare peak abundances of 7–240 hares/km² (Dolbeer and Clark 1973, 1975, Boutin *et al.* 2002). They are also higher than those found for white-tailed jackrabbits from elsewhere in its range over the last 30 to 40 years (Table 4).

Table 3

White-tailed jackrabbit population densities in Edmonton and region. The survey areas were 310.1 km² and 21.6 km² for the city and rural areas, respectively.

Year	City	Rural
1992	4.2 hares/km² (1302 total)	--
1993	--	0.27 hares/km²
1994	3.1 hares/km² (973 total)	0.026 hares/km²
1995	--	0.01 hares/km²
2001	3.6 hares/km² (1129 total)	0.28 hares/km²
2002	3.9 hares/km² (1231 total)	< 0.01 hares/km²

Members of the genus *Lepus* are well known for their cyclical population dynamics. The snowshoe hare has been studied over numerous 10-year cycles (Boutin *et al.* 2002), including a detailed examination of a population by Keith and Windberg (1978) in central Alberta. There are historic records of outbreaks in white-tailed jackrabbits on the prairies (Smith 1986), but the classic microtine rodent prairie cycle has apparently disappeared both in Alberta and in Saskatchewan. Harris reports that in Saskatchewan "population peaks for white-tailed jackrabbits occurred in 1960, again in 1970 and 1980 but the expected peaks for 1990 and 2000 did not occur." (Harris 2001).

Boutin, S, C J Krebs, R Boonstra, A R E Sinclair, and K E Hodges. 2002. Understanding the Snowshoe Hare cycle through large scale field experiments. pp. 69 – 91. In: A. Berryman (ed.), Population cycles: the case for trophic interactions. Oxford University Press, Oxford, UK. 192 pp.

Keith, L B and L A Winberg. 1978. A demographic analysis of the snowshoe hare cycle. Wildlife Monographs 58: 1-70.

Smith, H C. 1986. Mammals of southeast Alberta. Nat. Hist. Occ. Paper No. 7, Royal Alberta Museum, Edmonton, AB. 52 pp.

Table 4

White-tailed jackrabbit densities in the more southern parts of the species' range.

Location	Density	Reference
North Dakota	107–135/km²	Bailey (1926), reported in Mohr and Mohr (1936)
Minnesota	27–32/km² 4–8/km²	Mohr and Mohr (1936)
Iowa	11/km²	Kline (1963)
Wyoming	7/km²	Rogowitz and Wolfe (1991)
NE Colorado	0.4–2.3/km²	Flinders and Hansen (1973)

Kline, P D. 1963. Notes on the biology of the jackrabbit in Iowa. Iowa Academy of Science 70: 196-204.

Kurki, S, A Nikula, O Helle, and H Linden. 1998. Abundances of red fox and pine marten in relation to the composition of boreal forest landscapes. Journal of Animal Ecology 67: 874 – 886.

There are no comparable numbers to the present results for urban populations of rabbits or hares in North America. But many other mammal species, as well as birds, reptiles, amphibians and insects, have been studied for their response to human alteration of habitat from both agriculture and urbanization (Kurki *et al.* 1989). Depending upon the constellation of species three responses commonly occur (McKinney 2002). First, many herbivorous mammals experience population increases from predator release. Large predators are urban avoiders and this creates a predator free shadow in and near built centres. Second, human-subsidized food supply increases in urban areas. This is especially helpful to omnivorous species, and to generalist herbivores such as white-tailed jackrabbits. Third, the suppression of large predators can release medium-sized generalist predators who will then suppress prey species. In a study of predators in fragmented boreal forest landscapes Kurki *et al.* (1989) found that red fox did cause increased predation pressure, but pine marten (*Martens martens*) did not.

Implications

Hares are a permanent component of the urban landscape in Edmonton. They are here to stay and are flourishing in the non-forested habitats of our northern city. Their greatest numbers will continue to be found in the light-industrial zones in and around the city. City parks with extensive open-space also favour these animals. The least favourable areas are the high-density zones in the inner city, and suburban neighbourhoods with extensive fencing between housing units. It remains to be seen whether this species will expand its range northward as the climate changes. Further research needs to be done in smaller urban centers in Alberta and across the Canadian prairies.

Acknowledgements

The King's University College students who worked on this project included S Wildeboer in 1992, W Kelsch in 1993, and C Rasmussen in 1994; their unpublished reports were used to make some of the calculations in this paper.

A Vision for Converting Edmonton's Ribbon of Green to a Conservation Net

Ross W. Wein and **Jeff Truscott**, University of Alberta

Abstract

Modern urban development overpowers natural ecosystems leaving only fragments that, individually, are not conducive to supporting biodiversity and genetic flow. Edmonton has many ravines in the city and geologically unstable river valley sides along the 45 km North Saskatchewan River that naturally limit development and act as corridors for biological movement. The much promoted ribbon of green is a 74 km² backbone for a conservation net; this backbone extends up- and down-river through several jurisdictions. As special places are considered for inclusion in the protected area system, their long-term usefulness for biodiversity protection will only function if they are directly connected to the streams and ravines.

Introduction

The world's protected areas are under a greater range of threats than ever before in history; threats are industrial growth in some areas and human population pressure in other areas. Increasing human impact leads to fragmentation of ecosystems and losses of biodiversity. Seeking protection for the less disturbed and unique areas is important work that must continue. Unfortunately, if these areas are too small and/or too isolated, they are susceptible to loss of both genetic and species diversity. Not only is the loss likely to occur during extreme events such as fire, drought, biological infestations or social unrest, but also during long-term climatic shifts. As a result, these areas become islands where gene flow is restricted, extinction of local plant and animal populations occur and local people lose future social and economic options. The urgency in conservation work stems from fragmentation of landscapes (by urbanization, agriculture, forestry, petroleum and mining and other industries) that is occurring worldwide and more rapidly than ever before in history (Noss and Cooperrider 1994, Forman 1995). Over the past two decades there has been a movement to protect more landscapes for biodiversity protection and to link these areas. The theory has developed out of the field of island biogeography (MacArthur and Wilson 1967, Diamond and May 1976). There have been many studies on the negative consequences of fragmentation but now there is increasing interest in the field of landscape ecology (Hudson 1991, Huston 1994, Noss and Cooperrider 1994, Forman 1995) and conservation biology (Hunter 1996, Meffe and Carroll 1997).

In highly industrialized countries, the conservation movement is currently focused on linking isolated fragments of habitats (e.g. Great Britain – Kirby 1995, Bennett 1999, 2003). This linking usually requires the protection and even restoration of units of

Noss, R F and A Y Cooperrider. 1994. Saving nature's legacy: protecting and restoring biodiversity. Island Press, Washington, DC. 416 pp.

Forman, R T T. 1995. Land mosaics: the ecology of landscapes and regions. Cambridge University Press, NY. 632 pp.

MacArthur, R H and E O Wilson. 1967. The theory of island biogeography. Princeton University Press, Princeton, NJ.

Diamond, J M. and R M May. 1976. Island biogeography and the design of natural reserves. 163-186 pp. In: R M May (ed.). Theoretical ecology: principles and applications. W B Saunders, Philadelphia, PA.

Hudson, W E. 1991. Landscape linkages and biodiversity. Island Press, Washington, DC. 196 pp.

Huston, M A. 1994. Biological diversity: the coexistance of species on changing landscapes. Cambridge University Press, Cambridge. 681pp.

Hunter, M L. 1996. Fundamentals of conservation biology. Blackwell Science, Cambridge, MA. 482 pp.

Meffe, G K and C R Carroll. (eds.) 1997. Principles of conservation biology. Second edition. Sinauer Associates, Sunderland, MA. 729 pp.

Kirby, K. 1995. Rebuilding the English countryside: habitat fragmentation and wildlife corridors as issues in practical conservation. English Nature Science No. 10. English Nature, Peterborough, UK. 39 pp.

Bennett, A F. 1999. Linkages in the landscape: the role of corridors and connectivity in wildlife conservation. IUCN – The World Conservation Union, Gland, Switzerland. 254 pp.

Bennett, A F. 2003. Habitat fragmentation. In Ecology: An Australian perspective. (Editors: Attiwill, P. and B. Wilson) Oxford University Press. 500 pp.

Baldwin, A D. 1994. Beyond Preservation: Restoring and Inventing Landscapes. University of Minnesota Press, MN. 280 pp.

Harker, D F, G Libby, K Harker, S Evans, and M Evans. 1999. Landscape restoration handbook. 2nd ed. Lewis Publishers, Inc., 880 pp.

Whisenant, S and A D Bradshaw. J L Craig, W Jordan, S L Pimm, D S Saunders, and M B Usher (eds.). 1999. Repairing damaged wildlands: a process-orientated, landscape-scale approach. Cambridge University Press, Cambridge. 324 pp.

Higgs, E. 2003. Nature by design: people, natural process, and ecological restoration. The MIT Press, Cambridge, MA. 341 pp.

Jongman, R H G and G Pungetti (eds.). 2004. Ecological networks and greenways: concept, design, implementation. Cambridge Studies in Landscape Ecology, Cambridge University Press, Cambridge, UK. 345 pp.

Flink, C A and R M Searns. 1993. Greenways: a guide to planning, design and development. Edited by L.LaB. Schwarz. Island Press, Washington, DC. 375 pp.

Fabos, J Gy and J Ahern (eds.). 1996. Greenways: the beginning of an international movement. Elsevier, Amsterdam. 491 pp.

The divided highway of Fox Drive and the Whitemud Equestrian Centre are seen as major barriers to mammal movement between the forested valley slopes and the North Saskatchewan River to right of photo (photo by Ross W. Wein, 2004).

landscape between fragments. This field of basic and applied studies has a vast literature (Baldwin 1994, Harker *et al.* 1999, Whisenant *et al.* 1999, Higgs 2003, Jongman and Pungetti 2004). In urban areas where fragmentation is the most extreme, the linking of all green spaces (school play fields, golf courses, recreation parks) has been studied under the title of greenways (Flink and Searns 1993, Fabos and Ahern 1996). The most intuitively attractive, but least practiced approach to reintegrating the natural landscapes with human systems, is to establish an interconnected network of functional conservation units. We term this a Conservation Net. However, few comprehensive conservation nets have been designed and tested even though they

136

are of critical importance and universal applicability. There is a window of opportunity for conservation planning and for testing a conservation net effectiveness over time. It may not be possible to take this action a decade or more from now when urban population growth and land-use decisions may have foreclosed green area options.

Collapsed Keillor Road that even massive piles could not prevent shows the instability of valley sides in Edmonton (photo by D. Kramm, 2004).

Our goal in this paper is to apply conservation net ideas to the Edmonton region, to the North Saskatchewan River Valley, and to our ribbon of green and associated protected areas.

What Is Our Conservation Legacy?

The industrial and urbanization period after 1900 AD is well documented in the literature (e.g. Anonymous 1914, Hesketh and Swyripa 1995, The Fort Edmonton Historical Foundation undated). By the time Edmonton was officially founded (1904), the local and upstream valley forests were long stripped of commercial-sized trees and sawmills, coal mines, brickyards and gravel pits were common in the fragmented valley. Photographs of this era show stands of young aspen trees. By the 1920s, Edmonton became a strong vacuum into which resources flowed from increasing distances. Housing, roads, railways and bridges were being built; but, in contrast to many other cities, the potentially massive earth flows in the valley restricted building on

Anonymous. 1914. Edmonton: Alberta's capital city. The Esdale Press Ltd. and McDermid Engraving Co. Ltd., Edmonton, AB. 180 pp.

Hesketh, B and F Swyripa (eds.). 1995. Edmonton: The Life of a City. NeWest Publishers Ltd., Edmonton, AB. 336 pp.

Anonymous. Undated. Edmonton … the way it was. The Fort Edmonton Historical Foundation. Edmonton, AB. Unpaged.

Collapsed valley side destroyed houses that were built on the table land (photo by Ross W. Wein, 2003).

Godfrey, J D. 1993. Edmonton beneath our feet. Edmonton Geological Society, Edmonton, AB. 150 pp.

Anonymous. 1992. Ribbon of green: North Saskatchewan River Valley and Ravine System Master Plan. Edmonton Parks and Recreation, City of Edmonton, Edmonton, AB. 112 pp.

the river and ravine valley slopes. Resource extraction and the building of suburbs shifted to the tablelands. Valley ecosystems began to re-establish around golf courses and other low intensity development areas, including parks. In other areas disturbance continued and transportation corridors, gravel pits, and waste disposal areas prevented ecosystem recovery.

The winter city of Edmonton at 53°33'N latitude has a present area of approximately 700 km^2. The 45 km of the North Saskatchewan River (with 14 associated ravines) within the city boundary has cut to a depth of 100 to 150 m into the sedimentary geological formations (Godfrey 1993). The greater 74 km^2 ribbon of green (Anonymous 1992) is one of the longest single urban-park river valley corridors in Canada and thousands of citizens are active on the 150 km of trails in the valley on any given weekend. The ribbon of green is the backbone of biodiversity conservation within the city boundaries, even though this is better described as a greenway that includes sports fields, golf courses, recreation parks, and trails. Much of the valley is not under active management except for problem animals, birds, insects, and plants. Soil flows are not uncommon along the unstable valley slopes and, in low snow and rainfall years, fires are common. Over the past 50 years the number of grass fires averaged 320 and in five of those years the number was over 500 per year (Source: City of Edmonton, Emergency Response Department, July 24, 2002).

Protected areas outside of the ribbon of green (i.e. on the tablelands) have been proposed for protection over the years. Anonymous (1980) lists hundreds of areas worthy of protection. After a decade, O'Leary *et al.* (1993) identified over 300 ecologically sensitive areas and significant natural areas; subsequently, many of these have been lost to subdivision development. After another decade Westworth Associates Environmental Ltd. (2001) brought forward 13 areas as worthy of immediate attention, through the Conserving Edmonton's Natural Areas Committee. Unfortunately, there is a tendency to see these special areas only as individually valuable parcels. The status of each patch depends solely on its own merits, with little reference to the surroundings or proximity to other habitat patches. In addition almost all of these areas are on private land and the City has designated only a small fund for such purchases. The conservation net concept has not yet been implemented and most of these special areas are isolated from other protected areas and corridors.

The Future: the Theory of Conservation Nets

Conservation groups have sought to protect small and unique areas but theory and practice have shown that these areas are often too small and/or isolated to prevent loss of both plant and animal diversity, especially during times of environmental stress. Also,

Anonymous. 1980. Environmental inventory and analysis of the North Saskatchewan River Valley and Ravine System –Wildlife. pp. 145-202. In: North Saskatchewan River Valley and Ravine System Biophysical Study. Technical Report. EPEC Consulting Western Ltd., Edmonton, AB. 391 pp.

O'Leary, D, J Bentz, D Ealey and A Schwabenbauer. 1993. Inventory of environmentally sensitive and significant natural areas – City of Edmonton. Prepared for Planning and Development, City of Edmonton by Geowest Environmental Consultants, Edmonton, AB. 303 pp. plus map.

Westworth Associates Environmental Ltd. 2001. Conserving Edmonton's Natural Areas; a framework for conservation planning in an urban landscape. Community Services, City of Edmonton. 174 pp. (also see Executive Summary. 19 pp.)

when natural connections among conservation areas are broken, the consequences include everything from biodiversity loss to traffic hazards. The theory and practice of conservation in urban areas have undergone a renaissance in the past two decades. There is a window of opportunity for regional based planning for conservation. We have the chance to establish a conservation net for the Alberta Capital Region and to test its effectiveness over time.

A definition

We are defining conservation nets as a scale-independent concept that includes a series of protected areas with buffer zones that are linked by multiple corridors which also have buffer zones. The forces that drive natural ecosystem change are permitted to function, where possible, within the pressure of industry and other social goals of communities. From a dynamic point of view, the conservation nets function as a larger ecosystem than the total area of the nodes and corridors.

An analogy

Conservation nets can be viewed as a fish net lying over the landscape. The knots are the nodes of high biodiversity and the strings are the corridors. Over time individual strings may break because of roads, buildings, and even green area development but the net will still function. Broken strings can be retied (through natural succession or restoration) to be more effective. Carrying the fish net analogy further, the floats and weights attached to the edges of the net can be viewed as subdivision and industries which must be considered as conservation management proceeds.

Conservation Net Components

Nodes

A conservation net should be built on existing nodes of protected areas, which vary widely in terms of size, biological/physical condition and degree of protection. These nodes may have been established for scenic or recreation reasons rather than biodiversity protection and may have been managed under a wide range of intensities. Nodes which are damaged but will recover over time should be included because they will contribute in the future (Thomas 2002).

There is one example where the concept of nodes is well recognized and that is where water birds are the focus of interest. The nodes are the water bodies, which can be separated by great migratory distances.

Corridors

There is a good deal of controversy about the importance and effectiveness of corridors for the maintenance of biodiversity (Saunders and Hobbs 1991, Hobbs 1992, Schaefer 1992, Simberloff *et al.* 1992, Dawson 1994, Naiman *et al.* 1993, Rosenberg *et al.* 1997, Bennett 1999, 2003). There are even more critics in resource development circles because corridors are perceived to restrict development and may be too costly for industry to repair. In our region, organisms must move seasonally because of climatic extremes; obvious natural corridors on the landscape are the rivers and valleys. In other cases corridors are not so obvious, but it should be possible to identify corridors through less disturbed fragments of the landscape.

Landscapes can be so fragmented that only a series of fragments remain; researchers have referred to this scenario as a corridor composed of stepping stones, as in a path. Nodes with

Thomas, R. 2002. English Nature habitat restoration project final report. English Nature Research Report Number 377. 64 pp + appendices.

Saunders, D A and R J Hobbs. (eds.). 1991. Nature Conservation 2: The Role of Corridors. Surrey Beatty and Sons, Chipping Norton, New South Wales. 442 pp.

Hobbs, R J. 1992. The role of corridors in conservation: solution or bandwagon? Trends in Ecology and Evolution 7: 389-392.

Schaefer, J M. 1992. Designing and Protecting River Corridors for Wildlife. Rivers 3 (1): 14-26.

Simberloff, D, J A Farr, J Cox, and D W Mehlman, 1992. Movement corridors: conservation bargains or poor investments? Conservation Biology 6: 493-504.

Dawson, D. 1994. Are habitat corridors conduits for animals and plants in a fragmented landscape?: a review of the scientific evidence. English Nature Research Report 94. English Nature: Northminster House, Peterborough, UK. 89 pp.

Naiman, R G, and H Decamps and M Pollock. 1993. The role of riparian corridors in maintaining regional biodiversity. Ecological Applications 3: 209-212.

Rosenberg, D K, B R Noon, and C E Meslow, 1997. Biological corridors: form, function, and efficacy. BioScience 47: 677-687.

Subdivision in the valley with city-centre in the background. There is concern that subdivisions, roads, and bridges in the river valleys prevent wildland species movement up- and-down river (photo by Ross W Wein, 2002).

high conservation value separated by low movement-inhibiting spaces between fragments may be very useful. For example, agricultural land may have nodes with relatively short distances of land-use types that may be conducive to species protection. In other examples, corridors may exist even when spaces separating nodes are high-hazard areas, such as utility and transportation corridors. The wildlife hazards of these corridors must be balanced against the value of the node to node movements of wildlife.

Although the emphasis here has been terrestrial corridors, we should be aware that there are also water and air corridors. Aquatic systems are natural corridors for more that just aquatic species and to remain effective they should not have impediments such as dams and diversions and should not be contaminated; urban aquatic ecosystems are particularly susceptible to degradation. Air corridors are not as widely recognized, but there are corridors as evidenced by problems of birds flying into tall buildings and colliding with airplanes.

Buffer zones

It is generally accepted that smaller nodes need wider buffer zones to protect normal ecological processes. The purpose of buffer zones is to limit human activity in concentric circles around a core node that needs the greatest protection (e.g. see Noss and Cooperrider 1994). In an inner buffer zone, low impact human activities such as wildlife viewing and ecological monitoring might be permitted. In the outer buffer zone, more intrusive human activities, such as biking and skiing, are permitted. A refinement of this buffer zone concept, promoted by authors such as Hough (1995) and Sayer (1991), places more emphasis on integrating ecosystem needs of conservation with the needs of humans. The central point is still the core protected zone but there are other forms of human activities that are separated spatially. In urban areas this is difficult to zone because the protected areas are so small.

Conservation net dynamics

Ecosystems are dynamic with populations and habitat changing naturally over days, seasons, years, and decades. Even with a well-managed balance of protection and human use in protected areas, subtle forces such as climate shifts and catastrophic events such as storms, outbreaks of insects and diseases change protected nodes and break corridor continuity. A challenge for protected area managers is how to respond to these natural forces without causing instability. In urban areas, the goal is to offer at least some protection to fragments of ecosystems and to protect these from severe human impacts at the very least. In many cases the natural forces (e.g. fire) cannot be used because of threats to people or property. Thus only cultural techniques (e.g. vegetation cutting) are acceptable to the community.

Hough, M. 1995. Cities and natural process. Routledge, NY. 326 pp.

Sayer, J. 1991. Rain forest buffer zones: guidelines for protected area managers. Forest Conservation Programme, IUCN-The World Conservation Union, Gland, Switzerland. 94 pp.

Soulé, M E and J Ternorgh. (eds.). 1999. Continental conservation: scientific foundations of regional reserve networks. Island Press, Washington, DC. 227 pp.

Soulé, M E and G H Orians (eds.). 2001. Conservation biology: research priorities for the next decade. Island Press, Washington, DC. 307 pp.

Applying the Concept at Different Scales

Over the last decade, the vision of continental scales (10 000+ km²) of conservation nets (Soulé and Ternorgh 1999) have captured the imagination of the public, land managers and researchers (Soulé and Orians 2001). Most major mountain chains and geological faults are being considered (e.g. Yellowstone to Yukon, Central American Corridor, Andean Corridor, Great Rift Valley). The complexity of land ownership, jurisdictions, and many other issues is simply staggering and yet for long-term biodiversity protection the development of sub-continent conservation nets is a noble goal.

At the regional or national scales of 100 to 1,000 km², the spatial relationships between human populations and protected areas are well known. At this scale, extensive agriculture, forestry and other resource extraction industries have caused and are causing widespread modification of natural ecosystems and habitats. Transportation and communication corridors lead to increased conflicts with animal movements. As a result, conservation areas tend to be located in remote areas, mountains and wetlands where resource extraction is limited by cost. At these scales, several ecosystem types and political jurisdictions are usually included in a conservation net. In landscapes of mountains and foothills, there is long-term built-in conservation protection because these areas are less amenable to high intensity human activity. Seasonal animal movements are usually up and down mountain slopes and in times of greater climatic stresses (e.g. drought, low temperatures) or even longer term climate change, plants and animals need only to move short distances to survive. In regions of low topographic relief, rivers, wetland, and escarpments are critical because these are less amenable to high intensity human activity. At this scale (such as the North Saskatchewan River watershed or the Greater Edmonton region) there may be strong societal views that the quantity and quality of water must be protected for the long-term health and economic development of the region or country.

At local scales up to 10 km², individuals and conservation groups promote the protection of remnants of formerly larger ecosystems within farms and ranches, small national parks, or urban-rural fringes of cities. Urban conservation has been studied for decades as a wildlife issue (Murphy 1988, Soulé 1991, Adams 1994, White 1994) and recently the urban planning literature includes information on rural-urban fringe conservation such as city farms (Roseland 1998 and especially Hough 1995). At this scale, there are many issues of private land ownership and the high cost of land; this usually means that protected areas are small and lack corridors and buffers. Protected areas are usually associated with rivers and valleys, which are natural corridors. There is also a desire to conserve examples of distinctive plant communities and the creation of stepping-stones between protected areas outside of the valleys.

The Future: Implementing a Conservation Net in Edmonton

Characteristics of pre-industrial ecosystems

The potential for mature natural ecosystems of the Edmonton region are well described (Strong and Leggat 1992). Ecosystems are at a tension point among the boreal forests to the north (Alberta Environmental Protection 1998), the aspen parkland and grassland to the south (Alberta Environmental Protection 1997) and the ecosystems up-river in the foothills (Alberta Environmental Protection 1996). Most of the upland would be aspen forest with white spruce in areas naturally protected from fires. Black spruce would be located in very wet soils with deep organic matter. Lakes and wetlands are common in the tablelands. In the river and

Murphy, D D. 1988. Challenges to biological diversity in urban areas. Pages 71-76 in E. O. Wilson, (ed.). Biodiversity. National Academy Press, Washington, DC. 521 pp.

Soulé, M E. 1991. Land use planning and wildlife maintenance: guidelines for conserving wildlife in an urban landscape. APA Journal, Summer 1991: 313-323.

Adams, L W. 1994. Urban wildlife habitats: a landscape perspective. University of Minnesota Press, Minneapolis, MN. 186 pp.

White, R R. 1994. Urban environmental management. Wiley, New York, NY. 233 pp.

Roseland, M. 1998. Toward sustainable communities. New Society Publ., Gabriola Island, B.C., Canada and Stony Creek, Connecticut, USA. 240 pp.

Strong, W L and K R Leggat. 1992. Ecoregions of Alberta. Alberta Forest Lands and Wildlife, Edmonton, AB. 59 pp. plus map.

Alberta Environmental Protection. 1998. The boreal forest natural region of Alberta. Alberta Environmental Protection, Edmonton, AB. 312 pp. plus maps.

Alberta Environmental Protection. 1997. The grassland natural region of Alberta. Alberta Environmental Protection, Edmonton, AB. 229 pp. plus maps.

Alberta Environmental Protection. 1996. Selecting protected areas: the foothills natural region of Alberta. Alberta Environmental Protection, Edmonton, AB. 16 pp. plus appendices.

Recent drought killed many birch and some pine and spruce. This reminds us that the force can change valley ecosystems (photo by Ross W. Wein, 2004).

Fires in the North Saskatchewan River Valley of Edmonton occur every year, especially in the spring (photo by Ross W. Wein, 1993.).

ravines the south-west slopes would be aspen-grassland, the north facing slopes would be white spruce and recovering vegetation of fire and landslide areas would be mixtures of these vegetation types.

What do our ecosystems look like now?

The forested ecosystems are recovering from complete harvesting over the past 100 years or more; this means the early succession species (e.g. aspen) are widespread. In addition there have been many plant and animal introductions that originate in other Canadian or overseas ecosystems. Examples include insects, diseases, and weeds. We should also recognize the older residential areas of our city are now tree dominated (Figure 1). It is noteworthy that boulevard and home-owner trees are non-native to the area; a few examples include scots pine, blue spruce and bur oak.

What could a conservation net look like?

At the North Saskatchewan River watershed landscape level, the river valley should be afforded better protection for a continuing supply of ecological services. Biodiversity will benefit as well from this protection. For example, the seasonal movement of animal species is up- and down-stream and in and out of the valley from the upland. In times of environmental stress such as drought or low temperature winters, the valley is critical for wildlife survival.

At the regional level, there must be links between the watershed protected areas and the local urban conservation nets. In our region there are many communities in the Greater Edmonton area and the conservation nets of these would be most effective if the corridors were planned in a co-ordinated fashion. One obvious linkage would be through the protection of the ribbon of green from encroachments both up- and down-river.

Coyotes Still Sing in My Valley

Figure 1
A satellite image showing the North Saskatchewan River Valley, streams and lakes, and the ravines which reach out toward the urban suburbs and into the rural-urban fringe of agricultural land.

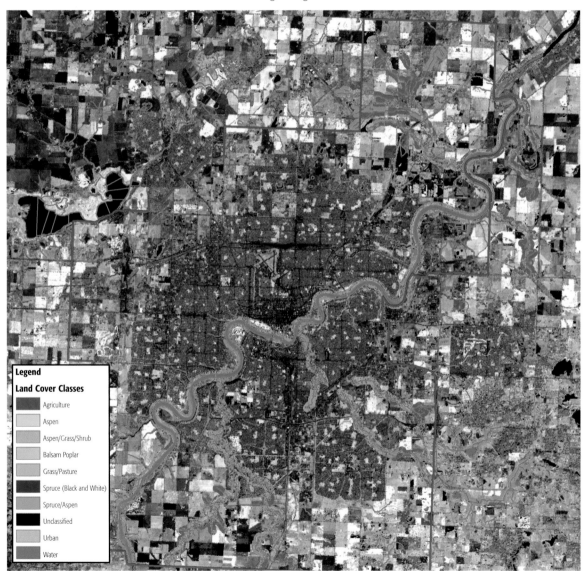

Legend

Land Cover Classes
- Agriculture
- Aspen
- Aspen/Grass/Shrub
- Balsam Poplar
- Grass/Pasture
- Spruce (Black and White)
- Spruce/Aspen
- Unclassified
- Urban
- Water

The North Saskatchewan River Valley and ravines should be considered as the backbone for a conservation net (photo by Ross W. Wein, 2003).

The landscape on the tablelands surrounding the Greater Edmonton urban areas is a patchwork of regenerating aspen parkland and agricultural land-use. To the east of the city, across this patchwork, is Elk Island National Park. Stepping-stone corridors, composed of larger forested fragments interspersed with agricultural land, may connect this protected area with the ribbon of green.

In the City of Edmonton, the conservation net would include the main North Saskatchewan River Valley and the 14 ravines and streams. Figure 1 is an image that was developed through a supervised classification approach from satellite imagery; it shows the connection of the main river valley and the ravines that reach from the city centre, out through the suburbs, to the surrounding agricultural land. Table 1 is a summary of vegetation types (with the urban areas removed) in the North Saskatchewan River Valley and

Table 1

Landscape cover types of the North Saskatchewan River Valley and Whitemud Creek buffered to a 500 m width. The water and urban areas are removed.

| | Land Cover Types | | | | | | | |
	Spruce	Spruce/aspen	Aspen	Poplar	Aspen/grass	Grass/pasture	Crops	Total
North Saskatchewan River Valley								
Area (ha)	409	415	301	575	476	659	416	3,251
Area (%)	12	13	9	18	15	20	13	100
Number of patches /100 ha	35	75	52	62	56	35	27	
Whitemud Creek								
Area (ha)	158	188	149	326	281	526	727	2,355
Area (%)	7	8	6	14	12	22	31	100
Number of patches /100 ha	10	46	40	43	43	32	27	

Whitemud Creek. The two creeks are surrounded by much more agricultural land and much less spruce forest than the main valley. In addition, the density of patches shows the high degree of fragmentation of all land cover. This information gives only a coarse overview of a conservation net backbone. A more thorough assessment should be made using the more detailed spatial data sets held by the city. Hopefully, in the conservation net, the streams would be protected by buffers that also encompass the wetlands that support the streams. There will be many suggested unique and special areas for the conservation net. Those that are easily linked to the stream and ravines are valid candidates for long-term protection. Hopefully, these can be purchased for the public good and managed as protected areas.

What is Needed for Implementation?

There are a number of steps that are usually suggested in the establishment of a conservation net. Any conservation net will not be secure until the land ownership question is solved and until communities that border the nodes and corridors benefit economically and socially. All too often people are seen to be a major problem for conservation; yet, local communities may have the most to gain through business and ecotourism opportunities if ecosystems are protected. Planning for and establishing conservation nets requires facilities, equipment, and trained personnel (men, women, and youth). There are many real and perceived problems that must be solved by researchers with people at the local level. Finally there is an important role for monitoring to ensure that planned protection goals are being achieved. Funding is critical for success and the high economic return on investment needs to be emphasized. A conservation net is infrastructure for quality of life and a well planned conservation net will reduce the level of conflict between developers and other stakeholders.

Step 1: Communication

Local involvement and control is essential to gain credibility and so a range of communication formats is a high priority throughout the building of conservation nets. Frequent discussion fosters information flow to and from many people in local communities. Information on protected area development and management must be synthesized to guide further research, training and management. As residents of communities take control, community conservation focus groups and regional workshops could assist professionals to find solutions to real and perceived problems; community leagues are a natural group to lead such initiatives. While some

In heavily modified agricultural areas, connectivity is still identified through stream configurations (photo by Ross W. Wein, 1990).

conservation groups perceive residents of new suburbs as the major problem for biodiversity protection, others recognize that these urban citizens can speak strongly for their local conservation nets (Brandon and Brandon 1992, Wells, Brandon and Hannah 1992, Ceballos-Lascurain 1996). Suburbs near protected nodes or corridors are especially well located to take advantage of recreational opportunities that require ecosystem protection for greater quality of life. In the rural-urban fringe, where communities are just being planned and developed, there is much opportunity to develop conservation nets. Urban developers certainly recognize the economic advantage of building near protected areas.

Brandon, M W. and K Brandon. 1992. People and parks: linking protected area management with local communities. The World Bank, Washington, DC. 99 pp.

Wells, M, K Brandon and L Hannah. 1992. People and Parks: linking protected area management with local communities. The International Bank for Reconstruction and Development/ The World Bank, Washington, DC. 99 pp.

Ceballos-Lascurain, H (ed.). 1996. Tourism, ecotourism and protected areas. IUCN – The World Conservation Union, Gland, Switzerland. 301 pp.

Step 2: Identification of established and potential protected fragments

In most cases conservation nets will be built around established protected areas which have a unique history. Information on current protected areas in Edmonton is already synthesized and there are large sets of spatial data on which to build. There is a need to identify and gain ownership of additional conservation nodes and corridors. This is especially true for rare, mature ecosystems; most valley and ravine ecosystems are recovering from industrial disturbance that was only reduced within the last five to ten decades. There is also a need to evaluate the conservation integrity of the ribbon of green, ravines, and streams. Few large areas will be set aside in the future because the majority of land is privately owned. Small areas might be readily purchased as protected areas if their uniqueness can be demonstrated and if they can be linked to corridors. Areas of known conservation value (naturalness/high species diversity) have been identified through the City and through consultation and public meetings. These potentially protected areas and corridors need to be evaluated in terms of conservation integrity (naturalness, biodiversity, rare and valuable species). The critical goal is to identify multiple corridors wherever possible because corridors can be broken.

Step 3: Short-term evaluations

Often there is much effort applied to identify and secure areas through direct purchase and easements; much additional effort is required to collect information needed for development and management of a conservation net. While there tends to be many opinions, there are fewer quantitative evaluations on the characteristics that make a node outstanding or a corridor effective in the short-term. There are even fewer data on which to evaluate

Green spaces should be considered as nodes or corridors because protection over time can increase biodiversity (photo by Ross W. Wein, 2003).

long-term effectiveness. Many of the available observational and experimental studies are oriented to species behavior. Space and time models might be more effective to test the value of corridors for effective movement of animal and plant species among nodes.

For example, it is critical to know which nodes can be most effectively joined by multiple corridors. Some nodes will be connected by potential corridors made up of unbroken bands, while others will consist of stepping-stones of suitable habitat separated by inhospitable terrain. Information on how corridors function in time and space can be gained by modeling plant and animal movement and using driving variables such as change in habitat type and predators. Ultimately, the validity of these predictions must be verified through field studies. For plants, field studies might involve measurements of seed dispersal distances along corridors by wind and animals. For animals the effectiveness of corridors can be verified by surveying the movement of selected species among nodes by a variety of methods such as observations

Hawrelak Park and the Mayfield Golf and Country Club were established after this bend in the river was mined for gravel and sand. Revegetation of the mined area has renewed biodiversity (photo by Ross W. Wein, 1991).

of tracks in winter and summer, direct observations of animal movements, radio and satellite tracking, trapping surveys and experiments. Coyotes and deer are often suggested as corridor-effectiveness indicators but other wildlife guilds (i.e. groups of species with similar ecological requirements of the landscape) should be considered. With considerable resources, checks on historic patterns of dispersal can be made from comparisons of genetic similarity through DNA fingerprinting techniques between selected areas within metapopulations.

Once the characteristics of successful corridors are established for different plants and animals it will be possible to prescribe management actions to enhance the corridors for key species and guilds. For example, it may be possible to identify where

154

management strategies should be changed to strengthen protection or restore habitat. The effects of disturbance are important to consider, not only in the protected nodes but also in the corridors. Disturbance in corridors could repel organisms from moving or attract organisms to move faster and for greater distances.

Step 4: Solving longer-term problems

After corridors have been identified and verified over the short-term, research is needed to support defensible management decisions. Data are needed to understand how to maintain the conservation value of the nodes, as well as improving and completing corridors. An important management goal is maintaining viable populations at the nodes and improving the flow of species along corridors that have suitable habitat. This suitable habitat is often seen as critical staging posts for species with limited powers of dispersal (especially among plants and invertebrates). If corridors are too long or unsuitable, there will be limited development of viable populations.

Solving boundary and buffer zone issues will be a continuing concern because of modified ecosystems. If the ecosystems outside the conservation net are strongly modified, the buffer zones need to be wide. Those who control the ecosystems outside may insist that the buffer zones be inside the corridor, rendering the corridor ineffective. Without long-term research and management plans, management becomes crisis oriented on specific issues at specific locations. Ultimately management solutions must be ecologically sound and acceptable to nearby communities.

At the watershed level, issues will include rapid intensification of agriculture, forestry or petroleum industries or wildfire threats. At the regional level, issues might include the spread of unwanted plants, insects, diseases or pollution. At the local urban level issues

Urban areas have many exotic species that have been introduced and that may spread by corridors. In this photo, there are at least five non-native tree species (photo by Ross W. Wein, 2004).

might include problem animals or plants at the personal, home owner, subdivision, or utility and transportation levels.

As solutions are found they should be integrated into the overall management of the conservation node or corridor. Demonstrations, through benchmark areas, can be an effective tool to convince managers about solutions. Research and management issues may rely on specialists, but the larger community can play a role especially by providing background information through monitoring.

Step 5: Monitoring

Since ecosystems are dynamic and can change dramatically over time, it is necessary to monitor them to determine if changes in the conservation net are acceptable within the stated goals. Benchmark sites have long been used as a method of monitoring local changes. Generally benchmark plots should be established at ecotones between vegetation types, at paired sites where adjacent management strategies are distinctly different, or at sites where dramatic changes, such as erosion, are expected to occur. The goal is to demonstrate the first signs of directional ecosystem change. These plots are also effective as demonstrations of changes that result from management treatments. Often benchmark plots can be short-term experiments that are left in place for the collection of longer-term results.

Who Would Benefit?

Although a basic goal of conservation nets is to protect wild plant and animal species, this goal is often not recognized by society as a priority. Ecological services, however valuable, are difficult to quantify for small areas. On the other hand, there are well-recognized economic, recreation, health, and education benefits of a more fully developed conservation net. There are many city administrators who wish to decrease the conflict between developers and conservationists by focussing on conservation areas at the planning stage rather than at the implementation stages of suburb development.

Investors, developers and many city residents recognize the economic benefits of conservation; a simple examination of the names of subdivisions conjure up views of natural surroundings (Aspen Gardens, Twin Brooks, Quarrie Ridge) and it is well known that ravine-edge properties are sold at a premium.

Many citizens recognize the quality of life benefits to individuals, families, and clubs. For example, the health benefits of exercise on walking, cycling, and skiing trails and the therapeutic benefits of simply experiencing the relative quiet of the conservation net are well known. The city administration could promote tourism of our valley even more than at present. The tourist literature promotes the City of Edmonton as our Alberta capital city and as the home of West Edmonton Mall, the Muttart Conservatory, the Alberta Legislature Building and Fort Edmonton Park. There is mention of the scenic river valley but little information is provided.

The value of conservation nets for environmental and heritage education of all ages is shown by the number of current and potential activities in the valley. Many curriculum modules in primary and secondary school students can be effectively taught in the conservation net that is close to the school. University teaching and research has always been practiced in the valley. Life-long learners reconnect with their natural heritage through clubs. Cultural celebrations and meeting places in the valley are important for the 40,000 citizens of Aboriginal descent (2001 Census of Canada).

Conclusions

To many Edmonton residents the North Saskatchewan River Valley defines the quality of life of our city and the protected areas represent long-term infrastructure investments. We need to begin to adopt a conservation net to guide the development of a concrete, comprehensive local and regional conservation plan.

Acknowledgements

In clarifying our thinking on this conservation topic, we recognize Jon Meade, Alastair Franke, Robert J. Hudson, Michael J. Salomons, Richard M. Roth and more recently, Adele M. Mandryk, John R. Wood and Colleen Cassidy-St. Clair.

Useful Websites

http://www.gov.edmonton.ab.ca/fort/
http://www.pma.edmonton.ab.ca/human/archaeo/research/fort.htm
http://www.gov.ab.ca/aboutalberta/history_firstnations.cfm

Special Urban Conservation Places

Achivements and Lessons Learned

Anonymous. 1992. Ribbon of Green. Edmonton Parks and Recreation, Edmonton, AB. 112 pp.

Godfrey, J D. 1993. Edmonton beneath our feet. Edmonton Geological Society, Edmonton, AB. 150 pp.

Anonymous. 1980. Environmental inventory and analysis of the North Saskatchewan River Valley and Ravine System. Wildlife. pp. 145-202. In North Saskatchewan River Valley and Ravine System Biophysical Study. Technical Report. EPEC Consulting Western Ltd., Edmonton, AB. 391 pp.

O'Leary, D, J Bentz, D Ealey and A Schwabenbauer. 1993. Inventory of environmentally sensitive and significant natural areas – City of Edmonton. Prepared for Planning and Development, City of Edmonton by Geowest Environmental Consultants, Edmonton, AB. 303 pp. plus map.

Westworth Associates Environmental Ltd. 2001. Conserving Edmonton's Natural Areas; a framework for conservation planning in an urban landscape. Community Services, City of Edmonton. 174 pp. (also see Executive Summary. 19 pp.)

Chapman, R. 1991. The discoverer's guide to Elk Island National Park. Lone Pine Publishing and The Friends of Elk Island Society, Edmonton, AB. 96 pp.

Saley, H, D H Meredith, H Stelfox and D Ealey. 2003. Nature walks and Sunday drives 'round Edmonton. Edmonton Natural History Club, Edmonton, AB. 80 pp.

The ribbon of green (Anonymous 1992) is considered the backbone of biodiversity conservation within the city boundaries, even though this is a greenway that includes sports fields, golf courses, recreation parks, and trails. Much of the remainder of the valley is not under active conservation management except for problem mammals, birds, and insects; weeds and trees that are deemed a hazard also receive attention. The forested ecosystems are recovering from deforestation through mining and many other activities early in the last century; soil flows are common along the unstable valley slopes (Godfrey 1993). In low snow and rainfall years, grass fires occur, especially in the spring.

Areas outside of the ribbon of green (i.e. on the tablelands) have been proposed for protection over the years. Studies include Anonymous (1980), in which hundreds of areas were identified as worthy of protection. After a decade, O'Leary *et al.* (1993) identified over 300 ecologically sensitive areas and significant natural areas; many of these have since been lost to subdivision development. After another decade Westworth Associates Environmental Ltd. (2001) brought forward 13 areas as worthy of immediate attention, through the Conserving Edmonton's Natural Areas Committee. Unfortunately, there is a tendency to see these small areas only as individually valuable parcels. The status of each parcel depends solely on its own merits, with little reference to the surroundings or proximity to other habitat patches. In addition almost all of these areas are on private land and the City has designated only a small fund for such purchases. Non-purchase options must be considered.

Beyond the boundaries of our city, protected areas that quickly come to mind include Elk Island National Park (Chapman 1991) and others described in Saley *et al.* (2003). These represent the aspen parkland ecosystems (Bird 1961, Kabzems *et al.* 1976, North 1976, Strong and Leggat 1992) and contribute to biodiversity protection. Several of the protected areas have northern prairie pothole lakes. The more southern pothole lakes are more thoroughly studied (van der Valk 1989, Weller 1994, Galatowitsch and van der Valk 1994, Murkin *et al.* 2000); fortunately much of the science is applicable to our area. Naturalists recognize that these lakes feature spectacular waterfowl viewing in the spring and fall migrations. Most importantly, the status of conservation of our wildland species is now being documented (Anonymous 2001).

In this section, specific areas are featured that make unique contributions to biodiversity protection, that attract the attention of naturalists, and that sometimes act as the focus of conflict. Much has been learned from the successes of establishing and managing these sites. We also learn from the failures; but, of course, we celebrate the successes with more enthusiasm. As we look forward to protecting additional sites, we also think about corridors that are necessary for the long-term protection of biodiversity in our region.

Bird, R D. 1961. Ecology of the aspen parkland of Western Canada in relation to land use. Canada Department of Agriculture, Ottawa, ON. 155 pp.

Kabzems, A, A L Kosowan and W C Harris. 1976. Mixedwood section in an ecological perspective Saskatchewan. Tech. Bull. No. 8, Tourism and Renewable Resources, Government of Saskatchewan, Saskatoon, SK. 118 pp. plus map.

North, M E A. 1976. A plant geography of Alberta: an interpretation based on the 1965 vegetation map. Department of Geography, University of Alberta, Edmonton, AB. 147 pp. plus map.

Strong, W L and K R Leggat. 1992. Ecoregions of Alberta. Alberta Forestry, Lands and wildlife, Edmonton, AB. 59 pp. plus map.

Van der Valk, A (ed.). 1989. Northern prairie wetlands. Iowa State University Press, Ames, IA. 400 pp.

Weller, M W. 1994. Freshwater marshes: ecology and wildlife management. 3rd edn. University of Minnesota Press, Minneapolis, MN. 154 pp.

Galatowitsch, S M and A G van der Valk. 1994. Restoring prairie wetlands: an ecological approach. Iowa State University Press, Ames, IA. 246 pp.

Murkin, H R, A G van der Valk, and W R Clark (eds.). 2000. Prairie wetland ecology. Iowa State University Press, Ames, IA. 413 pp.

Anonymous. 2001. The general status of Alberta wild species 2000. Alberta Environment/Alberta Sustainable Resources Development, Edmonton, AB. 46 pp.

Elk Island National Park: A Conservation Island in an Agricultural Landscape

Ross Chapman, Elk Island National Park

Introduction

Located 45 km east of the city of Edmonton, Elk Island National Park is a 194 km^2 wilderness refuge in a sea of agricultural development (Figure 1 and 2). The rectangular-shaped park is located on a dead ice moraine in the transitional lower boreal mixedwood forest dominated by aspen. Glacio-fluvial, morainic and lacutrine deposits are found within the park, with glacial till being the dominant form of surface deposits. The park is characterized by low hills up to 20 m higher than the surrounding landscape. Some 20% of the park is wetlands.

Perhaps the most impressive characteristic of the park is the density of wildlife found within its borders. The park contains a native ungulate guild of hundreds of plains bison, wood bison, elk, moose, and white tail and mule deer. The biological inventory of the park includes over 600 species of native plants, over 200 species of birds, five species of amphibians and over 40 species of native

Figure 1
Location of Elk Island National Park in relation to Edmonton and Beaverhills/Cooking-Lake Moraine (Source: Elk Island National Park).

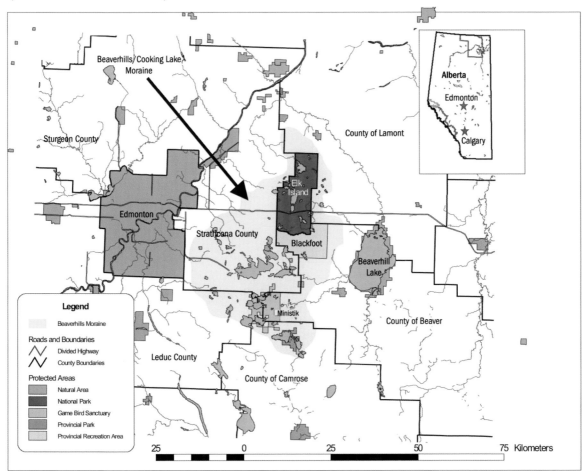

mammals (Chapman 2003). Cougars are recent arrivals to the park, possibly via the North Saskatchewan River Valley. While the park is fenced to prevent the bison from wandering into Edmonton and elsewhere, the bison freely roam most of the park.

Chapman, R J. 2003. Memorable wildlife encounters in Elk Island National Park. Human Dimensions of Wildlife. 8: 235-236.

The park has provided bison for many new herds in Canada (photo by Ross W. Wein, 2000).

Kaye, R. 2004. Personal communication.

Cool, R. 2004. Personal communication.

Elk Island National Park encompasses a number of outstanding features that attract visitors. Human dimension studies show that visitors are mostly attracted to visit Elk Island by the assurance of seeing large wildlife such as bison (Chapman 2003). In fact, roadside viewing of bison and elk is the most often talked about experience by park visitors and usually dominates visitor's memories of the park. Canoeing on Astotin Lake with its many species of waterfowl is also often cited as a memorable experience. Occasionally trumpeter swans are visible on Astotin Lake; these native birds were re-introduced starting in 1985. Picnicking and camping is featured but swimming is not recommended because of swimmers itch (a non-threatening skin rash caused by a parasite which ordinarily infects birds, semi-aquatic mammals, and snails). Serious birders find Elk Island attractive because of the chance to witness rare migrating birds and some of the warblers that breed in the park. In the winter, over 30 non-migrating birds are an attraction for the visitor. Hiking and cross country skiing on the more than 60 km of trails within the park is a highlight for many visitors; while the frequent sightings of wildlife give people a feeling of being deep in the wilderness.

The park contains several species of rare plants (e.g. moonworts), and on a wider North American scale has provided source herds for many herds of elk and bison, including herds relocated to British Columbia, Saskatchewan and Ontario, as well as other locations in Alberta. Several shipments of elk have been trans-located to Tennessee, Kentucky and other USA states (Kaye 2004). While many herds of plains bison in North America are contaminated with cattle genes from early cross breeding experiments (Cool 2004), plains bison from Elk Island are considered the purest in the world. The most recent trans-location was to a grasslands area in southern Saskatchewan in 2003.

Over 200,000 visitors use the park annually (Chapman, 2004). Most visitors are from the Greater Edmonton area and most take day trips lasting up to five hours. Today's visitors focus on wildlife viewing (mostly bison), hiking and picnicking. There is also an international component of visitors; they visit Elk Island while visiting attractions in the Edmonton area, or are en route to the mountain parks such as Banff and Jasper. There are visitors with different levels of ecological knowledge ranging from the advanced birdwatcher to the visitor who only has a limited knowledge of bison. Most wildlife viewers are in their automobiles on the parkway when viewing wildlife.

Majestic elk walking silently at dusk or through the mist is nature at its finest (photo by Ross Chapman, 2004).

History of Development

Elk Island's original role was to preserve one species. In 1905, concerned hunters and local conservationists petitioned the federal government to set aside land to preserve a remnant herd of native elk (*Cervus elaphus* spp. *manitobensis*) in part of the Cooking Lake forest reserve. Subsequently, approximately 10 km² of land was fenced. In 1913, the park, which by then had grown to 194 km² in size, was established as a National/Dominion Park.

From 1905, the park has evolved from a phase of preserving elk, to a phase where tourist facilities, roads, swimming, power boating and golfing were emphasized with little thought to ecological integrity. Over time the elk, bison and moose

There is a resident population of moose held by this fenced park (photo by Ross W. Wein, 1999).

Parks Canada. 1994. Guiding principles and operational policies. Parks Canada.

populations outgrew the capacity of the habitat to support them and slaughter programs were necessary. In 1979, the relocation of excess elk, bison and moose became policy. A goal to better monitor the ecological status of the park gained emphasis beginning in the 1980s and today is the main focus of the park. Secondary management mandates include the provision of visitor experiences that are compatible with maintaining the ecological integrity of the park. Canoeing on Lake Astotin is allowed, but power boats are not permitted in the park today.

Management of the Park

National parks protect representative examples of Canada's landscape. To accomplish this goal Parks Canada Agency has identified 39 distinct natural regions that capture ecosystem diversity in geology, physiography, vegetation and wildlife. Efforts are underway to establish one national park in each natural region (Parks Canada Guiding Principles and Operational Policies 1994). Elk Island represents the southern boreal plains and plateau natural region. Less than 5% of the lower boreal mixed wood forest dominated by aspen survives, and is therefore considered as one of Canada's most endangered habitats. Elk Island thus provides an important conservation role from an ecosystem sense.

Recent studies show that Elk Island is heavily fragmented from earlier resource management practices such as internal fencing and

Coyotes Still Sing in My Valley

visitor facilities. However, when compared species by species to areas surrounding the park, the park still offers much biodiversity protection. For example, western toads thrive in the park and forested areas which make up a large portion of the park and still retain a high degree of naturalness. One of the goals of the Elk Island ecosystem conservation plan is to manage ecosystem dynamics to duplicate the natural processes that drive the park and surrounding area ecosystems (Cool *et al.* 2003). Elk Island has a robust controlled burn program to re-establish fire as a process on the landscape. The earliest controlled burn program was implemented in 1979 (Dixon 2004). Controlled burns have subsequently been conducted on an annual basis, but have stopped for the last couple of years because of the drought and low soil moisture levels, which makes the hazard unacceptable. More pre- and post-monitoring is now being planned to ensure the desired vegetation targets are being met.

Research

Elk Island and the surrounding Beaver Hills have been subject to scientific studies, especially through partnerships with the University of Alberta because of its close proximity to the park. This has allowed for the ongoing development of a pre- and post-monitoring program and a strong database that has stimulated new ideas in managing natural landscape and human interfaces. Landmark biophysical studies include a biophysical inventory by Hardy and Associates (1986) and several smaller inventories on small mammals, birds and plants. The four wetland types found in Elk Island National Park include bogs, fens, swamps and marshes. Nicholson and Vitt (1990) studied wetlands in the park and assessed paleo-vegetation in varying vegetation types in the park.

Trumpeter swans returned to Elk Island National Park in 1987 (photo by Edgar T Jones).

Cool, N *et al.* 2003. Elk Island ecosystem conservation plan. Parks Canada Report.

Dixon, J. 2004. Personal communication.

Hardy and Associates. 1986. Ecological land classification of Elk Island National Park. Parks Canada Report.

Nicholson, B and D Vitt. 1990. The wetlands of Elk Island National Park, Alberta: a resource inventory, evolutionary analysis and suggestions toward their management and interpretation. Parks Canada Report. 43 pp.

Bates, L and R Chapman. 2002. Ozone balloon release. Air Bulletin, Ottawa, ON, Canada.

Bates, L, A Tremble and R Chapman. 2002. Assessing sources of particulate matter in Elk Island National Park. Parks Canada Spring Edition.

Parks Canada Agency. 2003. Annual Elk Island National Park archeological monitoring report. Parks Canada Report.

Current graduate student research include fire behaviour, ungulate interaction, beaver ecology, red squirrel habitat interaction, saw whet owl habitat fragmentation, and resident bird studies to name a few. Much graduate work on fragmentation and disturbances now focuses on the 900 km² Cooking Lake moraine that includes Elk Island. In addition, recently completed Masters and Doctoral research have helped redefine indicators for aquatic and riparian health. Partnerships with industry are also strong, with Elk Island operating one of thirteen regional air quality stations. Results show that the air over the park is impacted by industrial activity in the Greater Edmonton area (Bates and Chapman 2002, Bates *et al.* 2002). These air quality indicators are presently being assessed to evaluate the level of impact on the ecosystem.

Elk Island's rich wildlife assemblage over the past thousands of years has made it a favourite place for Aboriginal hunters. Over 200 archaeological sites have been mapped in Elk Island National Park (Parks Canada Agency 2003). Most of these sites, some dating back thousands of years, are hunting sites consisting of fire burned rock, the occasional arrowhead, and pottery and bone fragments. The earliest archaeological surveys were conducted in the mid 1980's with a survey now being conducted by Parks Canada archaeologists on an annual basis.

The Future

The vision for Elk Island National Park is that it will continue to protect a portion of the southern boreal plains and plateau natural region and will form an integral part of the Beaver Hills/Cooking Lake ecosystem. It will also remain a renowned destination where visitors can view and appreciate nature. The park will play an important role in re-establishing species such as the trumpeter swan and wood bison. Key processes such as fire, herbivory, and beaver flooding will be maintained. With these efforts it will be possible to sustain a representation of the boreal forest to the north and the grassy plains to the south (Elk Island National Park 2003).

On the negative side, development is occurring in the Cooking Lake moraine at an astonishing rate. One of the largest concentrations of heavy industry including many refineries is located on the edge of the moraine, a mere 20 km from the park. Noise from this industrial complex impacts park ecosystems and visitors. Other accelerating developments such as oil and gas wells are being developed within 1 km of the park. Cell phone towers pose a visual pollution problem. As Edmonton, with a population of close to one million, edges toward the park, greater co-operation with neighbouring jurisdictions will have to occur if the park is to preserve its native wildlife and plant guilds and its natural processes.

The patch-like, privately-owned, natural areas and areas such as the Blackfoot Recreation Area to the south and Ministik Bird Sanctuary to the southeast are important to the long-term survival of Elk Island; they connect the park to the larger ecosystem. Recent ongoing research shows the astonishing amount of native biodiversity even in small natural areas that are part of acreages, farms and ranches. One pond, surrounded by a cultivated field, was surveyed in 2001 and contained over 100 tiger salamanders (Eaves 2003). Rare plants are known to inhabit the creek banks of intermittent streams such as Astotin Creek. One recent survey of plants also revealed a provincially rare sedge (*Carex pseudocypress*) growing just metres inside the park boundary as well as less than 100 metres outside the park next to a county road that runs parallel to the boundary (Cornish 2000). Some birds such as the saw whet owl appear to do well in the highly fragmented land surrounding Elk Island. The red backed vole, one

Elk Island National Park. 2003. Draft management plan. Parks Canada Report.

Eaves, S. 2003. Personal communication.

Cornish, B. 2000. Personal communication.

of the favourite prey species of the saw whet owl, is found in abundance on the forest patches that surround the park.

One of the goals of the current park management plan is to continue to understand how Elk Island National Park contributes to the protection of natural remnants of the Cooking Lake moraine. New partners, such as the Nature Conservancy of Canada, are now busy setting aside conservation easements and purchasing parcels of relatively undisturbed land in the 900 km² area. Research studies are helping to define which parcels to preserve in order to achieve greater connectivity between protected areas such as Elk Island, the Blackfoot Grazing Reserve and Ministik areas. Linkages such as the Astotin Creek drainage to the North Saskatchewan River are also very important. Working with neighbours is a goal of Elk Island in preserving the biodiversity of the Cooking Lake moraine.

Lessons Learned

Elk Island National Park is managed by the Canadian Government Department of Environment. The maintenance of park roads and picnic areas, the enforcement of the National Parks Act, and the preservation of ecological integrity is the responsibility of the Canadian Government. However, the fact that public funding is often given to other priorities highlights the importance of partnerships to achieve ecological integrity goals, and Parks Canada Agency encourages partnerships with other organizations that share a similar mandate.

There is conflict with neighbouring farms; this conflict must be resolved. Some park animals roam outside the park on a regular basis; coyotes are a good example. Although a large part of their diet is rodents, they sometime interact in a negative way with neighbouring domestic birds on farms. Deer and beaver also travel in and out of the park underneath the fence on a regular basis. Weeds and even domestic animals from farms are a concern to the park, and a regular weed control program has been established in the park in co-operation with neighbouring jurisdictions to combat this problem. Scientists regularly review the weed control program for environmental implications.

Elk Island will truly become an ecological island unless efforts are continued to preserve areas surrounding the park and corridors to the greater ecosystem. Elk Island managers are committed to engaging in discussions with park neighbours. To this end, park managers are working closely with agencies such as the Nature Conservancy of Canada that is establishing conservation easement and other mechanisms for preserving habitat in the Cooking Lake moraine.

Acknowledgements

Discussions with Steve Zoltai (in 1987), Beth Cornish (in 2000), Sarah Eaves (in 2003), and Rob Kaye, Norm Cool, and Jeff Dixon (in 2004), were much appreciated.

Further Reading

The selected papers and reports given below introduce the range of information that is available in the Park library:

Chapman R. 2002. An environmental assessment of water use for the Elk Island National Park Golf Course. Parks Canada Report.

Chapman, R. 2002. Rare plants discovered in Elk Island National Park. Parks Canada. Research Links, Summer Edition, Parks Canada.

Chapman, R J. 2002. Exploiting the human need for nature for successful protected area management. George Wright Forum Journal 19 (4): 52-55.

Chapman, R J. 2002. Biological invasion risks and the public good: an economic perspective. Journal of Conservation Ecology 6:1 p. 33.

Chapman R and R Brown. 1991. The discover's guide to Elk Island National Park. Lone Pine Publishing, Edmonton, AB.

Chapman R and S Therrian-Richards. 2000. An environmental assessment of the Elk Island National Park Management Plan.

Eaton, B R, C Paszkowski and R Chapman. 2003. *Rana sylvatica* parasite. Herpetilogical Review 34: 55.

Griffiths, G. 2002. Rare plant checklist. Elk Island National Park Report.

Parks Canada. 1999. Visitor survey Elk Island National Park. Parks Canada Report.

Paszkowski, C, B Eaton and R Chapman. 2002. Amphibian monitoring in Elk Island National Park. Research Links, Spring Edition, Parks Canada.

Techman Ltd. 1979. Vegetation classification and evaluation – Elk Island National Park. Parks Canada Report.

Walker, J and R Chapman. 2004. Thinking like a park: The effects of sense of place, perspective and intentions. Journal of Parks and Recreation Administration [accepted for publication].

Walker, G and R Chapman. 2001. Visitor motivation in Elk Island National Park. Research Links, Winter Edition, Parks Canada.

The Clifford E. Lee Nature Sanctuary: Bringing People in Touch with Nature

Marg Reine and Lu Carbyn, Clifford E. Lee Nature Sanctuary

Introduction

The 137 ha Clifford E. Lee Nature Sanctuary was established in 1978 (Figure 1). It is located just west of Highway 60, south of Stony Plain Indian Reserve, 135.5 km from the west boundary of Edmonton, 2 km from the 450 ha Devonian Botanic Garden, and 2 km from the North Saskatchewan River Valley (Saley *et al.* 2003). The origin of the name is from the Clifford E. Lee Foundation, which funded the purchase of the land. This was the first nature sanctuary set aside by the Canadian Nature Federation and is operated by a volunteer management committee. The mission is to protect a variety of habitats with the associated flora and fauna, to educate the general public regarding natural areas and their significance, and to provide the opportunity to enjoy nature.

A unique feature of the sanctuary is that it represents the 80 km² Devon sandhills complex that has a northwest-southeast 10 km axis. In the matrix of sand dunes, dominated by jack pine,

Saley, H, D H Meredith, H Stelfox and D Eale. 2003. Nature walks and Sunday drives 'round Edmonton. 80 pp.

Figure 1

Air photo of 137 ha Clifford E. Lee Nature Sanctuary showing the shallow lake and surrounding marshes of *Typha latifolia*. The southeast to northwest axis of the lake is about 2 km (Source: City of Edmonton).

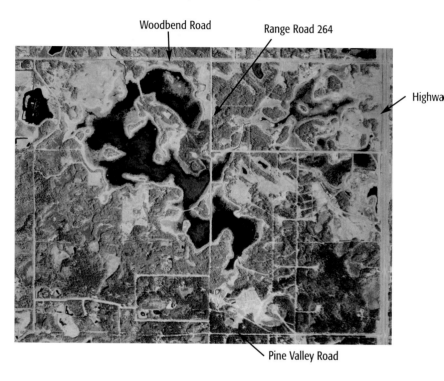

Woodbend Road   Range Road 264

Highwa◄

Pine Valley Road

Griffiths, C D G and D E Griffiths. 1979. Avifauna flora of the Clifford E. Lee Nature Sanctuary.

Hervieux, D. 1981. Mammals of the Clifford E. Lee Nature Sanctuary.

there are aspen parkland stands, intermittent ponds and lakes, as well as fens and marshes. Land-use is acreages and farms, with many oil well installations. More than 100 bird species have been documented with many of them breeding within the sanctuary (Griffiths and Griffiths 1979). Wildlife such as ducks, geese, beaver and muskrats are common in the network of lakes and marshes, part of which is impounded by a dyke that Ducks Unlimited constructed. Upland animals such as white-tailed deer, moose, and coyotes are found in the pine and aspen forests (Hervieux 1981).

The varied habitats boast 267 species of vascular plants, including some that are unique in the region (Griffiths and Griffiths 1979). The terrestrial and aquatic insects provide interesting study material for school field trips (Corkum 1978). A few species of insects are at their most northerly limit (Griffiths and Griffiths 1980).

Facilities of the sanctuary include 6 km of trails, including about 1.1 km of boardwalk that passes along the fringe of the marsh. Three viewing platforms installed along the boardwalk permit the observation of waterfowl on the open water. These platforms have signs that facilitate self-guided nature interpretation. Eight pamphlets that have been developed to highlight the plants and animals of the sanctuary are also distributed to visitors. Records show that the majority of the annual visitors (about 5,000) come from Edmonton; however, they also come from the surrounding communities and from all parts of Alberta and Canada. Approximately 2% are international visitors.

Funding has been provided as a small operating budget by the Canadian Nature Federation and from granting agencies for specific projects that have included boardwalks, signs, interpretative material and displays. All funding is used for the development of the sanctuary so that the general public, local schools and community groups can utilize the area as an outdoor classroom or as a natural area to enjoy the outdoors.

A management committee of local volunteers manages the sanctuary on the basis of three to five year plans, including an interpretative plan, a resource management plan and a site maintenance plan (Butler 1981). The committee has close ties with the Devonian Botanic Garden, the County of Parkland, Natural and Protected Areas of the Environmental Protection Branch of the Government of Alberta, and is in partnership with Ducks Unlimited, who built a dyke and manage the impounded water body.

Red squirrels are common in the pine and spruce forests of this nature sanctuary (photo by Ross W Wein, 2000).

Corkum, L. 1978. Limnological study. Clifford E. Lee Nature Sanctuary.

Griffiths, C D G and D E Griffiths. 1980. Preliminary insect survey of the Clifford E. Lee Nature Sanctuary.

Butler, J. 1981. Clifford E. Lee Nature Sanctuary interpretative concept plan.

The sanctuary does not have sufficient resources to operate regular programs but encourages educational institutions (primary, secondary and post-secondary) and other local groups to utilize the sanctuary as an outdoor classroom. Volunteers from the committee speak to various organizations. The John Janzen Nature Centre has brought numerous groups to the sanctuary and Junior Forest Wardens, 4-H Associations and Scout and Guide movements use the sanctuary for work on their nature study badges. Some of these groups assist with spring and fall clean up. In the last two years, home schooling associations from Fort Saskatchewan and the Edmonton region have begun to use the sanctuary as a classroom. The local natural history club and bird club continually take field trips to the sanctuary to study birds, flowers and insects throughout the field season.

History of Development

The sanctuary was established in September 1978 with the signing of a lease between the Canadian Nature Federation and the Clifford E Lee Foundation, which had funded the purchase of 140 acres of marsh from Mr Hector Cunningham. Mr Cunningham retained a 20-acre parcel of the original quarter section. In 1982, a 160-acre parcel was purchased from Mr Clevette, again with funds provided by the Clifford E Lee Foundation, and title to the 300-acre sanctuary was transferred to the Canadian Nature Federation. In 1992, the sanctuary was further expanded when the County of Parkland transferred the title of a 16-acre parcel adjacent to the southern boundary of SE 20 to the Canadian Nature Federation. Finally, the management committee became volunteer stewards of a 28-acre parcel lying immediately east of SE 20 that was purchased by the province under the natural areas program. In 1990, the provincial government designated the sanctuary a watchable wildlife site, one of 34 in the province.

Coyotes Still Sing in My Valley

Scientific studies completed at the sanctuary include limnology, avifauna and flora, mammals, insects, and an interpretative concept plan (see references). These studies were completed before development in order for the management committee to plan the trails and to produce accurate interpretative signs and literature.

Lessons Learned

To be a successful natural area there are a few key things that managers need to keep in mind.

- Finding a suitable natural area and developing a plan for preserving it is the first requirement.
- Assembling a group of people who have interest in and knowledge of the environment and a commitment to volunteer for the management of a conservation area is essential.
- Learning more about the biodiversity is important in developing interpretive programs.
- Seeking professional assistance in preparing a long-term development and management plan is important.
- Following through with the management plans to the best of one's abilities and a willingness to re-evaluate and alter the management plan goals periodically is a continuing issue.
- Being vigilant to problems that might affect their natural area (power lines, gas and oil lines, vandalism, local water management and county development) is a continuing effort.
- Being alert to ways of continually improving the natural area (wildlife corridors, new land, water management) is important in attracting the public.
- Encouraging the public to use and appreciate the area so they will develop an appreciation for the environment and its associated flora and fauna is critical; it is always necessary to strike a balance between nature preservation and nature interpretation programs and activities.

The Future

Land acquisition is an integral part of the overall management plan for the sanctuary's future. It is critical to have an upland area of sufficient size to maintain the diversity of plants and animals within the sanctuary. The sanctuary should also increase the marshland area to have more control over the water. Adding a buffer around the existing sanctuary would allow for more effective wildlife corridors.

In addition to the sanctuary land, the management committee acts as volunteer stewards for a 26-acre parcel of land to the east of the sanctuary. The acquisition policy is to try and secure more of the marsh to the east of the sanctuary and to extend to the west where there is a diversity of upland habitats and additional marsh. The property in the center of the sanctuary has now been bought and a land swap of an island for land at the edge of the road has been negotiated. The use of restrictive covenants, easements and leases could be used to acquire additional lands.

Ideally, an endowment fund would enable the committee to develop and maintain educational programs; unfortunately, natural area committees have not been particularly successful in attracting sufficient funds for endowments that would provide continuing operating funds, let alone purchasing land.

The sanctuary serves the general public as more people are walking, hiking and bird-watching than ever before and these activities require areas where people can safely enjoy and appreciate nature. People enjoying nature and the outdoors find a sense of rejuvenation, which affects their mental well-being and their lives in general. Education will continue to be a major focus of sanctuary activities. To encourage groups to use the sanctuary as an outdoor classroom, to update scientific information, to produce new literature, and to produce a web site will be priorities for

future management plans. To bring these plans to fruition
dedicated volunteers will be required, along with financial and
professional expertise from municipal and provincial governments.

Acknowledgements

Thanks to all the dedicated people who have worked over the last
twenty-five years on the management committee to make the
Clifford E. Lee Nature Sanctuary a success story of conservation.

References

Reports and others cited in this paper are available as reference
material at the Devonian Botanic Garden and at the Concordia
University Library. A set of eight sanctuary pamphlets is available
on request.

The Wagner Natural Area

Patsy Cotterill, Edmonton Natural History Club

Wagner Fen: Its *Raison d'Etre*

A visitor driving west from Edmonton on Highway 16 (Yellowhead Highway) may be surprised to see the shapes of dark spruce and feathery larch trees appearing suddenly to the left, about 5 km west of the Edmonton city limit. This forest is an anomaly in the surrounding landscape of open fields, housing and commercial buildings. Why, the environmentally conscious visitor might ask, is there coniferous forest in the aspen parkland natural region? The answer is that conifers are growing on a peatland, a particular type of wetland. Where the soil is waterlogged and the oxygen content low, plant remains decompose only slowly. The cold, wet peat substratum produces conditions similar to those of the boreal forest to the north in the province. Much of the early information on this special area has been summarized in Thormin (1982).

Wagner is located approximately 6.5 km west of the Edmonton city limits at 53°34'N, 113°50'W, directly to the south of Highway 16 and east of Atim road (Range Road 270) (Figure 1). The

Thormin, T. 1982. The Wagner Bog. The Edmonton Naturalist 10(2): (Special Issue). 52 pp.

quintessential parts of these peatlands between Edmonton and Spruce Grove have been preserved in a 2.16 km^2 area of provincial Crown land known as Wagner Natural Area. This is a hotspot of biodiversity dominated by a complex of sedge fens, strips or islands of vegetation alternating with marl ponds, and shallow pools with clear, amber-coloured water and greyish-white bottoms (Figure 2). Only on the fen strings between the pools is the plant mat thick enough to bear the weight of large mammals. These strings are made up of dwarf bulrushes, sedges, colourful wildflowers, dwarf willows, dwarf birch and some stunted tamarack and spruce. Adjacent to the fens, where the water table is a little lower and there is enough oxygen for tree roots, black spruce, tamarack, and even white spruce may grow to normal heights, creating a treed fen or swamp (often popularly referred to as muskeg).

Before Wagner Natural Area became protected by provincial legislation, it was popularly known as Wagner Bog. Indeed, the moniker dies hard. But ecologically speaking, bog is a misnomer. Bogs are peatlands whose water supply is precipitation and consequently mineral-poor. Sphagnum moss predominates under these more acidic conditions, whereas in fens the vegetation is in contact with water that is relatively rich in minerals. In Wagner, the water is rich in minerals and highly alkaline. Wagner Natural Area lies on the edge of the broad shallow valley containing Big Lake and the Sturgeon River. Groundwater moves down-slope through glacial outwash sand and gravel buried some 8 to 25 metres below the surface between varying thicknesses of clay and silt. The water comes to the surface as seepages and springs. The recharge area is believed to be located some 3 to 5 km up-slope to the south.

Figure 1

Air photo (facing north) of the north end of Wagner Natural Area bounded by the Yellowhead Highway on the north and Atim Road on the west (Source: City of Edmonton).

Range Road 270

Highway 44

Yellowhead Highway

Atim Road

Water Chemistry: Cause and Consequence

As weakly acid groundwater percolates laterally through the soil it dissolves carbonate and bicarbonate anions; where the groundwater is pushed to the surface, the carbonate is precipitated as marl. Deposition of marl is also aided by the green alga, stonewort or *Chara*, which removes CO_2 from the water during photosynthesis, becoming encrusted with calcium carbonate and brittle to the touch. Other minerals, such as magnesium, sodium, iron and sulphur occur in Wagner's spring water, and some may come from deeper aquifers, but calcium is the most abundant. The

Figure 2

Cross-section of a spring fen and adjacent coniferous treed swamp, indicating wetland environments during deposition, in the Wagner Natural Area, Spruce Grove, Alberta. From: Zoltai *et al.* 1988. Wetlands of Boreal Canada. Adapted from National Wetlands Working Group, Canada Committee on Ecological Land Classification, Wetlands of Canada. Polyscience Publications Inc.

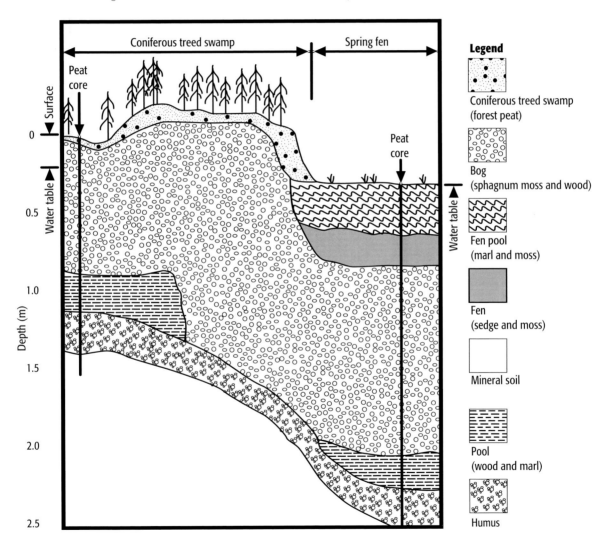

spring water may feed marl ponds directly, or it may seep out and accumulate as ditches (flarks) and ponds, generally oriented across the direction of water flow.

The biodiversity reflects the habitat diversity. Approximately 340 species of higher plants, 67 moss species, 11 liverwort species, and 80 lichen species have been recorded at the site. Typical boreal species of mammals (41), birds (150), reptiles (2), amphibians (4), fish (2) and invertebrates (thousands) also live in the natural area or use its habitats at some point in their life-cycles.

Wagner is of particular interest to bryology students because of the brown mosses growing in its calcareous fens. To many, Wagner's chief claim to fame is its astonishing array of orchids: 16 of the 25 species native to Alberta have been recorded on the property. Orchids depend on symbiotic relationships with fungi for growth, and fungi thrive in the cool, moist, organic soils. Equally fascinating are the carnivorous plants: the round-leaved sundew of sphagnum hummocks in the treed fens, the oblong-leaved sundew and common butterwort of the fen strings, and the bladderworts of the marl ponds. The site is perhaps most famous for its invertebrates (of which the mosquitoes are the most prominent, eager to greet all visitors). Personnel from the Royal Alberta Museum conducted a series of collections of terrestrial invertebrates in the late 1980s, and they are still identifying new species. There have also been surveys of mosquitoes, dragonflies, butterflies, moths, snails, and diatoms. Unique species include *Dolomedes striatus*, a small water spider (Family *Pisauridae*), discovered in 1988. Previously, this species was known only from eastern Canada.

History of Protection

Wagner's geographic location in proximity to Edmonton has led to rapidly increasing urban development pressure. Naturalists, university and government scientists, and educators were aware of the peatland's ecological value in the 1950s and were eager to see it preserved. Wetlands are not conducive to traditional crops, and fortunately a scheme to exploit the marl deposits commercially was opposed by the landowner and abandoned. But it was recognized that without legal protection this fen could be lost. In 1970 the Alberta Wildlife Foundation obtained a one-year option to purchase the north half of section 7 in township 53, range 26, west of the 4th meridian from the farmer-owner, Mr William Wagner (Hendry 1983). These 320 acres (130 ha) were purchased by the Lands Assembly Division of Alberta Environment in 1971. In 1975 the Wagner property was turned over to Alberta Energy and Natural Resources (ENR) for administration by the Public Lands Division under their natural areas program, as a resource for educational groups. By the early 1980s the area was perceived to be under threat from further development of Highway 16, especially with respect to the proposed construction of an interchange linking Highway 16 to Secondary Highway 44. This put two government departments, Alberta Transportation, responsible for roads, and ENR, responsible for the welfare of Wagner Natural Area, into conflict. Concern for the future of the natural area was high, and in late 1982 a group of people representing various stakeholders and local residents got together to form the Wagner Management Committee, with a mission to lobby both government departments for protection of the site and to embark on management programs. The committee incorporated in 1983 as the Wagner Natural Area Society. It was thus in a position to participate in a major way (for example, by assisting

Hendry, A. 1983. Interview summary. Conducted with Mr. William Wagner, former owner of Wagner Natural Area on January 7, 1983.

with environmental impact assessments and having representation on a special negotiating committee) when the road issue became active and the interchange was being designed, from 1989 to 1991. An important outcome was that the interchange alignment was moved farther to the east than had been originally planned, to avoid the springs and some of the fen complexes, which by then had been incorporated into the natural area with the addition of a further 22 ha (54 acres) on the east side. There have been additional development threats to the site. In 1995-1996 plans for a service road on the north and east sides of Wagner were stalled after opposition by the Society. Drainage from the Acheson industrial sites to the southeast through Morgan Creek has been an ongoing concern. Since 2000, the Society has opposed the construction of a storm-water management pond by a neighbour to the north on the grounds that it could divert groundwater from the aquifer, drawing down water levels in the fens. A recent compromise resolution of this issue includes changes to the pond design and depth and the installation of wells by Alberta Environment to monitor groundwater. Almost from the beginning, the Society has recognized the importance of protecting the groundwater recharge area to the south. For this reason, the purchase by the provincial government in May 2001 of an additional 160 acres (65 ha) to the south, was a huge step forward in assuring the longevity of the fen. The natural area now stands at 534 acres (216 ha) and the Society is currently seeking to acquire more land contiguous to the existing property on the southwest, for the purpose of providing a buffer for sensitive parts of the fen.

Lessons Learned

A number of factors have contributed to the successful protection of Wagner. First, the Wagner Society, which became the official volunteer steward of the site under the government's new stewards program in 1986, has an active executive of about a dozen people, who collectively carry out an array of activities. The executive committee is supported by a voting membership, and a wider circle of non-voters. The management or executive committee moved quickly to establish its stewardship interests by acquiring a 21-year recreational lease to the site (1983), a management plan (begun in 1986 and periodically updated), and a water licence permitting ecological use of water (1987). Wagner Natural Area was among the first of the government's natural areas and under the Society's stewardship (which included such things as constructing a self-guiding trail and basic facilities for the public, compiling checklists and supervising and funding research projects), it quickly acquired the status of the government's flagship natural area. The Society has continued to promote the natural area in a number of ways, including media articles and public talks, production of an orchid poster supplied free to area schools, a trail guide, twice-yearly newsletters, organized field trips and annual members' nights (for voting members and the public).

Another lesson the Society learned early was the importance of communicating and co-operating fully with the provincial government, the municipal government in whose jurisdiction Wagner lies (Parkland County), local landowners, and local residents. The Society takes a keen interest in land- and water-use issues in the region, and spends a considerable amount of time corresponding with authorities and attending private and public meetings. As a result it has earned credibility and respect for its conservation work, as well as a fearsome reputation for persistence! Another important point is that the natural area is appreciated locally. Moreover, the Society's work in promoting the site to the scientific community and in obtaining grants to fund various studies has fostered its reputation as a field laboratory for biological, peatland and hydro-geological research. All this is the result of prolonged hard work by people dedicated to a worthy cause. By the end of 2002, 20 years after its inception, the Society had logged over 18,000 volunteer hours. This does not of course count the efforts of the pioneer conservationists!

The Future

Don Prosser, a hydro-geologist with Alberta Environment, made a key statement in 1982.

> "The important point is that the bog is not a small patch of land which can be preserved, in the long-term, by fences and special status. It is a small expression of a much larger groundwater flow system and the whole system must be considered if the bog is to survive."

Don Prosser's statement remains as true today, and for the foreseeable future the Society's main conservation objective is to expand the land base of the natural area in order to protect the groundwater recharge area and to provide the largest possible buffer against disturbance from the outside. The Society's lease to the area will be renewed, possibly to reflect a focus on conservation and research rather than on recreation. Scientific studies and monitoring, both of biological diversity and groundwater, will continue to direct conservation and management actions. For example, the 30 species of mosquitoes (especially *Culex tarsalis*) are of interest because of the spread of West Nile virus in western Canada.

In conclusion, there are conservation challenges and advantages to Wagner's location in a densely settled area. How interesting it would be to look into the future and see if this area maintains its ecosystem functions and its biodiversity. Groundwater, both quantity and quality, will be the key.

Acknowledgements

The Society would like to thank the Government of Alberta, Parkland County, the federal government, and all the various agencies that provided funding for facilities, educational materials, and research projects over the years.

Further information on the Wagner Natural Area Society can be found on their website at www.wagner.fanweb.ca.

Further Reading

Acorn, J. 1994. Wagner butterflies: the groundwork has been laid. Wagner Natural Area Newsletter 8 (1): 1-2.

Banak, L. 1992. Hydrogeologic study of the Wagner Natural Area and surrounding region. Unpublished B.Sc. Thesis, Department of Geology, University of Alberta, Edmonton, AB. 36 pp.

Belland, R. 1998. Moss diversity in Alberta peatlands. Wagner Natural Area Newsletter 12 (1): 7.

Cotterill. P. 1985. The Wagner Natural Area: safeguarding a jewel. Alberta Naturalist 15: 37-41.

Finnamore, A T. 1994. Hymenoptera of the Wagner Natural Area, a boreal spring fen in Central Alberta. Memoirs of the Entomological Society of Canada 169: 181-220.

Johnson, J D. 2001. Soil surveys of Wagner Natural Area. Wagner Natural Area Newsletter 15 (1): 6.

Jones, E. 1998. Surveying breeding birds in Wagner: a summary. Wagner Natural Area Newsletter 12 (1): 5-6.

Locky, D A and M N Thormann. 2003. Wetland Series. Part. 4. Western continental wetland plant communities. Wagner Natural Area Newsletter 17 (1): 3-6.

Locky, D A. 2003. Wetland Series. Part 5. Peatlands and creatures great and small: Part 1 – Vertebrates. Wagner Natural Area Newsletter 17 (2): 3-6.

Snails in Wagner Natural Area. 1997. Wagner Natural Area Newsletter 11 (2): 5-7.

Saley, H, D H Meredith, H Stelfox and D Ealey. 2003. Nature walks and Sunday drives 'round Edmonton. Edmonton Natural History Club, Edmonton, AB. 80 pp.

Thormann, M N. 2001. Wetlands – Shedding some light into their murky waters. Part 1. The importance of wetlands and their distribution. Wagner Natural Area Newsletter 15: 3-5.

Thormann, M N. 2002. Wetlands – Shedding some light into their murky waters. Part 2. What are wetlands, how do they form, and where are they in Alberta? Wagner Natural Area Newsletter 16 (1): 3-4, 7.

Thormann, M N. 2002. Wetland Series. Part. 3. Chemical and physical characteristics of wetlands – a tale of gradients. Wagner Natural Area Newsletter 16 (2): 4-7.

Vujnovic, K, L Nikiforuk, J Bentz, and P Beaudette. 2000. Soil and vegetation inventory of Wagner Natural Area, Alberta. Alberta Environment, Resource Data Division, Edmonton, AB. 67 pp. plus appendices.

White, A. 1998. Moths, spiders and lichens. A sampling of Wagner's biodiversity. Wagner Natural Area Newsletter 12 (2): 5.

Zoltai, S C, S Taylor, J K Jeglum, G F Mills, and J D Johnson. 1988. Wetlands of boreal Canada. Chapter 4. In: Wetlands of Canada. National Wetlands Working Group. Polyscience Publications Inc., Canada.

Big Lake Natural Area

Louise Horstman, Big Lake Environmental Support Society, St. Albert

Introduction

This 21.4 km² Big Lake Natural Area is situated at the northwestern corner of Edmonton and the southwestern edge of St. Albert (Figure 1). The lake is now part of the Lois Hole Centennial Provincial Park. In spite of the fact that two cities border Big Lake, a visitor to the lake can experience a feeling of solitude and wilderness. A 1969 report by the Canadian Wildlife Service observed, "in all of western Canada, no city or centre of population has such a potential beauty spot on its door step" (Lane 2001). This is still the case; although a proposed highway near the east end of the lake may alter public access and the hydrological regime. Lack of public access and the lake's shallow, eutrophic nature makes it unsuitable for direct use by swimmers and motor boaters.

Big Lake, centred at 53°36'N, 113°43', is part of the 260 km Sturgeon River, which begins at Hoople Lake and flows eastward to the North Saskatchewan River. Atim Creek and Carrot Creek also flow into the lake on its western and northern sides, respectively. The river system drains a watershed of 3328 km² (Big Lake

Lane, R. 2001. Big Lake Important Bird Area. Unpubl. report prep. for Canadian Nature Fed., Bird Studies Canada, Federation of Alberta Naturalists. 20 pp.

Figure 1

Air photo of the 21.4 km² Big Lake Natural Area. The surrounding landscapes include the old and recent Sturgeon River deltas that almost divide the lake and the extensive *Typha latifolia* marshes to the north and west of the lake. St Albert is located to the to the northeast. Agricultural fields surround the Natural Area (Source: City of Edmonton).

Big Lake Management Group. 2004. Big Lake Natural Area and surrounding lands: vision and guiding principles.

Management Group 2004). The Sturgeon River enters Big Lake on the northern side through a delta and exits from the southeastern end, from there flowing eastward through St. Albert en route to the North Saskatchewan River. Big Lake is about 8 km in length and 3 km at its widest point; at the delta the lake narrows to 100 m. The lake is shallow, with depths varying between 0.3 to 4.1

m (Big Lake Management Group 2004); its depth barely exceeds 1.2 m in most years (Thomas 2002). In recent years the water surface area has varied from 2.02 (1958) to 28.36 km² (1974). The southern shore is steep, restricting the lake's expansion, so during high water years water floods to the west, north and east.

The natural area habitats range along a moisture gradient from permanent freshwater, through wide areas of emergent *Typha* and *Carex* vegetation, to upland deciduous and conifer forest (Elliott *et al.* 2004). The flora of the Big Lake Natural Area has been surveyed and species lists have been compiled for certain sites. One of these is the forested area at the end of 215 Street in Edmonton. Another is the surviving remnant of old up to 160-year stands of white spruce in the uplands near the northeast corner of the lake. Both of these contain a highly diverse vegetative understory with unusual and rare plant species.

As a result of the wide fluctuations in surface water area and a wide band of emergent vegetation, the habitat is ideal for many species of waterfowl and shorebirds that migrate through or nest in the area (Thomas 2002). About 235 bird species have been seen in the area and over 180 are recorded annually, including many rare and declining species (Thomas 2002). At-risk species include trumpeter swan (Thomas), bald eagle, Sprague's pipit (Elliott *et al.* 2004), peregrine falcon and short-eared owl (Big Lake Environment Support Society 2001). Once thought important for breeding Franklin's gulls, the colony has not been active on the lake since 2001 (Demulder), although individuals have been seen (Elliott *et al.* 2004). It may be that the nesting habitat of this species has been altered by recent low water levels; it is possible that the colony may return if water levels rise (Elliott *et al.* 2004). The lake is important as a staging ground for tundra swans and pelicans. While swans usually number in the low thousands during the last few weeks of

Thomas, R. 2002. Big Lake and its bird life – a big picture perspective. Appendix F In: St. Albert Anti-Bypass Coalition (ABC). Response to the Environmental Impact Assessment of the City of St. Albert Western Regional Road (WRR). www.elkeblodgett/ABCResponse2.pdf. Accessed April 2, 2004.

Elliot, C, V Nelson and M Constable. 2004. Migratory and breeding bird survey of the Big Lake Natural Area, Alberta. Big Lake Environment Support Society, St. Albert, AB.

Thomas, R. Personal communication.

Big Lake Environment Support Society. 2001. Bird checklist- Big Lake and St. Albert area.

Demulder, P. Personal communication.

October, as many as 20,000 have been recorded in a single season (Canadian Nature Federation and Big Lake Environment Support Society, undated). Cormorants, loons, great blue herons and ospreys forage on the fish in Big Lake. In years of low water levels, lesser yellowlegs, dowitchers, American avocet and various species of sandpiper are present along the lakeshore. In recent years, ospreys have increased and Eurasian widgeons are now seen each year. Nationally-threatened peregrine falcons, probably from the government recovery program in Edmonton, can be seen hunting around the lake (Lane 2001).

The most abundant species of fish in Big Lake is northern pike. Goldeye, white sucker, walleye, sticklebacks, and minnows are also present. The goldeye are thought to move into the lake from the North Saskatchewan River. While some areas near the inlets and outlets of the lake provide year-round fish habitat, most of the lake provides only seasonal habitat because the lake freezes to the bottom or becomes anoxic. There have been a number of significant events related to low oxygen levels in the aquatic ecosystem. For example, on November 11, 2002 there was a serious fish-kill on the Sturgeon River near St. Albert City Hall. Local residents and government agencies collected fish that were still alive and transported them upstream to deeper water (Big Lake Environment Support Society 2003).

The area immediately surrounding Big Lake is rated as highly important wildlife habitat with regard to mammals, amphibians and reptiles, as is a large area immediately to the west and north of the lake and the Sturgeon River Valley below the lake (AMEC *et al.* 2002). Moose graze in the lake during summer and in the shrub edges of the lake in winter. Extensive travel corridors and habitats for white-tailed deer surround the lake and the Sturgeon River Valley connects these to the North Saskatchewan River Valley.

Big Lake Environment Support Society. 2003. Submission to Dept of Fisheries and Oceans regarding Environmental Impact Assessment, Proposed West Regional Road.

AMEC, EDA Collaborative Inc. and Alberta Community Development. 2002. Big Lake Natural Area management plan. Maps. Edmonton www.amecedmonton.com. Accessed April 2, 2004.

Beaver, muskrat, mink, skunk, coyote, red fox, porcupine, snowshoe hare, red squirrel, pocket gopher, meadow vole, Gapper's red-backed vole and dusky shrew have been identified in the area (IBI Group 1996).

History of Development

People have lived along the shores of Big Lake from prehistoric times, as indicated by stone tools and weapons found on the south and east sides of the lake. The entire area above the lake's floodplain, as well as the floodplain itself northeast of the lake, has been designated as possessing high historical/archaeological potential (AMEC *et al.* 2002). With the arrival of the Europeans, the St. Albert Mission was founded in 1861 and was known as Big Lake Settlement. Waterfowl hunting, muskrat trapping and fishing for many years supplied the needs of the settlers. The lake was a source of drinking water for settlers and livestock well into the 1900s. Although poorly documented, the clearing of forests for agricultural land and the subsequent accelerated erosion is suspected to have caused infilling of the lake.

While numerous isolated studies addressed problems facing the Big Lake wetlands in the 1970s and 80s (Bevan 1996), it was not until the efforts of the Edmonton Regional Planning Commission in the mid-1980s that a serious attempt at management planning was begun. Technical staff conducted a comprehensive planning study for Big Lake and shore area by drawing upon the input of many stakeholders and three levels of government. This study culminated in The Big Lake Plan, which set forth a detailed map and guidelines for land-use planning and management around the lake (Edmonton Regional Planning Commission 1989). The stated intention was to implement these plans within five years of publication, but this has not occurred.

IBI Group. 1996. City of St. Albert West Boundary Road EIA Report.

Bevan, C. 1996. The case for wetlands: Big Lake, Alberta. www.elkeblodgett.net. Accessed April 2, 2004.

Edmonton Metropolitan Regional Planning Commission. 1989. The Big Lake Plan. (summary report and several technical reports). Referenced in Lane, 2001.

St Albert physician Dr. Fin Fairfield and about 20 other founding members established the Big Lake Environment Support Society as a non-profit society in 1991 for the purpose of preserving the physical and biological integrity of the Big Lake wetlands. In the same year, the St Albert City Council approved a master plan for the long-term development of Red Willow Park, which extended from the city to the eastern shore along Big Lake. On May 1999, the Alberta Government created the Big Lake Natural Area consisting of 1,119 ha of the lake and wetland complex (Anonymous 2003).

Big Lake Environment Support Society nominated Big Lake for consideration by Alberta's Special Places 2000 program; subsequently, Big Lake was named a special place under the program and the society was later appointed as the official volunteer steward of the natural area. Recognition of the importance of Big Lake as a staging and resting area for large numbers of waterfowl during spring and fall migrations led to its designation on June 5, 2001 as a globally significant important bird area. The Wetlands for Tomorrow program of Alberta Fish and Wildlife Division and Ducks Unlimited Canada also recognizes the lake as one of Alberta's 20 most important habitat units in Alberta.

A water quality monitoring program was begun by Alberta Environment in 1997 to assess Big Lake's nutrient status, levels of contaminants, and the amount of chemical substances being contributed to the lake by major inflow streams. The east and west basins of the lake were sampled monthly between May and October in 1997 and 1998. Characteristics sampled included major ions, nutrients, chlorophyll a, pH, temperature, dissolved oxygen, conductivity, suspended and dissolved solids, metals, trace organics, pesticides, and *E. coli* (Mitchell 1998). Unfortunately, the

Anonymous. 2003. Red Willow Park: West Master Plan update. Report prep. for the City of St. Albert, Alberta by Gibbs and Brown Landscape Architects, Edmonton, AB. 98 pp plus Appendices.

data were never summarized in a report, but the data indicate that pesticides present in the lake and/or its upstream tributaries included atrazine, 2,4D, dicamba, Lontrel, MCPA, MCPP-Mecoprop, and picloram (Alberta Environmental Protection no date).

The Big Lake plan, which set forth guidelines for land-use planning and management around the lake (Edmonton Regional Planning Commission 1989) was not implemented and the province's regional planning commissions were dissolved. The four Big Lake bordering municipalities did pass land-use bylaws and plans related to the preservation and recreational use of the Big Lake area. For example, St Albert's Red Willow Park master plan (2003 update) calls for trails and a nature centre at the eastern portion of Big Lake (Anonymous 2003). In 2003, the master plan was updated to include the eastern portion of Big Lake that falls within the St. Albert city boundaries. Plans for the Big Lake portion of the park include the construction of trail systems (including interpretive trails) and the creation of a Big Lake nature centre (Anonymous 2003).

Today

Big Lake Environment Support Society is now a regional organization, with membership coming from the four municipalities bordering the lake. The organization has established, over the past 20+ years, facilities (shelter, viewing platform, trail), put on summer environmental education programs, hosted festivals and cleanup activities, published promotional brochures, collected field data including breeding bird counts and water levels, and provided input to consultation processes regarding proposed development around the lake.

Recreational use of the lake is mainly for wildlife viewing, canoeing, kayaking, and waterfowl hunting in the fall. There are

Mitchell, P. 1998. "Big Lake water quality monitoring program 1997/98". Unpubl report, Alberta Environmental Protection Water Sci. Br. 3 pp.

Alberta Environmental Protection. no date. Raw data from water quality monitoring program 1997-98 provided to Big Lake Environment Support Society.

few places in which the public can access the lake. One can access the SE corner of the lake via the driveway of the Kinsman Corral on Riel Drive in St. Albert. The driveway ends near the river's edge where a public shelter built by the Big Lake Environment Support Society can be used for picnics or as an outdoor classroom. Canoes can also be launched here. From the shelter, a foot trail leads to the lake's outlet and a public viewing platform built in 1995 with funds raised by the society and contributions from the city of St. Albert. In late April, when the outlet is the only open water on the lake, congregations of migrating waterfowl are in close proximity to this viewing platform. Access on the north side of the lake consists of a petroleum industry service road between Meadowview Drive and the lake. Ducks Unlimited and the St. Albert Rotary Club have arranged for public use of this road, as the sign "Big Lake Interpretive Trail" indicates. On the south side, the northern extension of Highway 60 (Range Road 263) ends at the SW corner of the lake. The north end of 231 Street in Edmonton also ends at the lake.

Lessons Learned

One of the major lessons is that a natural area surrounded by a rapidly urbanizing landscape will always have pressures. Solutions are needed to determine how to protect natural area features as suburban developments rapidly change the watershed.

Agriculture in the lake basin has grown steadily and much land in the lake basin was cleared and is still being cleared today. Forests and native vegetation have been removed for agriculture, private use, industry and golf courses, and contaminated runoff from some of these areas has entered the watershed. There are five golf courses within the lake's basin and these use lake water for irrigation and contribute fertilizers and pesticides to the lake during times of runoff. Infilling and dyking of lakeshore areas by landowners has also occurred as has water withdrawals for various uses including the golf courses. Large oil and gas extraction has been occurring for many years on the north shore and continues today, with numerous wells situated within the lake's floodplain. Informal meetings to discuss environmental considerations occurred on an *ad hoc* basis between the society and companies over a number of years. In 2003 a more formal process was set up whereby a multiple-stakeholder advisory committee meets monthly with the major petroleum company operating in the area. Indirect human activities in the lake's watershed have been impacting the lake's water quality for many years. Sewage from many municipalities was discharged into tributaries of the Sturgeon River until recently. Studies are needed to understand this legacy and how to rehabilitate where necessary.

In recommending the establishment of Big Lake as a special area, the Big Lake Special Places Local Committee stressed that partnerships with all surrounding municipalities would be essential to the protection of the natural area. In response to this, the four municipalities bordering the lake and Alberta Community Development began a management planning process in 2002. This plan aims to integrate the conservation, recreation, tourism and heritage appreciation of these five jurisdictions (Big Lake Management Group 2004). As most of the land around the lake is privately owned, the process will involve input from landowners and other interests within the natural area.

Results from additional studies will encourage more scientific management. A study of water quantity and management implications in the Big Lake Basin was commissioned in 2003 by a task force consisting of seven municipalities along the Sturgeon River and the provincial departments of transportation and environment.

This study examined the changes that have occurred in the Sturgeon River basin upstream of Big Lake over recent years and their expected impacts of increasing frequencies of extreme events on water levels in the basin and lake (Associated Engineering Ltd. 2004).

Associated Engineering Ltd., Edmonton. 2004. Draft summary report: Big Lake stormwater management plan. Prep for the Big Lake Basin Task Force.

The Future

As with other urban wildlands, the Big Lake natural area has been experiencing many threats to its ecological integrity. At the same time, a growing number of informed citizens, elected officials and government departments are becoming aware of the need to protect natural areas that remain and perhaps even restore some through good management. As the vision statement of the Big Lake Management Group (2004) states:

> "Big Lake is a wetland resource treasured by the surrounding region and recognized locally and internationally as a model for integration of residential development with the preservation and enhancement of a natural wetland environment; and for the delivery of world-class education and heritage tourism programs."

Challenges to this vision include:

- residential subdivisions within the watershed
- a proposed highway parallel to the eastern lakeshore, traversing the lake's floodplain at its NE corner and crossing the Sturgeon River near the lake's outlet
- sand and gravel extraction in the upstream river basin
- continued clearing of trees and other vegetation by landowners along the lake
- runoff into the watershed from agricultural operations, golf courses and industry, including the petroleum extraction industries in the north shore wetlands of the lake.

Acknowledgements

Many stakeholders must be recognized for their contributions to the conservation goals of Big Lake. These include Ducks Unlimited Canada, federal and provincial environment departments, Federation of Alberta Naturalists, Edmonton Bird Club, Edmonton Natural History Society, service clubs and both provincial and local Fish and Game Associations. The author also recognizes the long-term work of the Big Lake Environment Support Society membership and especially the assistance of Elke Blodgett, Peter Demulder and Richard Thomas.

Kinokamau Lake: An Industry-Owned Urban Conservation Area

Ernie Ewaschuk, Land Stewardship Centre, Edmonton

Galatowitsch, S M. and A van der Valk. 1998. Restoring Prairie Wetlands: an ecological approach. Iowa State University Press, Ames, IA. 246 pp.

Mitchell, P and E Prepas. 1990. Atlas of Alberta lakes. The University of Alberta Press, Edmonton, AB. 675 pp.

Murkin, H R, A G van der Valk and W R Clark (eds.). 2000. Prairie wetland ecology. Iowa State University Press, Ames, IA. 413 pp.

van der Valk, A G (ed.). 1989. Northern Prairie Wetlands. Iowa State University, Ames, IA. 400 pp.

Weller, M W. 1994. Freshwater marshes: ecology and wildlife management. 3rd ed. University of Minnesota Press, Minneapolis, MN. 154 pp.

Alberta Environmental Protection. 2004. www3.gov.ab.ca/env/water/swg/assets/trophicGc.pdf. Accessed August 15, 2004.

Introduction

Early maps and air photos show that Kinokamau Lake was once in a series of wetlands named Long Lake that drained in a northeast direction. Today, of the remaining lakes in the area the largest is Big Lake, the second largest is Kinokamau, and the smallest is Kirk Lake. The area is bounded on the east by 170 Street and also heavy industry, clay pits and clay storage areas closer to the lake (Figures 1 and 2). On the south is the Yellowhead Highway and on the west and north are fields and urban developments. The remaining natural upland vegetation of the region is characteristic of the aspen parkland, but this forest has been replaced almost entirely by farmland and urban development. This wetland with a lake of less than two metres depth is typical of many northern prairie potholes of the region (Galatowitsch and van der Valk 1998, Mitchell and Prepas 1990, Murkin *et al.* 2000, van der Valk 1989, Weller 1994). The lake is classified as eutrophic to hyper-eutrophic with about 100 mg/m^3 total phosphorus and 25 mg/m^3 of summer chlorophyll a (Alberta Environmental Protection 2004).

FIgure 1

Air view of Kinokamau Lake in the central part of the photo. The lake is bounded on the east by stockpiled clay and 170 Street. Foreground is Yellowhead Highway and CN Rail. The former aspen parkland around the lake has been replaced with hay fields. The shallow lake has a wide fringe of *Typha* and *Carex* (Source: City of Edmonton).

Baseline studies conducted in 1998 included: hydrology, water quality, benthosics, vegetation, small mammals, amphibians and birds. At water levels between elevations of 678.0 and 678.8 m above sea level, the water between 30 and 100 ha with water volumes between 300,000 and 1,300,000 m³, respectively. There are no significant inflow or outflow channels. Water levels show wide annual variation; in 1967 the lake was almost dry and in 1975 the lake was at its highest recorded level. A survey in 1998 showed a water area of 20 ha, a *Typha latifolia* area of 16 ha, and a *Carex anthrodes* area of 17 ha. Species lists are available from Ducks Unlimited; approximate numbers are: vascular plants (75), mammals (15), birds (128 – 50 confirmed breeding), and amphibians (2 – wood frog and possibly the striped chorus frog). There are no fish because each winter the lake freezes to the bottom or the unfrozen water becomes anoxic.

On the Inland Cement side of the lake an ecologically sensitive site has been designated by the Canadian Wildlife Service.

History of Development

By 1912, the Grand Trunk and Pacific Railway was constructed across the southern tip of the lake and the Slave Lake Railway was constructed through the northern section of the lake. Since then, construction of surrounding streets and the Yellowhead Trail have permanently modified local drainage. More recently, Kinokamau Lake and the surrounding area have come under intense pressure from Canadian National Railway, who bought land adjacent to the lake in order to build a new intermodal terminal, and Lehigh Inland Cement of Edmonton, who bought the rights to mine the clay from the lake. Once the environmental significance of the area was brought to the attention of the company, the decision was made to protect the lake for conservation purposes.

Figure 2
Southward air view of Kinokamau Lake. The vegetation of *Typha, Carex,* aspen remnant and hay fields are clearly visible (Photo by Ernie Ewaschuk).

On May 1st in 1998, Inland Cement Ltd. and Canadian National made an initial commitment to have Kinokamau Lake and surrounding lands placed under a conservation easement to Ducks Unlimited Canada. This agreement provides for management of the area's integrity and water levels and for vegetation management, including weed control in the surrounding uplands areas. The two conservation easement donations ensure Kinokamau Lake is retained as the largest wetland within Edmonton's city limits. The total area covered by the conservation easement is 100 ha. The area now represents one of the most significant land donations to Ducks Unlimited habitat in central Alberta with a combined value of more than $1.1 million dollars.

Because the impacts of developing a CN intermodal yard could not be fully avoided, CN Rail agreed to measures to minimize habitat losses and onsite enhancement measures as mitigation. As compensation for the remaining 8.1 ha of unavoidable wetland and upland habitat losses, CN Rail is in the process of purchasing 48.6 ha of unbroken land in the ecologically unique Beaverhills area southeast of Edmonton. A conservation easement will also be applied to this property and similarly administered by Ducks Unlimited Canada. It is intended that this property be subsequently incorporated into the adjoining Ministik Bird Sanctuary, thereby providing further assurance of sustained conservation.

Management

Since the lake is on private land, there is no public access to the site. Around the year 2001, the city developed an area structure plan for Kinokamau plains (see www.edmonton.ca under planning). A water outlet structure was built by CN in 2001.

Ducks Unlimited manages the area under a committee that has representatives from Ducks Unlimited, Inland Cement, and CN. To date, noxious weeds have been controlled, including the hand pulling of scentless chamomile (*Matricaria maritima*). Remediation has been funded by CN. Under contract, the fields around the lake have been cut for hay, but this contract was terminated in 2003. In the future, the watershed area will be maintained for waterfowl habitat and periodic removal of the grassland vegetation may be necessary to maintain stand health and vigor.

The Future

Although this area is seemingly isolated and there are no terrestrial conservation corridors to other conservation areas for terrestrial species, birds use the resources of Big Lake and other surrounding sloughs. The importance of incorporating an upland buffer area around the wetland was an important consideration in the long-term sustainability of Kinokamau Lake. There is still upland that is not within the easement area. In the long run, it is hoped that more of the upland watershed area will be included in the easement. The upland will be permitted to undergo natural succession which includes the increase in area of aspen forest. This will gradually shift the biodiversity toward more forest dwelling species of the aspen parkland in future years.

Acknowledgments

Thanks to Greg Norman and Jonathan Thompson of Ducks Unlimited Canada who provided details on the ecology and management of Kinokamau Lake.

Further Reading

Ducks Unlimited: www.ducks.ca/news/prov2001/010206.html. Accessed August 15, 2004.

Environment Canada: www.ec.gc.ca/ea-ee/communication/reports/annual_rep_1999_2000_e.asp. Accessed August 15, 2004.

Horsehills Creek:
An Urban Stream at the Rural-Urban Fringe

John R. Wood and Kimberley Tomiyama, King's University College

Introduction

Edmontonians are rightly proud of the remarkable natural heritage our river valley affords us with its verdant ravines, and streams feeding into the North Saskatchewan River. There are 14 ravines and 8 major streams within the city of Edmonton. They have formed because of the unique and highly erodable bedrock and surficial geology of glacial Lake Edmonton (see details in Cruden, Rains and Thompson 1993, Godfrey 1993). These dynamic environments have numerous spring seepages dotting their unstable slopes. These aquatic ecosystems are an important component of Edmonton's famous urban park system. Until recently, the common planning and development approach was to drain wetlands and redirect streams into culverts so that roads could be built. Construction has encroached by increments into the river valley and ravines. Today urban and near-urban watersheds have become vitally important to citizens, and their free ecosystem

Cruden, D M, B Rains and S Thompson. 1993. A - 8, A Short Walk in the North Saskatchewan River Valley. Field Trip Guidebook, Geological Association of Canada, Mineralogical Association of Canada, Joint Annual Meeting 1993, Edmonton, AB. Edmonton Geological Society. (see pages 9-11, 15, Fig 2.2).

Godfrey, J D. 1993. Edmonton beneath our feet: A guide to the geology of the Edmonton region. Edmonton Geological Society. 150 pp.

services are increasingly valuable. The streams and wetlands associated with river valley ravines are part of a natural biological water filter. After the contaminated drinking water disasters of Walkerton, Ontario and North Battleford, Saskatchewan we can no longer afford to take our urban streams for granted. It may be, if we learn to listen to their voice, that our ravines become the proverbial miner's canary of water quality. Public held attitudes are changing because we are now aware of the value of the ravine systems for recreation, for biodiversity protection, and for general quality of life benefits. The importance of water in our future is highlighted by Water for Life: Alberta's strategy for sustainability (Alberta Environment 2003). This report concludes that healthy aquatic ecosystems, and knowledge of our waters are vital to a high quality of life for Albertans and must be preserved. One of those ravine and stream ecosystems is in our city – Horsehills Creek. The Horsehills watershed is located in the near-urban northeast quarter of the city on agricultural land that was annexed in 1982 (Figure 1). It is a prime example of the challenges and opportunities posed by a creek on the rural-urban fringe (Watzin and McIntosh 1999).

It might seem surprising to suggest that urban streams in general, and their prairie/parkland counterparts, are largely understudied ecosystems (Paul and Meyer 2001, Dodds *et al.* 2004). We seem to know much more about the great salmon producing systems of the West Coast, the temperate forest streams of Ontario, the cascading wonders in the Rockies, or even desert streams (Cushing and Allan 2001). There are many reasons why prairie streams have received much less attention than mountain streams or large navigable rivers of Alberta. In the aspen parkland near Edmonton streams are low gradient and silty-bottomed, with no charismatic fish species to sustain a sports fishery. They are

Alberta Environment. 2003. Water for Life: Alberta's strategy for sustainability. www.waterforlife.gov.ab.ca. Accessed November 15, 2004.

Watzin, M C and A W McIntosh. 1999. Aquatic ecosystems in agricultural landscapes: A review of ecological indicators and achievable ecological outcomes. J. Soil Water Conserv. 4: 636-644.

Paul, M J and J L Meyer. 2001 Streams in the Urban Landscape. Ann. Rev. Ecol. Syst. 32: 333-365.

Dodds, W K, K Gido, M R Whiles, K M Fritz, and W J Matthews. 2004. Life on the Edge: The Ecology of Great Plains Prairie Streams BioScience 54: 205-216.

Cushing, C E and J D Allan. 2001. Streams: Their Ecology and Life. Academic Press, San Diego. 366 pp.

Figure 1

Air photo of Horsehills Creek ravine, where it enters the North Saskatchewan River (lower right side of figure). Adjacent to the ravine is agricultural land, the Evergreen Trailer Park, and Crop Centre North, with small experimental fields (Source: City of Edmonton).

slow moving, ice jammed each winter, run intermittently in spring, and often dry up in summer. Beaver dams may provide the only permanent water along their course, and even these ponds are subject to periodic drought. To the casual eye these streams often look indistinguishable from sloughs, potholes, or dugouts: nevertheless, there are great opportunities to learn from these systems. For many Edmontonians, their first interaction with natural water systems is in an urban stream. Our ravines are living classrooms, filled with interactive lessons waiting to be explored.

Public interest in enjoying and conserving the river valley and ravines remains high. The River Valley Alliance, established in 1996, is co-ordinating a regional system of parks called Alberta's Capital River Valley (River Valley Alliance 1998). Edmonton is also a vital link in the mountain to prairie waterway featured in the new North Saskatchewan River Guide (Milholland 2002). Some of the most popular city parks, including Whitemud Park, Mill Creek Park and Gold Bar Park, are ravines with prairie streams. Hiking, biking and cross-country runs are popular summer activities. And in the winter Gold Bar Park and Ravine is the "mambo hub" of cross country skiing in Edmonton (Maxfield 2004). Horsehills Creek is an urban park of the future. What it will look like in a decade is being decided by our study and planning today.

History of Development

Horsehills Creek is named for the nearby Horse Hills, a hill where in the 1870s the Hudson's Bay Company kept a horse guard or wintering ranch. It was also said that the NWMP had a temporary post on the hill, which gives views east across the North Saskatchewan River and west to the modern Canadian Forces Base at Namao. In 1891, one hundred quarter sections of land in the district were reserved by the Dominion for re-settlement of German immigrants who were abandoning their homesteads near Medicine Hat and moving north to find farms (Mardon and Mardon 1998). This was the advance group of many more newcomers to the area over the next few years. The settlers found remnant patches of prairie and open land from natural fires and human activity. With the construction of Fort Saskatchewan, and

River Valley Alliance. 1998. Alberta's Capital River Valley. Community Services Department, City of Edmonton.

Milholland, B. 2002. North Saskatchewan River Guide. North Saskatchewan Watershed Alliance, Edmonton, AB.

Maxfield, C. 2004. Skitown: Edmonton, Alberta. Cross Country Skier, February (2004).

Mardon, E G and A A Mardon. 1998. Community Names of Alberta. 2nd edn. Golden Meteorite Press, Edmonton, AB.

City of Fort Saskatchewan 2004. Our Historic River Valley Community. PDF at http://www.fortsask.ca/visiting/ab_facts.cfm

Harrison, T. 1990. Place Names of Alberta: Volume 3 – Central Alberta, Friends of Geographical Names of Alberta, Edmonton, AB.

the movement of the headquarters of 'G' division of the North West Mounted Police to Fort Saskatchewan, a challenging dirt trail wound its way around wetlands to link the new Fort to Fort Edmonton. A photo of the Fort Trail crossing Horsehills Creek taken sometime around 1903 reveals an open landscape almost devoid of trees (City of Fort Saskatchewan 2004). It became a busy thoroughfare with more than 170 horse and buggy teams reported on the trail one morning in 1905. A halfway hotel at Horse Hills operated briefly, and an official post office opened in April 1896 and closed in August 1919 (Harrison 1990), but the population did not develop to the level of a village.

In 1905 the Canadian Northern Railway arrived in Fort Saskatchewan. In 1926 the Fort Road trail was gravelled, and oiled in 1930 (City of Fort Saskatchewan 2004). This was one of the first paved roads in Alberta. From early in the 20th Century the surrounding land was purchased for agriculture. The federal and provincial land holdings included the site of the Alberta Hospital and the airfield at Namao (now CFB Edmonton). In 1949, a provincial tree nursery was established. Its role expanded, eventually becoming the Alberta Agriculture Crop Diversity Centre North. It is situated on over 340 acres of Class 1 (Canada Land Inventory) soils.

The entire Horsehills Creek watershed, except the CFB Namao, was annexed from the municipal district of Sturgeon into the city of Edmonton in 1982. Existing urban developments, such as the Evergreen Trailer Park and newer acreages and subdivisions, such as Eagle Ridge, have increased the number of people in the watershed. Agriculture continues to be an important activity; however, the municipal policy saying agricultural land will be held until needed for urban development is causing continuing land-use conflicts and concern. Market gardens, horticulture, and seed potato operations are increasingly using intensive agriculture approaches.

Today

Hydrologically, Horsehills Creek is an ephemeral stream that flows during the spring snow-melt and then almost completely dries up from the early to mid summer. As a result of this low summer flow, agricultural activity frequently reaches to the stream borders and even extends across the creek bed in the upper portions of the creek. This is especially true during dry climatic cycles. There are a few natural and man-made water impoundments containing water throughout the summer. The largest is the earth-filled dam and lake maintained for irrigation at the Alberta Agriculture Crop Diversity Centre North facility about 500 m west of the CNR culvert. Beaver dams are also common along the stream from the mouth of the creek to beyond the Manning Freeway.

Today impervious surfaces are increasingly covering the watershed as agricultural fields are converted to residential properties. This is a dominant feature of urbanization and leads to increased runoff, altering stream hydrographs (Paul and Meyer 2001). Analysis of satellite imagery shows that only 1% of the creek area is white spruce (total forest is about 9%) (Table 1). Much of the land is in pasture (aspen/grass and grass/pasture – 50%). Crops cover 41% of the area. Note that the number of patches is an indication that the landscapes are highly fragmented.

View of the mouth of Horsehills Creek taken from a vantage point over the North Saskatchewan River. Note the valley floor forest and steep valley sides of the ravine (photo by John R Wood, 2003).

Biophysical Assessment of Horsehills Creek Watershed

Physiographically, Horsehills Creek can be divided into major divisions of tableland and ravine (Figure 2). The upstream

Figure 2

Satellite image of the North Saskatchewan River and Horsehills Creek in northeast Edmonton. The interpretation of the land-use is given for a buffered width of 500 m (Source: Jeff Truscott; see Table 1 for more details).

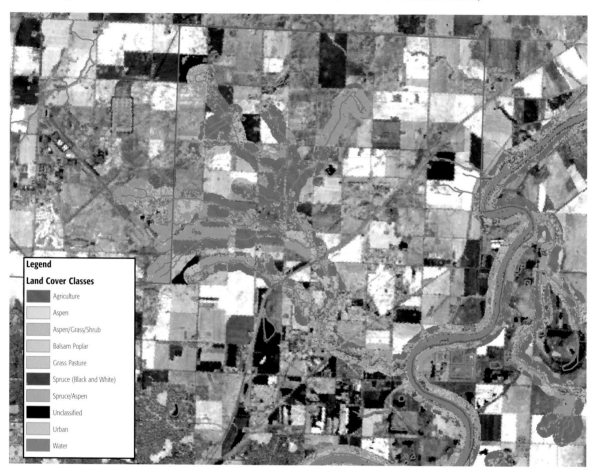

Legend

Land Cover Classes
- Agriculture
- Aspen
- Aspen/Grass/Shrub
- Balsam Poplar
- Grass Pasture
- Spruce (Black and White)
- Spruce/Aspen
- Unclassified
- Urban
- Water

tableland portion of the creek drains three hydrologic zones. To the north a major branch arises from Horse Hills and 2 wetland/lakes about one mile south of the city boundary (Highway 37). The flow is in a south-easterly direction towards the Manning

Table 1
Landscape cover types of the Horsehills Creek buffered to a 500 m width.

	Spruce	Spruce/ Aspen	Aspen	Poplar	Aspen/ Grass	Grass/ Pasture	Crops	Total
					Land Cover Types			
Area (ha)	22	47	41	71	253	763	826	2,024
Area (%)	1	2	2	4	12	38	41	100
Number of patches /100 ha	2	15	14	14	27	23	19	

Freeway. At 18th Street this branch intersects with a second network draining wetlands on the east side of the CFB Edmonton. In the south a third major branch drains wetlands near Little Mountain and Moran Lake to a confluence at Fort Road and 18th Street. The slope through the tableland is less than 0.5%, and there is little or no riparian vegetation in the agricultural zone. A survey by aerial photos and ground-truthing found this upper portion of the creek to be highly modified by canalization, water impoundments, roads/culverts, and agricultural usage within the creek bed.

In the second watershed division, east of the Manning Freeway, the creek channel is much more distinct. Over the last 3 km before the confluence of Horsehills Creek and the North Saskatchewan River the creek drops with a 1.3% slope and has formed a ravine of 50+ m depth. The ravine has an average width of 175 m, with a maximum of 310 m near the mouth. The sides are very steep in some places (over 60% slope) and most of the riparian and ravine banks are forested with communities of aspen, white spruce, balsam poplar, and scattered white birch; shrubs are the next most abundant covering. Woody vegetation in riparian areas provides a

Westworth Associates Environmental Ltd. 2001. Conserving Edmonton's Natural Areas: A Framework for Conservation Planning in an Urban Landscape. Technical Report, Alberta Environmental Network and Community Services, City of Edmonton.

Horsehills Creek south of the Manning Freeway showing illegal infilling of the channel. There are many examples of channel modification on this creek and also on other creeks and ravines in Edmonton (photo by John R Wood, 2003).

number of important ecological functions, including providing habitat for wildlife species, shading the snow accumulation, protecting stream banks from erosion, and controlling sedimentation, and thus water quality, in the stream channel.

Lessons Learned

The Horsehills watershed holds the distinction of containing 3 of 13 priority natural area reserve sites in Edmonton (Westworth *et al.* 2001). Moran Lake, the lower Horsehills Creek, and the Oxbow are regionally significant areas that meet multiple criteria of size, linkage, accessibility, and ecological importance for the park system in Edmonton. None of these sites has yet been protected.

Urban development is restricted to the tablelands, but the human impacts are significant even in the ravines of Edmonton (Westworth *et al.* 2001). The Horsehills Creek area is currently under many threats, and is one of the most modified of all of the ravines within the city of Edmonton. The land-use has traditionally been agricultural due to the highly productive soils, easy access to irrigation water, and a unique beneficial microclimate. Upstream dams for agricultural uses have altered the flow of the creek. Residential impacts (pets, fires, dumping, damaged vegetation) are noticeable within Horsehills Creek Ravine near the Evergreen Trailer Park. The northern portion of the ravine has been extensively disturbed by agricultural and off-highway vehicle use. Fortunately, the lower portion of Horsehills Creek ravine has a relatively intact riparian zone.

When examining the creek as a wildlife corridor, we identified wildlife movement barriers in the upper reaches of the creek that range from a major freeway, fences and dams, to sparse or non-existent cover vegetation. While the steep slopes of the ravine section of the creek have forested vegetation, the roadway at Meridian Street, the railroad track, and oil and gas pipelines all act as barriers. In spite of habitat fragmentation and increased activity in the ravine the diversity of riparian plant species appears high.

The Future

Urban aquatic habitats were once considered mostly a nuisance. They were either an engineering problem impeding roads and building construction, or the site of mosquito problems. If they had a use it was only for draining excess water. Urban runoff into our ravines has become an important source of pollution as a study of Whitemud Creek in Edmonton showed decades ago (Whiting and Clifford 1983). It seems nature and the urban environment are at odds. Sabloff (2001) has noted, "we manifest a poverty of discourse related to nature" in the city. Agriculture and the environment have also traditionally been thought of as being at odds. In fact, agriculture and urban development are the number 1 and number 2 causes of stream loss in North America (Imhoff and Carra 2003). Habitat fragmentation, destruction, and the subsequent biodiversity loss have set conservationists on a collision course with farmers and developers. These conflicting views are having expensive consequences for residents now and in the future.

Attitudes toward wetlands, wildlife and near-urban agriculture are rapidly changing in Edmonton's city planning, as elsewhere (Imhoff and Carra 2003). The concept of farming with the wild is challenging traditional notions of clean-land farming. The challenge for Edmonton is in making both agriculture and urban

Whiting, E R and H F Clifford. 1983. Invertebrates and urban runoff in a small northern stream, Edmonton, Alberta, Canada. Hydrobiologia 102: 73-80.

Sabloff, A. 2001. Reordering the Natural World: Humans and Animals in the City. University of Toronto Press, Toronto, ON.

Imhoff, D and R Carra. 2003. Farming with the Wild: Enhancing biodiversity on farms and ranches. Sierra Club Books, San Francisco, CA.

Adams, L W. 1994. Urban wildlife habitats: a landscape perspective. University of Minnesota Press, Minneapolis, MN. 186 pp.

Fitch, L and N Ambrose. 2003. Riparian Areas: A User's Guide to Health. Lethbridge, Alberta: Cows and Fish Program.

Fitch, L and B W Adams. 1998. Can Cows and Fish Co-exist? Can. J. Plant Sci. 78: 191-198.

Briody, F and K Yakimishyn. 2002. Getting to Know Your Local Watershed. Alberta Agriculture, Food and Rural Development; Agriculture and Agri-Food Canada. Agdex # 576-8.

Abma, G S. 2003. An implementation framework for an agricultural business development zone: the case for Northeastern Edmonton. Master's Degree Project, Faculty of Environmental Design, University of Calgary, Calgary, AB. 112 pp.

growth more harmonious with biodiversity (Adams 1994). Much more attention is being given to the planning and conservation of aquatic ecosystems of all kinds – lakes, ponds and wetlands as well as the river valley, with some notable successes (Westworth *et al.* 2001). Federal and provincial government departments are advocating the value of streams and increasing standards for wastewater discharge. They have sponsored community-based programs, such as the Riparian Areas: A User's Guide to Health (Fitch and Ambrose 2003). These actions are educating people on the importance of riparian areas for maintaining water quality, increasing agricultural sustainability, restoring biodiversity and buffering the impacts of floods and droughts. Up until recently the Cows and Fish program has been focused on prairie streams in the southern part of the province (Fitch and Adams 1998). Now it has expanded into the aspen parkland district, but is still primarily a rural focus. We need to place publications, like Getting to Know Your Local Watershed (Briody and Yakimishyn 2002) into the hands of urban and suburban citizens too.

Horsehills Creek was once a recognized landmark between Edmonton and Fort Saskatchewan. This riparian corridor could be an effective connector from the North Saskatchewan River through Namao to the ravines and streams in the Sturgeon River drainage. A network of parks, reserves, and ecological right-of-ways would conserve the rich cultural, historical, agricultural and environmental heritage of this watershed. It would add economic value to adjoining properties and help create a vibrant community in northeast Edmonton. There are many obstacles to affording greater protection to Horsehills Creek watershed. Many of these have been detailed in Westworth *et al.* (2001). A recent thesis by Abma (2003) provides some planning guidelines for alternate development strategies. Horsehills Creek deserves better protection; its value for local citizens will increase into the future.

Acknowledgements

Kings University College students Blaine Johnson, Thea Koeppen, Dennis Perrin, and Dennis Vroom are recognized for their contributions to the biophysical assessment project titled Corridors and Connectivity: the State of the Horsehills Creek Ravine System over the past three years. Jeff Truscott kindly provided the satellite imagery analysis of Horsehills Creek. Bob Priebe, Community Services, City of Edmonton, kindly provided aerial photos for the vegetation analysis.

Paul M J and J L Meyer. 2001. Streams in the urban landscape. Annual Reviews of Ecology and Systematics 32: 333–365.

Wang L, J Lyons, P Kanehl and R Bannerman. 2001. Impacts of urbanization on stream habitat and fish across multiple spatial scales. Environmental Management 28 (2): 255–266.

Wang L, J Lyons, P Kanehl and R Gatti. 1997. Influences of watershed land use on habitat quality and biotic integrity in Wisconsin streams. Fisheries 22(6): 6–12.

Booth D B and L E Reinelt. 1993. Consequences of urbanization on aquatic systems – measured effects, degradation thresholds, and corrective strategies. Proceedings of Watershed '93 Conference: 545–550.

May, C, C Cooper, R Horner, J Karr, B Mar, E Welch and A Wydzga. 1996. Assessment of cumulative effects of urbanization on small streams in the Puget Sound Lowland Ecoregion. Paper presented at Non-Point Source Pollution and Water Quality Monitoring Session of the Urban Streams Conference, November 15 – 17, Arcata CA, 1996.

Booth D R and C R Jackson. 1997. Urbanization of aquatic systems: degradation thresholds, stormwater detection, and the limits of mitigation. Journal of the American Water Resources Association 33(5): 1077–1090.

Schueler T and R Claytor. 1996. Impervious cover as a urban stream indicator and a watershed management tool. In: Effects of Watershed Development and Management on Aquatic Ecosystems. Proceedings of an Engineering Foundation Conference, August 1996, Snowbird, Utah. American Society of Civil Engineers, New York, NY. pp 513–529.

Lost Creeks and Wetlands of Edmonton

Kathryn A. Martell, University of Alberta

Introduction

As cities grow they become important regional elements affecting a great number of biophysical processes. Some of the most pervasive and far-reaching impacts are those on aquatic systems – urban infrastructure has significant effects on hydrology, channel morphology and aquatic organisms for many kilometres both up- and down-stream (Paul and Meyer 2001). These impacts are linked to the impervious area (roads, buildings, parking lots) (Wang *et al.* 2001, Wang *et al.* 1997, Booth and Reinelt 1993). Stream degradation begins very early in the urbanization process (May *et al.* 1996) and becomes severe beyond a threshold of approximately 20% impervious area (e.g. Booth and Jackson 1997, Schueler and Claytor 1996). Several studies have concluded that our ability to repair this damage is minimal, and that perhaps the only means of preventing damage to aquatic systems is through limiting watershed development (Booth and Jackson 1997, Schueler and Claytor 1996).

Urban drainage design evolved to get water out of cities as efficiently as possible (Jones 1991). As a result, creeks are often culverted and filled in to make land available for residential and commercial construction. The cumulative impacts of these activities result in changes to drainage density (stream length per catchment area) and flow regime (Paul and Meyer 2001) and in direct loss

While many wetlands have been drained, some wetlands remain in northeast Edmonton and in the region (photo by Ross W Wein, 2003).

of habitat for aquatic and riparian species. Since its incorporation, the city of Edmonton has been expanding rapidly in population and area. In 1999, Edmonton's population was 650,000 residents. Edmonton planners anticipate 44,000 new residents over the next five years and by 2020, the population of Edmonton is expected to be almost 900,000 (UDI 2001). Extensive development and expansion into agricultural lands are planned to accommodate new residents within the boundaries and in all of the surrounding communities and counties. Edmonton's system of protected creeks and ravines is often promoted as the largest connected river valley greenways system in North America and is certainly a striking feature of city maps. Despite the high-profile river valley system, Edmonton's growth has resulted in loss of wetlands and creeks that connect to the greenways system.

The first step towards changing, planning and management is to appreciate the need for that change; understanding the extent of current impacts is a critical foundation for that realization. In the lower Fraser basin, as the city of Vancouver has expanded, wetland

Jones, D E. 1991. Historic perspectives, questions and future directions. In Multi-Objective River Corridor Planning, Proceedings of the Urban Stream Corridor and Stormwater Management Workshop, Colorado Springs, Colorado, 1989. E Gruntfest, editor. Association of State Floodplain Managers, Inc. pp 200 – 206.

UDI. 2001. A fact sheet about urban development in Edmonton. Urban Development Institute. Fact sheet for a meeting between UDI and Edmonton City Council.

In subdivisions, developers commonly remove wetlands and build flood water retention ponds (photo by Ross W Wein, 2003).

areas have decreased from 10% to 1% of the land base since 1827 (Boyle *et al.* 1997) and many small creeks have been paved over. As Edmonton's development proceeds, a variety of citizens' groups have lobbied City Council to pursue smart growth strategies (e.g. Sierra Club Prairie Chapter Smart Growth Campaign) and to protect the existing natural areas within the city (e.g. Edmonton Natural History Club). An understanding of the impacts of Edmonton's past development will be a valuable tool for these groups and their campaigns.

Objectives

Our specific objectives were to create a graphic account of impacts to aquatic systems within the city of Edmonton, and to produce a map to serve as a focus for evaluating urban impacts and a tool for directing future growth.

Methods

For this study, we defined "lost" as a creek or wetland where water no longer exists on the surface. The University of Alberta Map Library includes a series of 1924 aerial photographs of Edmonton. We compared these 1924 air photos to a 1999 MapArt map of Edmonton. Lost water bodies were sketched onto this base layer. The study was based on our ability to orient on these 1924 photos because lack of roads in outlying areas made it difficult to determine

Boyle, C A, L Lavkulich, H Schreier and E Kiss. 1997. Changes in land cover and subsequent effects on Lower Fraser Basin ecosystems from 1827 to 1990. Environmental Management 21: 185-196.

the precise locations. The study area was bordered by Whitemud Drive and 167 Avenue, and from Anthony Henday Drive to 17 Street. We also examined a series of historical maps such as Deane's 1883 map of Edmonton settlement and Munro's 1912 map and consulted historical accounts (e.g. McDougall 1896). We confirmed our findings for some areas using 1997 1:16,000 scale maps and 2000 air photos. In addition, we walked many of the creek beds in November, 2001 to determine culvert locations and to confirm our other findings. We obtained a 2000 air photo mosaic poster from the City of Edmonton and scanned this image to use as a digital base layer for our map. We then scanned the draught MapArt base layer. Both of these images were imported into CorelDraw and then we traced the lost creeks from the MapArt map as a separate layer.

Results

This research attempts to provide a broad perspective of lost water in Edmonton. Delineating creek courses and wetland boundaries was sometimes difficult due to lack of distinct reference points in early air photos and omissions in early maps. Early map surveys of Edmonton often did not include marsh areas, since they were slated for draining, and instead show the lot divisions. Further, the University of Alberta map library has only a few sections of the original 1882 survey (Simpson 1882) of the Edmonton area. Therefore, our analysis failed to capture losses that occurred prior to 1924.

Our analysis shows that many creeks and wetlands have disappeared as the city developed. Our research at Edmonton Archives and our readings of historical books highlights the cultural connections that early Edmonton residents had with these water bodies, notably McKernan's Lake, which was once a popular

McDougall J. 1896. Saddle, sled and snowshoe: Pioneering on the Saskatchewan in the sixties. Eaton and Mains, New York, NY. 282 pp.

Simpson G A. 1882. Plan of Township 53 Range 24 West of the Fourth Meridian (2nd Edition). Dominion Lands Office, Ottawa, ON.

picnic and skating spot. Areas with significant impacts include Fulton Creek, Groat and MacKinnon Ravines, and Second Rat Creek (a major tributary of Kennedale Creek), and marsh areas in industrial developments on the city's outskirts. Many of the creeks and ravines were lost in the 1960s to road and bridge construction. Several marshes and wetlands had already been drained by 1924, largely for agricultural purposes. Current city expansion of industrial areas is encroaching on remaining marshy areas.

Groat and MacKinnon Area

In west central Edmonton, Groat Creek and the surrounding ravines were culverted and filled for various road construction projects in the 1950s and 1960s. Groat Creek was completely buried and Groat Ravine used as the roadway for Groat Road; part of the ravine was filled to create a city park. Upper sections of MacKinnon Creek have been gradually culverted and paved to build residential neighbourhoods. In the 1960s, MacKinnon Ravine was selected for the highway that would run through central Edmonton. MacKinnon Creek and Ramsay Creek were culverted and the ravine filled for the roadbed. This roadway has since become a paved walking/cycling trail.

Figure 1

A comparison of the McKernan Lake area of Edmonton in 1924 (left) and 2000 (right). The lake visible in A is Lendrum Lake with the outline of the already-drained McKernan Lake visible just North. Note also Belgravia Ravine, whose creek has been culverted and paved over to create Belgravia Road (Source: City of Edmonton).

McKernan's Lake (Figure 1)

The McKernan area of west-central Edmonton is built on the McKernan homestead and McKernan's Lake. Many older residents are aware of the former lake because of the fine-textured soils of their yards and the occasional flood of low-lying areas. Few realise the 12 hectare size of the former lake. McKernan's Lake was an extremely popular skating, curling, and picnic spot. Early maps of Edmonton indicate that this lake was already receding by the early part of this century (probably due to draining for agriculture) and the 1924 air photo shows that the lake had largely disappeared. A smaller lake, Lendrum Lake, is now known as the Lendrum community.

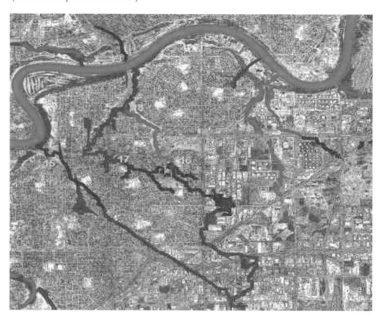

Fulton Creek (Figure 2)

Extensive sections of Fulton Creek, in eastern Edmonton have been culverted. Lower sections of the creek became the Capilano Freeway and Capilano Bridge; upper reaches are disappearing under industrial development. A western tributary has disappeared entirely. Fulton Creek flows into the city from the southwest, and first becomes a culvert as it enters Weir Industrial Park at 69 Avenue near 50 Street. The creek then emerges at 98 Avenue and Terrace Road (Fulton Place neighbourhood) – a culvert distance of more than 3 km. Fulton Creek flows through a relatively undisturbed ravine before going underground again at the Capilano Freeway.

Figure 3

A comparison of Brown Industrial Area. Left: 1924, showing extensive marshes; Right: 2000, showing heavy industrial use (Source: City of Edmonton).

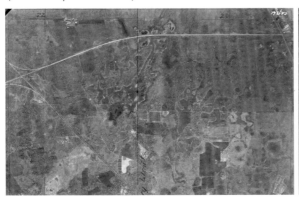

Marshes in northern Edmonton (Figure 3)

The Edmonton area once had many marshes and wetlands, as identified in 1924 air photos. An examination of early survey maps of Edmonton indicates that many wetlands and marshes had already been drained by 1924, for both agriculture and residential development, and these impacts continue. Many of today's industrial areas, in particular, were built on wetlands. Current city expansion of urbanized areas are infringing further on these marshes.

Lee, R G. 1992. Ecologically effective social organization as a requirement for sustaining watershed ecosystems. Chapter 4 in Watershed Management: Balancing Sustainability and Environmental Change. RJ Naiman, editor. Springer-Verlag New York, Inc., New York, NY, pp. 73–90.

Grimm, N B, J M Grove, S T A Pickett, and C L Redman. 2000. Integrated approaches to long-term studies of urban ecological systems. BioScience 50(7): 571–584.

Pickett, S T A, M L Cadenasso, J M Grove, C H Nilon, R V Pouyat, W C Zipperer and R Costanza. 2001. Urban ecological systems: linking terrestrial ecological, physical, and socioeconomic components of metropolitan areas. Annual Reviews of Ecology and Systematics 32: 127–157.

Meyer J L. 1997. Stream health: incorporating the human dimension to advance stream ecology. Journal of the North American Benthological Society 16(2): 439–447.

Dynesius, M and C Nilsson. 1994. Fragmentation and flow regulation of river systems in the northern third of the world. Science 266: 753–761.

Galli, J, J D Cummins and J B Stribling. 2001. Upper Sligo Creek: An integrated approach to urban stream restoration. In Watershed 96, Conference Proceedings. www.epa.gov/OWOW/watershed/Proceed/galli.html. 4 pp.

Discussion

Many problems in watershed management are fundamentally sociological (Lee 1992); therefore, planning frameworks that explicitly include humans will be much more likely to accurately inform environmental problem solving (Grimm *et al.* 2000). In light of this realization, bioregionalists are advocating the need to incorporate social dimensions in studies of urban ecology to see cities as social, biological and physical complexes (Pickett *et al.* 2001, Grimm *et al.* 2000) and to consider social aspects of such concepts as ecosystem health (Meyer 1997). As Dynesius and Nilsson (1994) assert, "In misreading landscapes and the interactions between people and place, we impose on those complicated places our own simplified visions of what their future should or will be." Social-based sustainable urban development must be guided and informed by an understanding of past impacts.

Several researchers (Galli *et al.* 2001, Burges *et al.* 2000, Booth and Jackson 1997) have expressed the opinion that the pervasive and persistent impacts of urbanization on aquatic ecosystems are perhaps neither repairable nor preventable. However, stream degradation is a cumulative process that is affected by each of the varying elements of physical, biological and social systems. Schueler (1996) concluded that a dynamic local watershed management plan is the best and most comprehensive tool to protect urban streams and wetlands from the cumulative impacts of land development. Many projects have shown that community involvement is essential to effective watershed protection and restoration plans (Burges *et al.* 2000; McGinnis *et al.* 1999) and to conserving nature in cities (Goode 1986). In fact, after an intensive survey of watershed organization members, McGinnis *et al* (1999) concluded, "...lack of a sense of community may be the single most important barrier to successful long-term watershed planning."

People are used to ignoring small changes and to thinking that changes to the landscape are inevitable. Several decades ago, development of many of the lost creeks we have documented (MacKinnon, Fulton, Quesnell) was quite controversial and citizens protested road construction, as reported by the Edmonton Journal. It is our hope that this study might generate this kind of concern for Edmonton's remaining creeks and wetlands. Although significant degradation of aquatic systems of watersheds occurs at low levels of urbanization, these effects are difficult to detect early in the process. Creek sections and small marshes are lost piece by piece, as exemplified by Fulton Creek. Air photos and maps serve to visualize the scale of human impacts to streams and wetlands. Effective bioregional maps serve as a focus for discussion and help to set a plan for positive and proactive change (LTA 1999). Current expansion and development threatens wetlands and creeks on the city's outskirts. By this documentation of past destruction, we hope to encourage city planners and citizens to consider alternative visions for the future – an Edmonton where we don't have to add any more red lines to this map.

Burges S J, D B Booth, S Shauman and J R Karr. 2000. Final Report: Urban stream restoration in the Pacific Northwest – physical, biological, and social considerations. National Center for Environmental Research, US EPA, Science to Achieve Results (STAR) Program. 7 pp. http://es.epa.gov/ncer/final/grants/96/wwshed/burges.html

Schueler, T. 1996. Crafting better urban watershed protection plans: twelve ways to ensure that the watershed plan actually protects streams. Watershed Protection Techniques 2(2): 329-337.

McGinnis M V, J Woolley and J Gamman. 1999. Bioregional conflict resolution: rebuilding community in watershed planning and organizing. Environmental Management 24(1): 1-12.

Goode, D. 1986. Wild in London. Michael Joseph, London.

LTA. 1999. Giving the land a voice: mapping our home places. S Harrington, editor. Land Trust Alliance of British Columbia, Salt Spring Island, BC. 75 pp.

DFO. 1995. Lost Streams of the Lower Fraser River. Fisheries and Oceans Canada, Fraser River Action Plan.

Acknowledgments

This project benefited greatly from the assistance of Bonnie Gallinger, Library Research Associate, University of Alberta Map Library; Stephen Pellech, City of Edmonton; and Bess Sadler and Omar Yaqub, Computer Network Services, University of Alberta. David Schindler, Eric Higgs and fellow students provided an interdisciplinary forum that encouraged us to explore bioregional mapping as a tool for addressing freshwater issues in Alberta. We appreciate the pioneering work of Fisheries and Oceans Canada (1995).

Losing Little Mountain:
A Personal Anatomy of a Campaign to Save a Remnant Aspen Parkland Site

Patsy Cotterill, Edmonton Natural History Club

Introduction

When I first set foot in the little piece of wilderness in northeast Edmonton that we informally called Little Mountain Natural Area one July day in 1988, I knew at once that it was my kind of place. I was on a birding trip led by Darrell Smith of the Edmonton Natural History Club, but what caught my attention was the incredible variety of plants and habitats that were packed into such a small space. Little Mountain reminded me of the wild places I sought out in my suburban childhood, where I picked flowers and berries, climbed trees, spied on nesting birds and ambushed voles. Places where I could lose myself for hours on end, but at the same time feel safe and conveniently close to home. After that first visit I came back frequently, either alone or with friends who had become as smitten with the place as I was.

The shadow of development lay over Little Mountain even then: the Pilot Sound Area Structure Plan had been approved in 1982. It was a typical municipal plan of the time, drawn on a blank piece of paper, without regard for anything that already existed on the ground, with the exception of the Little Mountain Cemetery. One day, during a particularly enjoyable sojourn, I stood in awe and sadness amidst its greenery and vowed that I would do what I could to save Little Mountain from development. If I didn't succeed, I would at least make sure that it did not disappear in silence, anonymously. People should hear about the loss, and care. In the end, this is probably all that those of us who fought the campaign to preserve Little Mountain did achieve. This, and galvanize the municipal authorities into some resolve and action to do a better job of conserving Edmonton's remaining natural areas in the future. Little Mountain was not saved, and so was lost a priceless piece of natural heritage, once typical of this region, but now, after a century of human disturbance of the environment, all too rare.

Natural History of Little Mountain

Little Mountain, its name derived from the eponymous cemetery which it enclosed to the north and east, lay to the east of 50th Street between 160 and 167 Avenues. It consisted of 16.9 ha in a squarish block of deciduous woodland with open or shrubby clearings full of herbs and grass. A pedicle formed by a shallow, partly wooded ravine, running eastwards to a freshwater marsh in the southeast, added another couple of hectares of natural vegetation. Between the pedicle were two fields at different elevations, also well-used by wildlife, the whole making up a rectangle of some 33.5 ha. In an ideal world this rectangle (NW36-53-24-W4M) would have been preserved as a whole, along with its natural corridors and connections to the river valley some 5 km to the east. With the exception of a couple of hectares in the west near the city cemetery, this area has been owned since 1993 by a

Little Mountain showing aspen parkland and a saline hollow. Although this unique site was lost to housing development, similar unique areas must be protected for the special groupings of species (photo by Patsy Cotterill).

development company, Brintell Joint Ventures, Inc. Indeed, it had been in the hands of development companies since 1974, when the farmer-owner, Alasdair Ferguson, whose parents had homesteaded in the area, retired and sold the land.

Little Mountain lay within the central parkland subregion of the parkland natural region of Alberta; a predominant feature of this natural landscape is poplar woods interspersed with open grassy areas. Balsam poplar forest grew on the moister soils to the south, aspen groves and grassland grew on drier, upland areas to the north and east, and meadow clearings, willow thickets and sedge meadows occupied low-lying areas where groundwater seeps indicated a high water table. South-facing banks were particularly productive of prairie species no longer common in the Edmonton area. Even more distinctive in their features and floristics were the shallow, eroded depressions in the grassy openings containing compacted, grey, intermittently wet, solonetzic soil. With its diversity of habitat, Little Mountain supported over 200 species of vascular plants, 36 species of birds, and most of the mammals common to the Edmonton region. Its cryptogamic flora and invertebrate fauna had yet to be investigated.

To understand the vegetation of Little Mountain one needs to know something also of its topography, geology and hydrology. Little Mountain occupied the upper portion of a gentle slope from a height of land near the Manning Freeway in the east. Here glacial till overlies bedrock which includes water-bearing coal seams. Where this bedrock has fractured below ground, the groundwater discharges to the surface as seepage springs and creates wet ground. These conditions likely accounted for the occurrence of the balsam poplar forest and a tufted hair grass–wire rush (*Deschampsia cespitosa-Juncus balticus*) meadow to the south, the peaty willow thicket and sedge meadows in the middle of the property, and the saline depressions to the north, depending upon the amount of flow and the nature of the local soil. Knowing the geology and hydrology of a site is also useful in planning conservation, because surrounding development can severely affect the natural water regime (e.g., by reducing the unpaved surface area over which precipitation can infiltrate the ground and recharge the groundwater, or by interrupting groundwater flow with drains and sewers). In turn, the peri- and post-glacial history of a site may shed light on the topography and hydrogeology of an area. For example, the fractured bedrock where the springs originate may have resulted from the shear forces generated by glaciers moving downslope, and the localized lenses of sandy soil that were found in the area may have been deposited as outwash from Glacial Lake Edmonton some 10,000 years ago. Moist sandy soil may have accounted for the unusual understory shrub, narrow-leaved meadowsweet (*Spiraea alba*), which grew in the easternmost aspen woods. Had Little Mountain been preserved, all this could have provided rich opportunities for interpretation at the site.

First Steps: Little Mountain Becomes a Significant Natural Area

In the early 1990s the City of Edmonton Planning and Development Department invited the public to nominate worthy natural areas. It had engaged consultants to draw up an inventory of sites having predominantly natural vegetation and an area greater than 1 ha that lay within the table lands (some 350 km² of mostly peripheral lands annexed to the city in 1982). This inventory would accompany a conservation policy (C-467) that was being developed. Here I saw my first opportunity to get Little Mountain on the conservation map, and on April 20, 1993 I wrote to the Planning Department to this effect. Apparently, the area did not meet the criterion of being within the tablelands; I argued successfully that since the object was to protect sites of ecological significance and the land was undeveloped, the criterion could be waived. Little Mountain was included, as site NE 8093, together with a number of other afterthought sites, in a supplement to the main inventory, published in 1993 (Geowest Environmental Consultants Ltd. 1993). This was important because now that the site had a formal designation it fell within the scope of the conservation policy and hence was eligible for bureaucratic action. By the time the policy was passed by a vote of City Council on July 25, 1995, its scope had expanded to include all undeveloped lands of appropriate size and ecological value, although the policy title still contains the tablelands wording.

City of Edmonton. 1995. City Policy C-467. Conservation of natural sites in Edmonton's table lands. Edmonton, AB.

Geowest Environmental Consultants Ltd. 1993. Inventory of environmentally sensitive and significant natural areas, City of Edmonton. Technical Report. Edmonton, AB.

Going Up a Blind Alley

Immediately after the policy was passed I wrote to Brian Mason, one of the two city councillors for Little Mountain's Ward 3 and he soon became a key figure in the all-important political initiative to keep Little Mountain. I asked that he instruct the Planning Department (presumably by means of a request in Council) to explore ways to save Little Mountain. In October, 1995, an Alberta Environment representative and I visited the site in the company of Mary Ann McConnell-Boehm of the Planning Department, who was also the temporary conservation co-ordinator, charged with administering the new policy. The co-ordinator was duly impressed and suggested that, given the imminent development pressure (an amended area structure plan, including the Brintnell neighbourhood which included most of Little Mountain, was in the works), our best option would be to apply to The Nature Conservancy of Canada (NCC) to purchase the site for the City to manage as a passive park, with trails and interpretive signage. Accordingly, over the next few months, the City worked with the Edmonton Natural History Club on a proposal to purchase, which included information about the site, its ecological significance and value to the community, and its management requirements. Useful in preparing this was a report on Little Mountain's human and natural history previously compiled by the Edmonton Natural History Club with the help of summer students. The proposal was submitted to the NCC in April, 1996. It wasn't until early 1997, however, that we received a definite reply—and it was negative. One cannot fault the NCC for its response: it specializes in acquiring less expensive rural land, but in retrospect, I believe we should never have waited that long for an answer. Time was of the essence; we should have sought a reply more aggressively and then moved on to other strategies.

Exploring Other Options

By early 1997, after discussions with City administration, Councillor Mason and the landowner, it had become clear that we should have to look for a more political solution. This would probably entail asking the City to acquire Little Mountain, either by purchase, possibly with the help of corporate donations, or – the option that the landowner/developer, Brintnell Joint Ventures, was prepared to consider – by means of a land exchange with City-owned land to the south of Little Mountain natural area. Since even a land swap was likely to cost public money, requiring Council approval, it would be important to have public support. Thus began the Herculean task of raising public awareness and support for the conservation of Little Mountain, a virtually unknown piece of bush in an unpopulated part of Edmonton!

Raising the Public Consciousness

One of our first actions to generate publicity was to develop a brochure about the site and the campaign to preserve it, which included a request for political action from the public. It was a professionally designed leaflet in black, white and grey, and it became a useful business card for the site, which could be handed out or mailed to city councillors, city staff, community leagues, schools and the public. It could be stuffed into letters, newsletters and media releases, and handed out at presentations and displays. Grant funding for the brochure came from the World Wildlife Fund local action fund. Another thing we did was to create a table-top display and an album of photos to go with it, which we later placed in two local libraries and the main downtown library, and took to events such as Earth Day and a booth which we rented for a weekend in a local (Londonderry) mall. We also put together a slide show and overheads of plans for use in presentations. Other forms of communication included a website set up with Edmonton Freenet and e-mail. I am particularly grateful to groups such as the Alberta Environmental Network, which transmitted group e-mailings and so enabled us to communicate to a significant number of people quickly and conveniently, to keep them informed or to request support (e.g., contacting councillors or presenting at Council meetings) at short notice. Nor was the old-fashioned method of writing articles in magazines and soliciting media publicity entirely ignored. Our efforts were puny compared to other campaigns I've since heard or read about, and we should probably have established a broader base of volunteers from the start, with which to launch our efforts. However, we received political and media attention. Little Mountain somehow managed to become a civic issue, and I can remember a feeling of pride and relief when I read the first article on Little Mountain that did not have any campaigners' names attached to it.

Development Puts a Straitjacket on Conservation Flexibility

Anyone involved in a conservation campaign learns very quickly that development plans, which have cost money to produce, put huge constraints on freedom to pursue options for conservation that make simple common sense to the public. In 1997, while we worked on our publicity campaign and pursued funding to cover our expenses, a new problem surfaced. The area structure plan called for realignment of 50 Street from its north-south alignment into a broad arc bowing out eastwards before swinging back to join a realigned 137 Avenue. The Planning Department had initially assumed that if Little Mountain were to be preserved, the original alignment of 50 Street could be retained; now, given transportation regulations and existing subdivision plans to the west, it appeared that it could not.

Nevertheless, the administration assured us that the road alignment could be re-engineered, at a cost, with a wider curve so that the road would merely clip the eastern edge of the natural area, not pass through a substantial part of it. In my darker moments I began to have doubts that we were doing the right thing in trying to preserve Little Mountain. I always envisioned it in the future as I knew it currently, along with the open, sweeping vista it presented to the east. But its tranquility would never be the same in proximity to a truck route, and surrounded by houses. And who knew what the incoming neighbourhood cats and dogs would do to the wild things there. Perhaps it would be better after all to let the patient die quickly, than force it to endure the pain and humiliation of deterioration!

Natural Site Assessments

In March 1997, the developer submitted a natural site assessment (NSA), as required by the conservation policy, to the Planning Department, in preparation for a Brintnell neighbourhood structure plan which would show complete obliteration of the Little Mountain site by development. The NSA contained no recommendation regarding the significance or conservation value of Little Mountain, and based on my and others' knowledge of the site and the regional biology we criticized it as being data-deficient and inaccurate. It had been derived from air photographs and lacked ground-truthing. The NSA had been done in the winter, with timing dictated by the developer's plan rather than considering the annual cycle of physical and biological landscape changes. The Planning Department demanded that another assessment be carried out, although it was restricted only to the Little Mountain site this time, not the whole neighbourhood. This was done by Spencer Environmental Management Services, again

Spencer Environmental Management Services Ltd., 1998. Stage one – Preliminary natural site assessment of significant natural area NE 8093. and Stage two – Detailed natural site assessment of significant natural area NE 8093. Edmonton, AB.

in winter (1997-1998), but including data the Edmonton Natural History Club had gathered over several seasons. On the basis of Spencer's NSA we were able to argue in the spring of 1998 that the site should be left as an intact block (rather than substantially reduced in size or fragmented) and adequate funding sought to acquire it by means of a land swap, rather than attempt to save only the small portion of it that would be feasible with the funding currently available.

Fund-raising Proves to Be a Tough Slog

By the summer of 1998, the Community Services Department had taken over from the Planning Department the chief responsibility for exploring ways to acquire Little Mountain, and we worked with their staff to develop a design for a trail and parking lot as part of the management plan the City would need if it acquired the site. It would also allow us, through the Edmonton Natural History Club, to apply for partnership funding to provide such infrastructure. At the same time we were applying for funding for land acquisition. Given that even a land swap would cost the City money, we invested considerable volunteer time in the fall of 1998 seeking corporate donations. We applied to 25 corporations in all and received only one small donation for our efforts. We were told that companies are generally unreceptive to requests for land purchase because there is no guarantee that the land will be used for the purpose indicated: it could be sold for the recipient's profit! We also applied to three grant-funding agencies for assistance with land costs and in December 1998 received a donation of $30,000 from the Alberta Sport, Recreation, Parks and Wildlife Foundation. The difficulty that small groups have in raising money for land purchase does, to my mind, point to the necessity of having land trusts or foundations dedicated to raising and managing conservation funds.

The Natural Areas Reserve Fund

On 26 November, 1998, during Council budget deliberations, Councillor Brian Mason introduced a motion, seconded by Councillor Michael Phair, to set up a conservation reserve fund, with a starting sum of $2 million, to acquire and conserve natural areas as defined in the conservation policy. The idea was that Little Mountain would have first call on the money. Unfortunately the motion was defeated. A second motion, that Brian Mason brought forward in December, that the City purchase Little Mountain for $1 m was also defeated. However, Council did give the Community Services Department a mandate to report on possible new strategies for natural area acquisition and conservation. By February 1999, Community Services was recommending as their main funding strategy that a Natural Areas Reserve Fund (NARF) be set up by withdrawing $150,000 from the existing Parkland Purchase Reserve Account (PPRA) and matching it with partnership funding, for a total initial deposit of $300,000. While most conservationists welcomed a fund, we were not impressed with the amount of money proposed, nor its source – since the PPRA is intended to acquire river valley properties it seemed like robbing Peter to pay Paul (the tableland sites).

The Land-Swap Mechanism is Approved

At a February 22 Community Services Committee meeting (the second meeting on this topic, since so many speakers registered to speak to this agenda item at the first meeting on February 8), Community Services' recommendations regarding the NARF were approved by the Committee. Of more relevance to the fate of Little Mountain, Councillor Mason, a current member of the four-councillor revolving committee, introduced a formal motion to the effect that Community Services pursue the land-swap strategy for preserving Little Mountain. On March 2, Council approved the establishment of the NARF. The recommendation from Community Services that "the Administration negotiate a land exchange with the owners of Brintnell Joint Ventures to acquire Little Mountain Natural Area, subject to final approval by City Council," was passed by Community Services Committee on March 24. Again, members of the public spoke in support of this motion at the meeting. April 6 was the big test day as the Committee's recommendations had to come before Council for final sanction. The public could only listen, not speak to the proceedings, as this was a regular Council meeting, not a public hearing, but Little Mountain supporters emerged jubilant at the end of the day. Council had voted 10-3 to authorize the start of negotiations for a land exchange. Incidentally, we demonstrated with banners and placards outside City Hall that day, but given the paucity of pedestrian traffic around City Hall and the sequestered nature of Council inside the chamber, we probably achieved very little. We did, however, get a good photo opportunity and an article in the *Edmonton Journal*.

With the City showing a commitment to acquire Little Mountain, we turned our attention to fund-raising for the proposed trail system. In mid June, the Edmonton Natural History Club submitted a request to Edmonton Community Lottery Board for $40,313 based on cost estimates provided by Community Services, and we were informed of our success in October.

Summer of Negotiations

Negotiations continued through the summer, in private. At first, the tenor of negotiations was positive. Community Services staff admitted there were some challenging financial obstacles, but assured us they could be overcome. Nevertheless, by August the word was out that the City and the developer were at an impasse over development servicing costs. The situation was this. The value of the adjacent developable land that the City would cede in exchange for 18.2 ha of Little Mountain was estimated at $1.125 million. The problem was that a debt was owing on this land or, in other words, the City's land bank (Land Revolving Fund) was under funded (to the tune of some $93 million), and that, according to new regulations to prevent the debt accumulating further, the $1 million plus would have to be paid back into the fund before the land exchange could take place. To make matters worse, the current market value of the land to be swapped was only about half what the City had paid for it in boom times, meaning the City stood to lose about $1.6 million because it would forgo the opportunity to recover this amount from development profits. As Little Mountain was undevelopable as a nature preserve, the City estimated the cost of keeping it at $2.7 million, with reinvestment into the land fund to come from reserves. However, there was a further critical complication. Servicing costs, such as roads and sewer lines, also known to planners as permanent area contribution, are normally covered by the developers of a site. The City pays such costs as a developer, but not on parkland or school sites, which the developer donates to the municipality under the requirement of the Municipal Government Act in the amount of 10% of the land to be developed. Little Mountain's area was greater than the legally required 10%, so the developer was demanding that the City pay its share of the costs, amounting to an extra $1 million. Community Services came back to Council for direction on whether or not to proceed with negotiations, and on August 31, 1999, Council gave them the green light to continue. But by October the negotiations were once again in trouble and there was talk of reducing the amount of area to be preserved to reduce the costs to the City. I received an urgent message from Community Services on October 28 asking me what parts of Little Mountain could be expended with the least amount of environmental loss. Another option discussed was that the City could defer paying permanent area contribution until it became clearer, later on in the development process, how much these would cost.

At a Council meeting on November 2, the crunch came. Nail-biting Little Mountain supporters spent the better part of a day in the Council chamber as Council debated the results of the negotiations both in camera and in public. The book value of Little Mountain now stood at $3.7 million (rounded up to $4 million for convenience by some opposing councillors). The idea of deferring the servicing costs was raised, but Council would not countenance committing itself to future costs that could not be foreseen. Councillors Phair and Mason made a last-ditch attempt to save the day by moving that a reduced area be considered for conservation with a total cost to the City of $2.1 to $3.1 million. Councillor Bolstad introduced another motion in an attempt to delay the decision on whether or not negotiations should continue. Both motions were defeated. One more desperate attempt was made to keep the preservation option open, but it too failed. The majority of councillors had had enough. Little Mountain had become just too expensive for those who weren't sure of its value as a community asset in the first place. The outcome was, of course, a crushing disappointment for Little Mountain supporters, especially after the high expectations of the spring. We found it hard to believe it was over. And we didn't. Not until December 1.

The Razing of Little Mountain

"Bulldozers flatten Little Mountain" ran the headline on the front page of the Edmonton Journal's City News on December 2, 1999. On December 1 someone phoned in the news that Little Mountain was burning, thick smoke drifting over northeast Edmonton. The developer had moved in swiftly to cut the trees and pile them into big bonfires. A television interview that night showed flames leaping up in the darkness. On December 11 we held a funeral for Little Mountain, in the Little Mountain Cemetery. About 80 people attended, including three councillors, eminent local conservationists, Aboriginal people, the public and the media. The outpourings of shock and sadness were sincere, even by people who did not know the site well.

Lessons Learned

The loss of Little Mountain did indeed make an impression on the city's psyche and its collective conscience. The difficulties encountered in protecting it had already spurred the creation of the Natural Areas Reserve Fund. It also engendered the concept of pro-active conservation, as the campaign drove home the fact that attempts to preserve a natural area when development is being planned are usually prohibitively expensive due to the costs that have already been incurred by the development process. It led to a comprehensive report (the Westworth Report) by a team of consultants with recommendations on how to do a better job of conservation (Alberta Environmental Network/Community Services, City of Edmonton, 2001). The City even adopted some of the recommendations, endorsing the report at a Council meeting on September 11, 2001. The position of conservation co-ordinator, to administer the conservation policy, has since been established. An enormous amount still needs to be done, including, most

Alberta Environmental Network/ Community Services, City of Edmonton, 2001. Conserving Edmonton's natural areas. A framework for conservation planning in an urban landscape. Technical Report. Edmonton, AB.

urgently, the setting up of a land trust. We must continue our efforts to educate both the public and our municipal politicians. Comments from our elected representatives such as "animals can go someplace else" (when habitat is destroyed) and "land only has value if it's developed" still rankle. As a community we need to gain experience in protecting urban natural areas, and showcase them to the public to clearly demonstrate their ecosystem and utility value.

Acknowledgements

Many people invested huge amounts of volunteer time into the campaign over the years. The dedication of these unsung heroes is to be applauded. Some volunteers have spent a good deal of time since 2000 rescuing native plants from the prairie portions of Little Mountain and growing and multiplying them in an effort to save the gene pool for naturalization and restoration projects elsewhere in Edmonton. Many continue to work on conservation issues in the city.

Significant Dates

1974: Farmer-owner Alasdair Ferguson sells land to Allarco Developments.

1982: Pilot Sound Area Structure Plan, which includes Little Mountain within the Brintnell neighbourhood, is approved. The natural area is not recognized. Edmonton's land area doubles in size to 700 km² as a result of annexation of tablelands – the boundaries now include many natural areas in undeveloped peripheral lands.

1993: *Inventory of Environmentally Sensitive and Significant Natural Areas, City of Edmonton* published, as well as a supplement to this Inventory. Little Mountain included as significant natural area in the supplement.

1997: Idea of a land exchange for City land south of Little Mountain, for Little Mountain land, now mainly owned by Brintnell Joint Ventures Ltd. is discussed.
Campaign to save Little Mountain, with various strategies to generate publicity began. Brintnell neighbourhood structure plan is submitted by the developer (showing destruction of Little Mountain site) but not actually sent to Council.

1998: A natural site assessment of Little Mountain is done by Spencer Environmental Management Services Ltd. The site is considered significant and viable if not reduced significantly in size or fragmented.
City of Edmonton Community Services designs a trail concept and parking area in case the site can be acquired and partners with the Edmonton Natural History Club (ENHC) to fund-raise.
November-December: First (unsuccessful) attempt is made during budget debates to establish an interest-bearing conservation reserve account that would have helped pay for the acquisition of Little Mountain.
December: ENHC receives $30,000 from the Alberta Sport, Recreation, Parks and Wildlife Foundation for Little Mountain land acquisition.

1999:   February: Community Services Committee (a subcommittee of Council) recommends creation of a Natural Areas Reserve Fund (total $300,000 initially) and a strategy for preserving Little Mountain that involves a land exchange.

April 7: Council votes for the City to begin negotiating a land exchange with Brintnell Joint Ventures Ltd. to acquire Little Mountain.

June: ENHC is successful in obtaining $40,313 for trail development in Little Mountain from the Edmonton Community Lottery Board.

August: Negotiations reach an impasse over who should pay development costs (permanent area contribution). Council tells the administration to resume negotiations.

November: The administration reports on progress with negotiations. Cost of acquiring Little Mountain has escalated from $2.7 million to $3.1 to $3.7 million. Council votes to break off negotiations.

November 30–December 2: Little Mountain is logged by the owners.

December 11: Eighty people attend a "funeral" for Little Mountain in Little Mountain Cemetery.

2001:   March: An amendment to the Pilot Sound area structure plan, and the Brintnell neighbourhood structure plan, are passed, allowing development of the area.

Getting Involved:

The Need for Support from the Public, Planners and Politicians

Kirby, K. 1995. Rebuilding the English countryside: habitat fragmentation and wildlife corridors as issues in practical conservation. English Nature Science No. 10. English Nature, Peterborough, UK. 39 pp.

Flink, C A and R M Searns. 1993. Greenways: a guide to planning, design and development. Edited by L.LaB. Schwarz. Island Press, Washington, DC. 375 pp.

Fabos, J Gy and J Ahern (eds.). 1996. Greenways: the beginning of an international movement. Elsevier, Amsterdam. 491 pp.

In highly industrialized countries, the conservation movement is increasingly focused on linking isolated fragments of habitats within cultural landscapes (Kirby 1995) and with involving local communities and stakeholders. To establish new protected areas requires the agreement of the community of stakeholders and this in turn requires multiple use of the landscapes. In addition, there is much concern that citizens are isolated from the realities of city dependency on landscape resources. Multi-use areas for nature protection, history, education, research, recreation, tourism and economic development are being promoted and developed to reconnect people to the rural landscapes. Usually there is one aspect of development that dominates over the others. A few specific examples from Europe include tourism (Sherwood Forest – England), city farms (La Ferme du Monceau – Belgium), and nature protection (Schliffkopf im Nordschwarzwald – Germany). In urban areas of North America, where fragmentation is the most extreme, the linking of all green spaces (school play fields, golf courses, recreation parks) has been studied and promoted under the title of greenways (Flink and Searns 1993, Fabos and Ahern 1996).

Beyond these greenways there are many types of special places. Examples in the USA include tourism, agriculture, forestry, watershed management, nature protection and cultural recognition. A similar list can be provided for Canada; examples include tourism (King's Landing, Mactaquac, New Brunswick), agriculture (Canadian Agriculture Museum, Ottawa), forestry (Canadian Model Forests), wetland protection (Oak Hammock Marsh, Stonewall, Manitoba), and Aboriginal culture recognition (Wanaskewan, Saskatoon, Saskatchewan). All of these developments have taken considerable effort, by many citizens, over many years and each development has its unique history.

Within the Edmonton region, greenways and other multi-use areas are taking shape as well; recreation is one of the driving forces. We love our protected areas and especially our valley! Telephone interviews with 2,417 individuals show the type of use and the numbers of visits to the river valley trail system and river valley parks over the preceding 12 months (Anonymous 1999). Many respondents indicated that they were involved in more than one activity. Of the respondents, 57% visited the trail system an average of 26 times for exercise (50%) or general recreation (17%). For the river valley parks, 75% of the respondents visited an average of 10 times and indicated benefits as general recreation (23%) exercise (20%), entertainment (20%) and family experiences (9%). Additional surveys in summer (1999 – 282 interviews) and in winter (2000 – 320 interviews) conducted by the City of Edmonton River Valley Park Rangers indicated that 65% of the summer visitors cite benefits such as walking and 23% indicate wildlife/nature benefits (unpublished data). Winter visitors indicated the following benefits: walking (70%), skiing (50%), ice skating (40%) and wildlife viewing (40%) (City of Edmonton River Valley Park Rangers, unpublished data). Translating these estimates to the population of Edmonton gives millions of visits to the valley annually. Since the number of users is expected to increase over time, the city must find ways of accommodating

Anonymous. 1999. River valley parks and trails user survey. Community Services, City of Edmonton, Edmonton, AB.

Citizens of Edmonton spend much time in the greenways all through the year. Walking, skating, skiing and wildlife viewing are popular activities (photo by John R. Wood, 2004).

citizen requests while conservation is also considered.

The Edmonton region landscapes are undergoing an unprecedented rate-of-change. Young ecosystems in the valley are recovering from agriculture activities in the 1900s and non-native species have become well established. More recently we have lost many unique areas through subdivision development. From a social point of view there is increasing pressure for recreation development within the valley and on the edges of the valley and ravines. At the interface of subdivisions and valley areas there are many unresolved people–wildlife issues. On the other hand, many of our citizens realize that conservation and protected areas are in the interest of all citizens because these areas support our long-term quality of life goals.

Over the past decade there have been many efforts in conservation planning and management as exemplified by the Conservation of natural sites in Edmonton's table lands (City of Edmonton 1995) and the Parks and Recreation Bylaw No. 2202 (City of Edmonton 1996). Conflicts between conservation and development groups are common in any urban area, but there have been a considerable number of conservation advances recently. For example, a natural areas committee functioned under co-chairs Councillors Bolstad and Phair for several years and fostered a natural areas acquisition and conservation report that was accepted by City Council on September 11, 2001. Ten days later (September 21–23, 2001), a conference hosted by the Edmonton Natural History Club brought forward many solutions to urban

City of Edmonton. 1995. Conservation of natural sites in Edmonton's table lands. Policy No. C467. Edmonton, AB. 15 pp.

City of Edmonton. 1996. Parks and Recreation Bylaw No. 2202. Edmonton, AB. 21 pp.

Coyotes Still Sing in My Valley

conservation (Van der Meer 2001). In 2002, an interdepartmental conservation co-ordinator was appointed by the City and an office was established to promote all aspects of conservation in the city. In September, 2003 an international conference titled Strategies for Urban Sustainability drew attention to many urban infrastructure issues.

van der Meer, K. 2001. A handbook for conserving nature in the Edmonton Region – a vision for the future. Edmonton Natural History Club, Edmonton, AB. 27 pp.

Reconnecting to Nature

Jim Butler, University of Alberta

Abstract

Nature in the occupied, built landscape is vital, not only environmentally but also because its presence is an affirmation of a standard for quality of life that embraces the health, social, psychological and spiritual needs essential for the human species. These needs are placed in the context of the pace and stress of current times and challenges of modern lifestyles that contribute to a sense of disconnectedness and unbalance. An historical perspective of green space in human society and urban parks is presented. This paper advocates that there is a primal need for contact and proximity to wild nature and a growing requirement for quiet places in nature for centering and contemplation. Walking and sitting for contemplation and meditation are very popular but are not adequately provided for in designs and recreational offerings. Urban nature places have become green hospitals.

People and Nature

Humans need nature. We need clean water, fresh air, healthy and nutritious food, and materials to construct improved habitats for ourselves. This much is indisputable. But that is generally the limit of any relationship to nature that we acknowledge. We no longer see ourselves as a part of nature or as having any reciprocal obligations to nature. Rather we have turned nature into various, individual commodities to be bought and sold in the marketplace. We have separated ourselves from our fellow life forms by only seeing them as resources and by denying wildlife, trees, streams and rivers their own intrinsic right to exist as acknowledged ecological partners in the ecosphere. When we subordinated nature in our lives, we actually imagined that we owned it. Even those who work for the environment and in conservation speak of it as our wetlands, our forests, our eagles and our natural resources. Commodities are objects, owned and traded, freely destroyed. This leaves little room for nature in our inspirations, spirituality or sense of community. This escalating disconnection of people from nature is most pronounced in our large population centers, affecting human attitudes, perceptions, values, ethics, and disassociated behavior. Additionally the ecological consequences of this separation are profound.

My observations and studies over the years of the people-nature interface have led me to conclude that wild nature is more central to our inner psyche than our activities, life style and daily behaviour would suggest. Wild nature, even if only in prints or paintings on an apartment wall, provides a balancing factor, something that counteracts the pace and madness of human society. It offers a place for psychological centering. It is not merely a decorative green necklace around our home or workplace: the indoor plants you can't forget to water; a place to resuscitate a

Thoreau, H D. 1853. Walden; or, life in the woods. Ticknor and Fields, Boston, MA.

neglected cardiovascular system, or run and sweat; where you go to sit or walk to make it difficult for others to find you; somewhere you can surreptitiously light up a cigarette where it is not illegal; or a place where the smoke of a barbecue doesn't set off your fire alarm. It is something much deeper; much more central to our very being; something that actually defines who we are; something primal to our existence. Whether we acknowledge its importance or not, it is there.

A new convergence of metaphysics and physics describes a universe that is somewhat different from what we were taught as we grew up. This fresh perspective sees a universe that is comprised of a unified field, a web of energy and consciousness that encompasses all and yet composes all, that is beyond space and time. All beings, all matter, are variations on the basic energy that composes that field. And because we are also made of the same energy, we are connected to all other beings and things in the universe. We cannot stand outside nature; nor truly detach ourselves from its influence, no matter how many ways we elect to alienate ourselves. We are linked to nature by our very substance and form. This is our primal connection. And this is our principal complication.

It is my contention that our disassociation from nature is a consequence of our disproportionate obsession with technology, materialism, sexual entertainment and observer sporting events. On the other hand there is an underlying search in most of us for our own identity, a sense of higher meaning, a need for balance, calmness, reflection, purpose, a re-connection to the roots of who we are, and an almost subliminal quest for happiness, contentment and joy. This paper explores these pathways and asserts that nature or green space in our cities is essential for our wellness and quality of life.

Urban Green Space

Green spaces are simply those portions of the landscape where nature still exists by purpose or circumstance. We measure it from aerial photographs by the presence and extent of tree cover. A high canopy ratio is used as a measure of environmental quality in comparing cities and neighborhoods, for the presence and extent of green space says much about our values, ethics, morality and the extent of our evolution.

Nature around our towns and cities exists as green spaces for the following reasons:

- Pollution absorption
- Buffers for site abatements, weather protection or territorial delineation
- General landscape aesthetics or urban beautification
- Watershed protection
- Noise and sound abatement
- Protecting regional biodiversity (plant and animal species)
- Wildlife movement corridors
- Settings for outdoor recreation activities, social events, and courtship activities
- Real estate value enhancement and desirability criteria
- Environmental education teaching sites for school children
- Pet and owner exercise pathways
- Civic and community pride
- Commemorative expressions of appreciation for public service or in memoriam
- Places in temporary reprieve from developers and highway engineers, usually due to site constraints or inaccessibility
- Abandoned recovery areas from former land-uses or residual toxicity.

The Origins: Protecting Nature for Our Health and Well-Being

The first efforts to incorporate nature in the forms of gardens and green space occurred in China about 4000 years ago. It was a concept that spread to the Mediterranean within a couple of centuries and eventually every culture and community that survived beyond the basic necessities of food, shelter, and self protection made purposeful efforts to incorporate the solace and workings of nature. Nature was a buffer to the labours and pressures imposed by the expansion of the built environment into the non-built environment of the natural world. Small remnant parcels and replicas served as an illusion of the wild land primeval. Japanese Zen rock gardens personify the concept of wild land replicas, which evolved its own form from earlier Chinese initiatives within the twelfth century. Zen monks and Samurai warriors learned to centre, balance, and seek spiritual connectedness within the influence of these natural parcels. Human beings had long sought sanctuary in the presence and proximity of nature, for their spiritual paths, psychological recovery, and escape from stress, as a source of aesthetic expression and as a buffer against the encroachment of urbanization.

To improve quality of life by setting aside nature preserves for the health and well-being of urban populations was a unique, novel idea that bloomed throughout North America through the vision of Frederick Law Olmsted (1822-1903) and was driven further by his apprentice Charles Eliot (1859-1897). Olmsted, the great landscape architect, was an idealist, social reformer, and a utopian socialist who believed parks and open spaces were vital to the physical and psychological well-being of people living in urban areas. Such parks were places of equality and replenishment, where people of all walks of life might enjoy glimpses of nature that formerly only the rich could experience through their seasonal retreats and vacations.

Charles Eliot was described at his Harvard convocation of 1882 as "a quiet man of rare, spiritual qualities." He was driven during his short life of 37 years by a strong sense of public responsibility and civic consciousness and extended Olmsted's perspective of urban parks to more greatly emphasize the importance of protecting wild nature for its biodiversity, as living museums. Eliot worked to establish the first organization in the world for the preservation of natural landscapes for public purposes, the Trustees of Reservations in Massachusetts, 1891. Eliot was outspoken that "a crowded population thirsts for the sight of something very different from the public garden, square, or ball field." Wildness rather than over-cleared, over-manicured parks were important because "each of these scenes is characteristic of the primitive wilderness ... of which, indeed, they are surviving fragments." It required a minimum size of fifty acres, Eliot believed, before visitors could experience "the subtle influence which skies and seas, clouds and shadows, woods and fields, and all that mingling of the natural and human which we call landscape sheds upon human life." (Abbott 1993). Always conscious of the human benefits of these living museums, he quotes in one of his speeches a Boston physician who claimed "a few hours' exposure of a child on a mother's lap to the freshness of a park will produce a sleep such as never follows opium, chloral or ether and will yield a chance for health such as no drug can give." (Abbot 1993). Our need to link to the subtle energies of green space, as large and as natural as possible, is an association of importance that must be affirmed and defended from time to time.

Australia's first national park (Royal National Park) was created beside Sydney as a health necessity following a terrible outbreak of the black plague. The health properties of national parks were important justifications for their creation, far more

Abbot, G Jr. 1993. Saving special places: a centennial history of the trustees of reservations: pioneer of the land trust movement. The Ipswich Press, Ipswich, MA.

initially than the ecological/biodiversity arguments stressed today. Politicians related to and understood the benefits-to-people argument. Steven Mather and James Harkin, the first directors of the U.S. and Canadian National Parks Services (respectively), both quoted in their speeches and reports the words of parks and wilderness advocate John Muir in this regard. "Thousands of tired, nerve-shaken, over-civilized people are beginning to find out that going to the mountains is going home; that wildness is a necessity; and that mountain parks and reservations are useful not only as fountains of timber and irrigating rivers, but as fountains of life." (Muir 1972). Henry David Thoreau, who is one of the earliest spokespersons for protecting wild nature, and who had a low opinion of the misdirected industry of human society, wrote in the essay What I Lived For, in Walden (1854) "A man is rich in proportion to the number of things he can afford to let alone."

Eco-Spirituality of Green Space

Clinebell (1996) stated in *Ecotherapy: healing ourselves, healing the earth*:

> "Sad to say, those suffering from severe alienation from wildness miss the energizing of their spirits, as well as of their bodies, minds, and sexuality, that comes from bonding with nature's wilderness."

He favoured growth-stimulating, hope-energizing, healing experiences that psychologist Abraham Maslow called 'peak experiences'.

> "These are mystical moments of self-transcendence in art, beauty, relating in depth to other people, and to the divine Spirit. Many people find their most energizing and healing peak

Muir, J. 1972. Trails of wonder: writings on nature and man. Hallmark Cards, Kansas City, MO.

Clinebell, H. 1996. Ecotherapy: healing ourselves, healing the earth. Fortress Press, Minneapolis, MN.

.

experiences by encountering the divine Spirit in the awesome beauty, wisdom and wonder of nature."

A movement from England called Deism, led by Puritan minister Jonathan Edwards, reached New England in the 18th Century. The Movement celebrated wild nature as the purest creative expressions of God. Ralph Waldo Emerson, one of the Transcendentalists, expanded on this theme in his book *Nature*.

In discussing caring for the soul, Thomas Moore adds an insight that illuminates the spiritual basis of earth bonding. Drawing on the ancient concept of the world soul, he declares: "Our soul, the mystery we glimpse when we look deeply into ourselves, is part of a larger soul, the soul of the world, *anima mundi*. The world soul affects [and is found in] each individual thing." Moore uses the term soul-ecology, reminding us that the Greek word *oikos*, from which ecology is derived, means home.

Connecting to the Earth: the Terminology of an Evolution

There are a number of terms that have arisen concerning the phenomenon of reconnecting to nature (other than world soul, earth bond, and soul ecology). Clinebell (1996) defines ecobonding as enjoying one's nurturing, energizing, life-enhancing connectedness with nature; ecophilia as the love of life associated with bonding with the earth; ecoalienation as seeking to distance oneself from our inescapable life-giving dependence on nature, and ecophobia as the fear of claiming one's dependence and bonding intimately with nature. E.O. Wilson (1984) states that "the urge to affiliate with other forms of life is to some degree innate, hence deserves to be called biophilia." Wilson elaborates: "I will make the case that to explore and affiliate with life is a deep and complicated process in mental development .... still undervalued in

Wilson, E O. 1984. Biophilia. Harvard University Press, Cambridge, MA.

philosophy and religion, our existence depends on this propensity, our spirit is woven from it, hope rises on its currents ... to the degree that we come to understand other organisms, we will place a greater value on them, and on ourselves."

Original trauma (Glendinning 1995) is caused by the systematic removal from our lives of nature, natural cycles, and the life force itself. Ecosophy is recognizing and drawing upon earth wisdom. Techno-addiction is an addiction to a mechanistic way of viewing the world and the addiction to specific machines such as computers, televisions, and high tech missile technology. Deep ecology is a movement and philosophy that calls for deep significant changes in our social and political values and in our behaviour towards nature and humans. (Nineteen basic fundamentals of deep ecology are presented in the closing paragraphs.)

Tuan (1974) defines Topophilia as the affective (emotional) bond between people and place or setting. Eco-therapy is a therapeutic process of healing the person through participation in sensible, selfless acts of contribution, and encourages a sense of reciprocal connection.

Eco-centredness (primal matrix), to be centred and rooted in the world, is a process, an aspiration and a goal of psychological therapy and meditation. Philosopher Simone Weil (quoted in Clinebell 1996) concluded, "to be rooted is perhaps the most important and least recognized need of the human soul." The Hopi describe the imbalance of modern life with a single word, *Koyaanisqatsi*, which translates as a world out of balance. Near the village of Oraibi, a petroglyph rock portrays when this out-of-balance period in human history began (Boissiere 1986). Having a firmly grounded relationship with nature grants us both balance and a profound sense of being, wellness and wholeness. Lakota (Sioux) refer to this state as walking in a sacred manner and the Navajo

Glendinning, C. 1995. Technology, trauma and the wild. In: T Roszak, M E Gomes, and A D Kannier (eds.). Ecopsychology, restoring the earth, healing the mind. Sierra Club Books, San Francisco, CA.

Tuan, Yi-Fu. 1974. Topophilia: A study of environmental perception, attitudes, and values. Columbia University Press, New York, NY.

Boissiere, Rt. 1986. Meditations with the Hopi. Bear and Company, Santa Fe, NM.

describe it as standing in the centre of the world. The Taoists simply see it as the balance of the yin and yang.

Psychologist Chellis Glendinning, in her 1994 book *My Name Is Chellis and I'm in Recovery from Western Civilization*, made the observation that people have a natural state of being. This has been acknowledged by many terms: being integrated, human potential, and the merging in unity of mind, body, and spirit. She refers to this state as the primal matrix, a healthy, wholly functioning psyche in full-bodied participation with a healthy, wholly functioning earth.

Glendinning, C. 1994. My name is Chellis and I'm in recovery from western civilization. Shambhala, Boston, MA.

Between Forest and City

Wilson describes how our bonds to nature have always been filtered through the influence of our culture. As a result, "They have suspended us between the two antipodal ideals of nature and machine, forest and city, the natural and the artifactual, relentlessly seeking, in the words of Tuan (1974), an equilibrium not of this world." The contrasting tension between civilization and pastoral simplicity has long been recognized. John Muir wrote that, "We gaze morbidly through civilized fog upon our natural world clad with seamless beauty ... civilized man chokes his soul as the ... Chinese their feet." (Muir 1972). At Pompeii the Romans built gardens next to almost every inn, restaurant, and private residence; they used spaced trees and shrubs, beds of herbs and flowers, pools and fountains. In courtyards too small to hold a garden, attractive pictures of plants and animals were painted on the walls (Wilson 1984). Glendinning (1974) concludes that "when we begin to heal ourselves of the traumas perpetrated through western civilization, lo! something miraculous ([which is] something entirely ordinary) takes place: the spirit-given resources of the primal matrix return to us." Primal healing is simplicity, centeredness, and balance, often felt and experienced in the presence of natural landscape.

The underlying shortcoming of modern psychotherapy is that it springs from the premise that we need to seek adjustment to society as it exists, and makes little attempt to challenge the premise that it is more typically the social, institutional and psychological models of modern society that are themselves dysfunctional and alien to our personal psyche and origins. It is our current dysfunctional model of industrial, high speed, high tech living/work environment that produces our disconnectedness. Being reconditioned to re-engage is shortsighted, and illusory. When confronted with external madness, it is a sane and logical response to choose to disconnect. This is no different from walking into a room with sound volumes turned up full and unplugging the stereo, radio and television. We need not seek to be reconditioned to the phenomenon. We need only acknowledge madness when we confront it and separate ourselves from it. Choosing an alternative to madness is neither withdrawal nor is it disconnectedness, but rather re-engagement and re-connectedness. Cahalan (1995) describes the primal therapy of nature contact. "Groundedness is a dynamic state of the person that includes the sense of confidence, pleasure and wonder resulting from progressively deepening contact with the wild and domesticated natural community of the person's neighborhood and larger land region; with unpaved ground, soil, or landscape; with weather and the diversity of native plants and animals; and with human family, neighbors, and local cultural activities."

Cahalan, W. 1995. Ecological groundedness in gestalt therapy. In: T Roszak, M E Gomes and A D Kanner (eds.). Ecopsychology. Sierra Club Books, San Francisco, CA.

Our Anaesthetized Autistic Generation

We are a product of our twentieth and twenty-first centuries' social conditioning and environment. We have been shaped by a bombardment of sensory noise and visual stimuli, and isolation from the natural environment as we move from one enclosed module to another enclosed module. We have become an organism which is experiencing a diminishment of our sensory capabilities and a severe constriction of our peripheral and depth perception. We have become, as Thomas Berry said, the autistic generation. Tuan, in Topophilia, writes, "Perception is an activity, a reaching out to the world. Sense organs are minimally operative when they are not actively used … It is possible to have eyes and not see, ears and not hear."

As a defense against excessive stimuli, senses tune down the numbing noise and visual bombardment of the modern world. Being anesthetized, as if on drugs, we have induced non-awareness and non-feeling. Clinical depression and the use of antidepressants have substantially increased. Both have radically dampened the senses. We don't notice much or feel as much. We are closed, and look but do not really see. We are no longer invaded and possessed by passion, as Laura Sewall (1999) wrote in *Sight and Sensibility*, by "shifting colors of grasses," nor are we "satiated by moonlight," or "permeated by the visible."

Sewall, L. 1999. Sight and sensibility. Jeremy P. Tarcher/Putnam, New York, NY.

We now believe that passion is important to assist the depth of our perceptions. Tuan says that our capacity to perceive is minimized by our passivity. Indeed the finger must slide across a surface to feel, and the eyes must roam across a landscape to see. Our ability to view wild landscapes seems to be further compromised by a growing propensity for staring at flat surfaces, from television and computer screens to sheets of paper. The muscles of our eyes are strained when we attempt to look into subjects finding it more comfortable to gaze at merely the surface. The consequence is we are impairing the acuteness of our depth perception.

We do a poor job of scanning the landscape for close and distant objects of our search. Apart from the impairment of our capacity to see depth in nature, we are also losing our peripheral vision, which is narrowing. There is an emphasis on our central vision for reading books and computers at a distance of 45 to 60 cm and a greater fixed distance for watching television. This perceptual conditioning has led to a new narrow centrality of the focus of vision which inhibits our ability to scan the landscape, see wildlife, recognize predators, and notice the approach of warring tribes which would have made us extremely vulnerable.

I have spent thousands of hours showing and attempting to show a distant bird, moose or basking turtle to students and park visitors. I can attest to seeing the change over forty years in their declining ability to locate and perceptually discern the animal despite the vast improvements in the optics of binoculars and spotting scopes. People are simply losing their capacity to locate and observe wildlife within the depths of a natural landscape whether on water surfaces, open grassland or forests. They no longer have practice in searching for and seeing wildlife. They do not innately perceive that a search is not for the whole object, such as a deer, with all features in their proper place and proportion and visible. Rather it involves visually scanning a broad landscape; searching for contrast and anomalies; for fractions rather than wholes (a leg or antler coming out of a bush); for movement across the field and small shifts in position; for the edges that blur; for fractures in the pattern; for singularities in color (an amber island of deer in the earthly beige of dried leaves); for the vertical shadow amidst the horizontal.

There is also a synesthetic collaboration of senses and faculties, which aids the ability to perceive wildlife. Hearing the voice of a meadowlark sing instructs the eyes to canvas for the image of meadowlark. Knowledge, memory, and experience narrow the form and environment of meadowlark, facilitating a perceptual readiness to locate a meadowlark. This combination leads to visual acuity. As these variables diminish, singularly and collectively, we are less able to see the life around us. We withdraw as our senses diminish. Most often we have no idea what we missed. We walk through a living museum, as though through a gallery of art with nine-tenths of the paintings turned with their face against the wall. And we probably do not even realize it. In short we become separate and disconnected from the natural world.

Our physiological and psychological response to noise, as opposed to music or silence, is profoundly contradictory. As Tuan describes in *Passing Strange and Wonderful*, noise is a clash of dissonant sounds that signals to us a response of tensing against danger, threat and chaos. Both silence and music signal comparative responses. They are the reconciliation after a quarrel, the calm after the storm, and a break for silence may be compared in music to the pauses between notes essential in compositions for their poignancy and serenity. Music, singing, chanting and the sound of wind, flowing water, leaves rustling and birds singing are again a welcomed withdrawal from noise and chaos, and we choose to focus upon them, be soothed by them, to the exclusion of clashing sensory bombardment. Visualize it. Why else do we close our eyes or have a vacant stare when we listen to music? I seem to naturally close my eyes when I focus on recognizing a distant or confusing bird song. We exclude the uninvited and enhance the desirable through selective sensory perception.

Tuan, Yi-Fu. 1993. Passing strange and wonderful. Island Press, Washington, DC.

Wild Landscapes as Green Hospitals: an Emerging Application

Urban parks are typically designed with trails, facilities, and managed vegetation suitable for an emphasis on recreating, running and sweating; moving people through, and maintaining safety and security. Opportunities for deeper and purposeful healing associations with nature, especially for introspective solitude, centering and green hospitals for mental recovery, are poorly accommodated. That such things do occur within this multiple use landscape is not denied. Researchers increasingly acknowledge the need of people for escape, withdrawal, and finding a psychological or spiritual centre. But if not purposely addressed during the planning and development phases, these needs are met as inadequately and unsatisfactorily as an attempt to play soccer on a golf fairway.

There is little interface between psychologists, who spend much of their time treating depression and stress, and the decision-makers and planners who authorize, plan, and design protected green spaces. We are beginning to see some signs of it, trails chosen and signed as quiet trails in the Great Smoky Mountains National Park. Recently I was invited to review the conceptual plan for a nature sanctuary by the young man who competently laid out a plan for trails, viewpoints, walking bridges, and environmental teaching locations through this rolling landscape of trees and small creeks. Here and there were placed a nontraditional symbol that was a bit of a hybrid between a child's drawing of a shining sun and a happy face. The map code described the symbol simply as MVP sites. The young naturalist planner was fortunately present and eager for, and anxious about, my scrutiny. Imagining these locations were something like most valuable places, I asked for clarification. "I call them 'Metaphysical Vibration Places'," he answered. "They are special spots that just feel good," he elaborated. "They feel special to me. There is something about them that deserves special protection and sensitive use. I have no other way of saying it. They don't emerge as special for their biophysical qualities. I just know these places are special." He was almost apologetic for not using some structured environmental assessment criteria for justifying his MVP designation. He had perceived this landscape more broadly than through empirical cognitive criteria. Henry David Thoreau would have certainly understood. He had embraced more holistic criteria. "Thumbs up," I thought. Wild nature offers unique and special experiences. They must never be compromised or sacrificed for a commonplace experience no matter how popular that commonplace experience might seem to be.

Conclusion and Vision

Green spaces have emerged more fully for their importance as green hospitals, not just for those sites used by people who drive for hours for a change of scene or a formal excursion, but especially for those easily accessible to people in urban areas. It's all about maintaining a balance. Our human psyche can only tolerate the sensory bombardment and the anxiety of human urbanization if it also has access to a sanctuary from its turbulence. Every race has a pause; a sporting event its time-out; a musical note measured by the silence around it; a waterfall against the pool beneath it; directed activity against passive reflection; the yin against the yang. This is an old rule of mental and physical well-being.

These green hospitals must be on emergency call, accessible at all hours. To embrace natural landscapes in regular doses is pro-active medicine, forestalling the mental/physical collapse that would require the trauma centre.

While any and all islands of nature in a built or modified landscape are beneficial for humans, these spaces typically fall short of the minimal requirement for the ecological special needs of wildlife. A pair of pileated woodpeckers requires old trees for nesting and feeding, and at least 200 ha per pair. Green spaces, comprising a natural state of living museums, as Charles Eliot called them, are also in short supply for the number of outdoor classrooms that are needed to teach ecology and environmental education fundamentals. Living museums are "scenes representative of the primitive ... of which indeed they are surviving remnants" (Abbott 1993).

My professional career began as a summer naturalist in Oglebay Park, a nationally respected urban park in Wheeling, West Virginia. Here, the A B Brooks Nature Centre was my source of inspiration, and its forests and programs nurtured my perceptions, values and a life-long bonding with nature. As early as 1911, Brooks, among the greatest and most inspiring of West Virginia's naturalists and early foresters, advocated a more advanced perspective of forestry in his book, *Forestry and Wood Industries*. "No one should underestimate the value of woodlands, even when maintained only 'for their aesthetic effects.' Those whose lives must be spent largely on paved streets between walls of buildings find a complete and refreshing change in the shaded parks and are benefited to the extent of their power to appreciate such surroundings ... Upon some, the forest has a fascinating effect, an influence that cannot be expressed in words, but which is capable of driving out every frivolous thought and stirring every deep emotion."

Brooks also believed in the power of natural forests to shape a person's character. "Natural forests, where there is no touch of the artificial, have a greater effect upon character. As long as the

Brooks, A B. 1911. Forestry and wood industries, Vol. V of West Virginia Geological Survey, Acme Publications.

beauty and grandeur of primitive forest scenery is preserved, it will have a powerful influence in shaping the character of people. Its influence ... manifested in their manners and customs and conversation ... [makes people] more thoughtful and less talkative and superficial..."

Lewis Mumford observed in England in the 19th century that throughout history concern for health has been a prime motivation for moving from urban centers. There seems to be a central, innate need for personal wellness, and we have a deep-rooted sense of place. This is accompanied by a centeredness, and connectedness to the natural world, physically, psychologically and spiritually.

As a society these connections individually and collectively are more than a lifestyle choice, they are essential for our personal well-being, quality of life, and ecological survival on this planet. They necessitate a critical reassessment of values, land ethics, and lifestyle.

Our surviving green spaces are indeed dynamic living museums where we must teach a new generation the wonder and fragility of the living landscape. And to teach, we ourselves must learn to reconnect. These are old pathways, from which we have strayed and in the process of becoming lost, have floundered into illiteracy with the earth, ecologically and spiritually.

Cahalan (1995) concluded, "There are various personality styles that foster disconnectedness, (including) a sense of emptiness, or a lack of groundedness. One of the most basic patterns involves clinging to core images of self as owner (of traits, things, land 'resources,' and people), rather than primarily sensing oneself as a process of relating."

Why do we need nature? Because we are nature! This maddening race towards the commoditization of all living things, of being measured for value on the market place, is the pursuit of a false god. Finding balance in our communities and the primal matrix of our inner spirit will lead to deep, significant changes, which will be the measures of our transformation and evolution. I would summarize these shifts as basic fundamentals. They include:

- modifying anthropocentric (human-centered) attitudes toward a new bio-centered philosophy (biocentrism),
- the intrinsic worth and right to life of other species,
- ecosystem thinking and the importance of biodiversity,
- the courage to take personal actions,
- questioning ourselves and the traditional ways we have interacted with nature,
- returning to our roots,
- cultivating deep interactions with nature through our intuitions and sensitivities,
- the search for meaning in an age of nihilism,
- seeking ecosophy or earth wisdom,
- defense and restoration of ecosystems,
- a strong identification with your own bioregion (bioregionalism),
- affirming our identification and solidarity with wild nature,
- encouraging introspection, purification, harmony and celebration of life,
- fostering an ecological, philosophical and spiritual approach to environmental threats,
- criticizing damaging resource practices and offering positive alternatives,
- fostering and practicing consistent personal and environmental ethics,
- favouring non-exploitive practices in science and technology,
- encouraging the introspection of solitude and rediscovering how to observe and listen,

- developing an ecological consciousness that recognizes connectedness, interdependence, fragility, biodiversity, and a personal sense of wonder and place (Butler 1994).

Through this we may transform and evolve to reach our potential on this planet and in the universe. We begin with ourselves and a journey of connectedness that is an inward path, empowered through a primal association with nature, engaging our primal matrix so that we stand in the centre of the world, more thoughtful, and less superficial.

Butler, J R. 1994. Dialog with a frog on a log. Duval House, Edmonton, AB.

Further Reading

Adorno, T W. 1997. Aesthetic theory. Univ. of Minnesota Press, Minneapolis, MN.

Bermingham, A. 1986. Landscape and ideology: the English rustic tradition, 1740-1860. University of California Press, Berkeley, CA.

Draper, M M. 2001. The nature of music: beauty, sound, and healing. Riverhood Books, New York, NY.

Jay, R. 1998. Gardens of the spirit: create your own sacred spaces. Sterling Publishing Co., New York, NY.

Kaplan, R and S Kaplan. 1989. The experience of nature: a psychological perspective. Cambridge University Press, Cambridge, UK.

Kellert, S R. 1996. The value of live: biological diversity and human society. Island Press, Washington, DC.

Kellert, S R. and E O. Wilson (eds.). 1993. The biophilia hypothesis. Island Press, Washington, DC.

Metzner, R. 1999. Green psychology: transforming our relationship to the earth. Rochester. Park Street Press, VT.

Nash, R F. 1989. The rights of nature: a history of environmental ethics. The University of Wisconsin Press, Madison, WI.

Snyder, G. 1995. A place in space: ethics, aesthetics, and watersheds. Counterpoint, Washington, DC.

The Building of the North Saskatchewan Watershed Alliance: Bringing Stakeholders Together

Adele M. Mandryk, University of Alberta

Abstract

The North Saskatchewan Watershed Alliance (NSWA) is a model of co-operation that brings together groups and individuals to solve conflicts on the river and its 80,000 km^2 watershed. There are a number of key factors that brought NSWA to its present state of development. These include

- management with a flexible, transparent, and accountable consensus-based decision and planning model,
- membership that is inclusive,
- a steering committee that has a flattened hierarchy, and
- a five-year business plan that firmly guides NSWA activities.

Measures of success include the expansion from the five original members to over one hundred, extensive community consultation, and the development and distribution of watershed toolkits and other publications. NSWA is in the process of developing a watershed management plan that meets the criteria of the

Government of Alberta and has a goal to provide tools for citizens and municipalities to protect their local sub-watersheds. Continuing and new challenges for the watershed and its people include climate change and rapid melting of the Saskatchewan Glacier, inter-basin water transfer pressures from the south, increasing demands for recreation, and cumulative impacts of industry, agriculture, forestry, mining, and urbanization.

Introduction

This is a missive of celebration. As the former manager of the North Saskatchewan Watershed Alliance I have a good news story to share. This is a story that speaks to the voluntary co-operation of many organizations that care about clean, safe water, biodiversity protection, soil conservation and economic well-being. This is about a group of people who have embraced a watershed perspective and a consensus model to work toward the common goal of a watershed management plan for the Alberta portion of the North Saskatchewan River and its 80,000 km² watershed. These dedicated individuals and organizations provide leadership and direction for a river and a watershed of low priority on the political agenda because it is not yet in crisis. Perhaps, because of this initiative and the growing awareness of local accountability in each of the eighteen sub-basins of the larger watershed, water quantity and quality, biodiversity, and soil conservation issues will not be at odds with economics. Perhaps the future holds a story that will show how an understanding of the true economic value of a river ecosystem helped guide governments, industry and environmental organizations to undertake co-operative watershed level planning to avert environmental degradation even while economic development and population growth relentlessly pushed ahead.

Watersheds, as a subject, have long been studied because of the connection between ecological functioning and the production of ecological services such as clean air, high quality water, and other resources. In short, healthy ecosystems translate into long-term high quality of life for humans and nature. Understanding the impact of human activities on ecosystem functioning, on economic resources, and on appropriately planning to mitigate them is the point of watershed planning. An impressive example of watershed planning is King County in the Puget Sound region of Washington State, U.S.A (King County 2004). King County is the 12th most populous county in the U.S.A. with 17 million people, including the City of Seattle. It also has a huge salmon fishery to protect and citizens of Seattle depend on the watersheds of the Cedar River and South Fork Tolt River for an estimated 160 million gallons of water per day (City of Seattle 2004).

With the human pressure for recreation, recent health scares due to contaminated water, and the collapse of salmon and cod fisheries, there is a growing realization among Canadians that watershed management issues impact them, and that solutions to the negative impacts of relentless urbanization and economic growth need to be found. Stakeholder polarization based on distrust and self-interest has proven ineffective in finding solutions that meet the needs of all parties involved and new approaches are emerging.

Canada's history with watershed level planning started with Ontario and British Columbia but many large cities are dependent on river water for drinking, waste disposal and economic activity. An example of Ontario's long history of watershed-based planning is the Grand River Conservation Authority, which has recently achieved Canadian Heritage River status for the Grand River in 1999 (Government of Canada 2004, Grand River Conservation

King County. 2004. King County watersheds. http://dnr.metrokc.gov/wlr/watersheds.htm. Accessed May 19, 2004.

City of Seattle. 2004. Seattle watersheds. www.cityofseattle.net/util/watershed/default.htm. Accessed May 19, 2004.

Government of Canada. Canadian heritage rivers system. 2004. www.chrs.ca. Accessed May 17, 2004.

Grand River Conservation Authority. 2004. www.grandriver.ca/. Accessed May 19, 2004.

Government of Ontario. 2004. Watershed-based source protection planning. www.ene.gov.on.ca/ envision/water/spp.htm. Accessed May 19, 2004.

Fraser Valley Regional Watersheds Coalition. 2004. www.fvrwc.org/ links.shtml. Accessed May 19, 2004.

EPCOR. 2004. Water source protection. www.epcor.ca/EPCOR+Companies/ EPCOR+Water+Services/Environmental+ Commitment/Water+Source+Protection/ default.htm. Accessed May 19, 2004.

Authority 2004). Further, the Government of Ontario has recently released a white paper on watershed-based source protection that includes recommendations for legislation and stakeholder and public involvement in finding solutions to secure quality drinking water (Government of Ontario 2004). The Fraser Valley Regional Watersheds Coalition has been formed to help communities in the Fraser Valley achieve healthy watersheds (Fraser Valley Regional Watersheds Coalition 2004). The City of Vancouver manages three watersheds to meet the drinking water needs of its citizens and engages in extensive watershed management planning, as does EPCOR Water Utility for the City of Edmonton (EPCOR 2004). These examples show that solutions are multidimensional and long-term, and exceed the mandates of any one city department, government agency, or water utility company.

Development of the North Saskatchewan Watershed Alliance (see Table 1)

The formation of the NSWA in Alberta was an attempt to address the limited mandates of individual organizations and foster long-term solutions. It is a model of co-operation that brings the awareness of the interconnection of human and natural systems together with the need for the co-operation of all parties involved to solve conflicts. Its focus is to co-operatively resolve the issues that arise from the conflicting needs of economic development and environmental protection in the Alberta portion of the North Saskatchewan River watershed by bringing together current, relevant, interdisciplinary knowledge about the watershed; integrating that knowledge; and planning in advance of crisis. The NSWA is unique because it is a model that arose voluntarily, without government mandate, simultaneously from within industry and non-government groups. When both groups realized their

Coyotes Still Sing in My Valley

Table 1

Characteristics of the North Saskatchewan Watershed Alliance model.

Voluntary:

Voluntary co-operation between industry, municipalities and non-government organizations to positively, co-operatively and pro-actively approach integrated water, soil and biodiversity protection.

Inclusive involvement:

Member directed, consensus-based decision and planning model.

Positive, inclusive, collaborative and equal involvement by those who are impacted.

All the people, municipalities and business in the watershed are partners in finding solutions.

Empowered management:

Manager empowered to lead the organization based on a reciprocal relationship with the membership and steering committee.

Well developed business plan:

A project based member approved business model based on a 5-year planning cycle to guide daily decisions and planning.

Responsibility for the watershed is extended to all members:

Local individuals and groups are encouraged to follow the NSWA model for their local water body or sub-watershed.

Clear purpose:

Protection and conservation of water quality and quantity, soil, and biodiversity without jeopardizing economic and social needs.

Clear jurisdiction:

North Saskatchewan River watershed in Alberta.

Clear management principles based on science:

Watershed management and integrated resource management are the disciplines.

mutual interests in watershed protection, they agreed to provide leadership and work together, co-operatively and equally, to maximize available resources. There are a number of key factors that brought NSWA to its present state of development. These are given below:

Management

In the spring of 2000, I was appointed manager of NSWA, with the mandate to catalyze the NSWA into a force that could speak authoritatively for the protection of ecological services and biodiversity in the North Saskatchewan River watershed in Alberta. The goal was to become recognized by policy makers at the municipal, provincial, and federal level by involving all the stakeholders in the watershed following a transparent and accountable consensus-based decision and planning model.

Membership

Visionary founding members of the NSWA were EPCOR Water Utility, Trout Unlimited Canada, Agriculture and Agri-Food Canada – Prairie Farm Rehabilitation Administration, Transalta Utilities and the City of Edmonton Drainage Services. Since then, membership has grown to over one hundred organizations representing many segments of the watershed, including industry, three levels of government, non-government organizations, and education institutions. This focus on inviting all watershed voices to the table contributes greatly to the success of the NSWA and invites a greater appreciation for local accountability for tributaries and sub-basin planning within the watershed.

Steering committee

The vision of NSWA's steering committee in recognizing the value of a flattened hierarchy and in doing so fostering a reciprocal, flexible relationship between themselves, the larger membership, and their manager was a major component in achieving success. In other words, everybody has an equal voice at the table, regardless of the size of financial contributions or political position. This approach is unique and has had an on-going pay-off in the speed in which the NSWA has been accepted as an authorative voice for the watershed, because it has fostered trust between diverse member organizations.

Business plan

Another key to success was the creation of a five-year business plan to firmly guide NSWA activities. This plan streamlines daily decision-making and allows the manager to move quickly and efficiently without the need for steering committee approval, so long as decisions fall within the expected outcomes of the business plan. This is also a unique approach and fosters a strong level of trust between the manager, the steering committee and membership.

Measures of Success Since 2000

- Expansion from the original five members to over one hundred.
- Development and distribution of the watershed toolkit to guide local stewardship.
- Development and distribution of the North Saskatchewan River Guide.
- Developing a watershed management plan that meets the criteria of the Government of Alberta.
- Developing a State of the Watershed baseline report.

Continuing and new challenges for the watershed and its people are on the horizon. Some of these challenges will be water quality and supply issues arising from climate change and rapid melting of the Saskatchewan Glacier. In addition, rapid population growth will lead to increasing demands for recreation, placing further pressure on the watershed, the river and the tributaries. Accelerating economic activity from the industries of agriculture, forestry, mining, and urbanization has cumulative impact of the finite land base. Increasing pressure will also be felt as drier more densely populated regions to the south of the watershed look north for new sources of water.

The list of successes indicate that NSWA has gained the trust and respect of government, industry, and other organizations and assists stakeholders to find solutions to challenges through co-operation, planning and local accountability. By working together these communities and the NSWA have reason to be proud and will continue to enjoy the natural and cultural heritage and the ecological services of the North Saskatchewan River watershed.

Acknowledgements

Thank you to the NSWA steering committee and member organizations for their support during the 2000 to 2002 period and for working together for the benefit of the watershed. Thank you to Sharon Willianen, the current manager, who embraces the vision of the NSWA and effectively leads the organization forward.

Protecting Natural Capital and Quality of Life Through Partnerships in an Urban Centred Region: The Beaver Hills Initiative

Guy S. Swinnerton, University of Alberta

Abstract

In many parts of the world such as Britain, Europe, and Japan, parks and protected areas have embraced lived-in landscapes and the heritage of local populations. More recently there has been worldwide recognition of the need to complement the natural landscape national park model with protected areas that include more human-oriented landscapes. In Canada, there is increasing acceptance of many of the principles and practices of the new paradigm. The Beaver Hills Initiative, located 45 km east of Edmonton, provides a working example of both the potential and the difficulties of implementing the new paradigm at the regional level. The initiative was stimulated in 2000 by proposed petroleum exploitation adjacent to the Elk Island National Park boundary. Beginning with 38 representatives from a diversity of stakeholders, the group is seeking ways to provide long-term protection to this large landscape through consensus. The Beaver Hills Initiative illustrates the need for collaboration and partnership and the adoption of innovative approaches to successfully conserve a region's biodiversity and natural capital while ensuring the sustainability of local communities and their quality of life. Many of the underlying principles and approaches being followed exemplify the new paradigm for protected areas. Particularly relevant is the potential of the Beaver Hills Initiative to demonstrate the applicability of this new paradigm within the volatile environment of an urban-centred region.

Introduction

Approaches to the planning and management of protected areas are constantly evolving. Over the past two decades the need has emerged to complement the traditional national park model with protected areas that include lived-in landscapes and modified natural systems that have been created by a long-established human presence (see Swinnerton 1999, Swinnerton and Buggey 2004). Many of the characteristics of this more recent approach are found within the new paradigm for protected areas (Phillips 2003). The essential elements of this new paradigm include:

- a bioregional approach involving trans-boundary collaboration,
- active and meaningful involvement and partnering with local people,
- recognition that protecting biodiversity can be achieved in conjunction with sustaining and enhancing the social and economic viability of an area and the quality of the community, and
- the realization that protected area planning and management requires not only the science of ecological systems and biodiversity, but also an appreciation for the social, economic, political, and institutional environment (see Mitchell *et al.* 2002, Munro and Willison 1998, Nelson *et al.* 2003).

Swinnerton, G S. 1999. Recreation and conservation: Issues and prospects. In: E L Jackson and T L Burton (eds.), Leisure studies: Prospects for the twenty-first century, pp. 199-231. Venture Publishing Inc., State College, PA.

Swinnerton, G S and S Buggey. 2004. Protected landscapes in Canada: current practice and future significance. The George Wright Forum 21(2): 78-92.

Phillips, A. 2003. Turning ideas on their head: The new paradigm for protected areas. The George Wright Forum, 20(2), 8-32.

Mitchell, N, B Slaiby, S Buggey, and M Benedict. 2002. Local community leadership: Building partnerships for conservation in North America. Parks, 12(2), 55-66.

Munro, N P and J H M Willison. (eds.). 1998. Linking protected areas with working landscapes conserving biodiversity. Proceedings of the Third International Conference on Science and the Management of Protected Areas. Science and Management of Protected Areas Association, Wolfville, NS.

Nelson, J G, J C Day, L M Sportza, J Loucky, and C Vasquez. (eds.). 2003. Protected areas and the regional planning imperative in North America. University of Calgary Press, Calgary, AB.

These and other underlying principles and processes are associated with Biosphere Reserves and the International Union for the Conservation of Nature (IUCN)'s Protected Areas Management Category V, Protected Landscapes/Seascapes (see Phillips 2002, 2003, Swinnerton 2003, UNESCO 1996).

Notwithstanding Canada's long involvement with the more traditional approach to parks and protected areas, there is now increasing acceptance of many of the principles and practices of the new paradigm (see Canadian Biosphere Reserves Association 2003, Curthoys 1998, Dempsey *et al.* 2002, Swinnerton and Otway 2003). For example, the panel on the ecological integrity of Canada's national parks (Parks Canada Agency 2000), while placing ecological integrity at the core of the Agency's mandate, recommended that Parks Canada participate in regional sustainable development strategies and in regional management plans where they may affect a national park's integrity.

More recently, the report by the National Round Table on the Environment and the Economy (2003) on nature conservation in the 21st century implicitly recognized that securing Canada's natural capital would require the implementation of many of the characteristics of the new paradigm for protected areas (see also Worbets and Berdahl 2003). However, the National Round Table has also identified a number of key barriers and challenges to making progress in nature conservation in this country including the lack of political will, the lack of conservation planning at the landscape level, and the lack of financial resources to support conservation and partnership.

This paper examines the Beaver Hills Initiative with its vision of integrating the protection of the natural capital of the region with sustainable community development. The initiative provides a working example of both the potential and the difficulties of implementing the new paradigm for protected areas at the regional level.

Phillips, A. 2002. Management guidelines for IUCN Category V protected areas: Protected Landscapes/Seascapes. IUCN, Gland, Switzerland and Cambridge, UK.

Swinnerton, G S. 2003. Forging partnerships to protect lived-in landscapes: the Canadian experience with Protected Landscapes – IUCN Category V., Fifth World Parks Congress, Benefits beyond boundaries. Durban, South Africa.

UNESCO. 1996. Biosphere Reserves: The Seville Strategy and the statutory framework for the world network. Paris: UNESCO.

Canadian Biosphere Reserves Association. 2003. Biosphere Reserves in Canada – Newsletter, No.15.

Curthoys, L P. 1998. For the love of Alberta: Ways to save your natural heritage. Private conservancy guide for Alberta. Federation of Alberta Naturalists. Edmonton, AB.

Dempsey, J, P Dearden, and J G Nelson. 2002. Stewardship: Expanding ecosystem protection. pp. 379-400. In: P Dearden and R Rollins (eds.), Parks and protected areas in Canada: Planning and management). (2nd ed.). Oxford University Press, Don Mills, ON.

Swinnerton, G S and S G Otway. 2003. Collaboration across boundaries – Research and practice: Elk Island National Park and Beaver Hills, Alberta. Fifth International Conference of the Science and Management of Protected Areas Association, Victoria, BC.

Parks Canada Agency. 2000. Unimpaired for future generations: Protecting ecological integrity with Canada's national parks. Vol. II Setting a new direction for Canada's National Parks. Minister of Public Works and Government Services, Ottawa, ON.

The Beaver Hills ecosystem includes Beaverhill Lake, which is well known as a migration stop for water birds including snow and Ross's geese (photo by Edgar T Jones).

The Beaver Hills Ecosystem

The Beaver Hills ecosystem, which lies 45 km east of Edmonton, is characterized by the knob and kettle topography of the Cooking Lake moraine. Approximately 1,500 km² in extent, Beaver Hills rises to 60 m above the surrounding plains and forms a disjunct portion of the dry mixed wood subregion of the boreal forest natural region within the central parkland subregion of Alberta. While this topography has restricted intensive agriculture, abundant tree cover and numerous water bodies have resulted in the area being highly productive for ungulates and other wildlife, waterfowl, and migratory birds; the topography constitutes part of the last remaining natural habitat corridor in east-central Alberta. In addition, the amenity value associated with these more natural landscape characteristics has provided highly sought after living and recreation space.

Designated protected areas of this landscape account for just over 25% of the area. Elk Island National Park (194 km²), the largest of these protected areas, was originally set aside as a dominion wildlife reserve in 1906 and gained national park status in 1913. Other designated protected areas include the Cooking Lake-Blackfoot Grazing, Wildlife and Provincial Recreation Area, the Ministik Bird Sanctuary, Miquelon Lake Provincial Park, the Strathcona Wilderness Centre, and a number of small natural areas designated by the Alberta provincial government. More recently, conservation initiatives involving private landowners have become increasingly evident (see Burak and Swinnerton 1998, Kwasniak 1997).

Located adjacent to Edmonton, with a census metropolitan area population of 782,101 (Edmonton Municipal Census 2005), the Beaver Hills and its immediate area is becoming increasingly impacted by one of the fastest growing metropolitan regions in Canada. The pressures of this growth exemplifies what is happening in many rural metro-adjacent areas, and includes residential development, infrastructure expansion, and the demands for outdoor recreation opportunities (Azmier and Dobson 2003, Worbets and Berdahl 2003). Agriculture and petroleum development also contribute to the intensification and fragmentation of land-use patterns that have significant implications for the long-term biodiversity and landscape character of the Beaver Hills. Not surprisingly, Parks Canada has been specifically concerned about these changes because of its mandate to protect the ecological integrity of Elk Island National Park.

As one of Canada's smaller national parks, and the only completely fenced unit within the national system, protecting the parks ecological integrity is a constant challenge that requires consideration of events beyond the park boundary (Parks Canada 1999). The 1996 management plan for the park noted the need to develop partnerships and foster regional integration by working co-operatively with other levels of government, agencies, and private

Burak, P G and G S Swinnerton. 1998. The Beaver Hills: An exploratory application of the biosphere reserve concept in the aspen parkland of Alberta. pp. 577-583. In: N.W.P. Munro and J H M Willison (eds.). Linking protected areas with working landscapes conserving biodiversity). Science and Management of Protected Areas Association, Wolfville, NS.

Kwasniak, A J. 1997. Reconciling ecosystem and political borders: A legal map. Environmental Law Centre (Alberta) Society, Edmonton, AB.

Azmier, J J, and S Dobson. 2003. The burgeoning fringe: Western Canada's rural metro–adjacent areas. Canada West Foundation, Calgary, AB.

Worbets, B, and L Berdahl. 2003. Western Canada's natural capital: Toward a new policy framework. Canada West Foundation. Calgary, AB.

Parks Canada. 1999. Elk Island National Park ecosystem conservation plan. Internal document. Elk Island National Park.

Parks Canada. 1996. Elk Island National Park Management Plan 1996. Parks Canada, Ottawa.

Parks Canada. 2003. Elk Island National Park of Canada management plan.

individuals (Parks Canada 1996). This need for partnership has been endorsed in the proposed new management plan for the park (Parks Canada 2003) which acknowledges that the park will co-operate with neighbouring jurisdictions to protect and manage natural resources that contribute to the long-term health of the ecosystem. A regional orientation is also evident within the plan by the park recognizing the contribution that it can make to local and regional economies through heritage tourism and sustainable land management initiatives.

The Beaver Hills Initiative

Over the last decade there have been a number of initiatives to develop a more integrated approach to protecting the valuable environmental, social, and economic assets of the area (Burak and Swinnerton 1998, Kwasniak 1997). These have met with varying levels of success. However, with the escalating development pressures being placed on the Beaver Hills and the vulnerability of this landscape to the forces of change, local residents, politicians, as well as park agencies have become increasingly aware that new initiatives are required to protect the fundamental qualities of the Beaver Hills.

The Process Leading to the Establishment of the Beaver Hills Initiative

An important impetus for the current initiative occurred in 2000 with the possibility of oil and gas development occurring in proximity to Elk Island National Park. In response to this threat, park staff began promoting the need for a more co-ordinated and long-term approach to land-use planning within the Beaver Hills. Parks Canada emphasized that the park was not solely concerned with protecting the ecological integrity of Elk Island National Park but wanted to ensure the socio-economic viability and quality of life of the local communities within the natural capacity of the regional landscape.

Coyotes Still Sing in My Valley

The importance of clean air and water, and the concept of sustainable communities were considered as touchstones to which everybody could relate. Over the next two years, a general agreement was reached for a co-ordinated approach by the park and many other stakeholders. These include provincial and federal government departments, five county councils (Strathcona, Lamont, Leduc, Camrose, and Beaver) whose jurisdictions contain portions of the Beaver Hills, industrial representatives, and environmental organizations.

On September 9, 2002, the first Beaver Hills focus group was held that involved a facilitator and 38 representatives from a diversity of stakeholders. The facilitator assisted the stakeholders to review the draft vision and operating principles, and representatives were chosen to establish a co-ordinating committee that would reflect the range of interests in attendance. The 38 representatives came from the following agencies and organizations:

- Municipal government: Beaver County, Camrose County, Lamont County, Leduc County, Strathcona County, and the City of Edmonton.
- Provincial government: Alberta Agriculture, Food and Rural Development, Alberta Community Development (Parks and Protected Areas/Cultural Facilities and Historical Resources), Alberta Environment, Alberta Municipal Affairs, and Alberta Sustainable Resource Development.
- Federal government: Parks Canada, Agriculture and Agri-Food Canada (Prairie Farm Rehabilitation Administration).
- Non-governmental: Alberta Conservation Association, Alberta Fish and Game Association, Ducks Unlimited Canada, Alberta Industrial Heartland, Nature Conservancy of Canada, Northeast Capital Industrial Association, North Saskatchewan Watershed Alliance.

Beaver Hills Initiative Co-ordinating Committee. 2004. The Beaver Hills Initiative: A sustainable community initiative. Fact sheet.

The Beaver Hills Initiative: Current Progress and Outcomes

The initial meeting of the co-ordinating committee took place on November 7, 2002 and since its formation, the co-ordinating committee has made progress in clarifying the purpose and direction for the Beaver Hills Initiative. The more significant of these are as follows (Beaver Hills Initiative Co-ordinating Committee 2004, Swinnerton and Otway 2003):

- Vision: The Beaver Hills Initiative values the region for its natural beauty, quality of life, and supports co-operative efforts to sustain the quality of water, land, air, and community development.

- Mission: Working together for a sustainable region, through shared initiatives and co-ordinated action.

- Develop a regional plan that explores and demonstrates how industry, parks, agriculture, and residents can co-operatively support and plan for a high quality of life, which includes a natural landscape and economic productivity.

- Implement the regional plan by identifying and prioritizing issues, sharing data and developing and promoting information resources. This will assist stakeholders and citizens in achieving and maintaining a sustainable communities' approach to development within the region.

Working within these overall guidelines, sub-committees have been established for specific tasks including hiring consultants, submitting funding applications, and developing a communication strategy. In addition, long-term goals and objectives are complemented by shorter-term targets with measurable outcomes. These include invasive alien species management, fire protection, information and data sharing, and watershed/landscape planning.

Preliminary Achievements on the Beaver Hills Initiative

Although the Beaver Hills Initiative is in its early stages, a number of preliminary achievements are noted (Swinnerton and Otway 2003):

- The process being followed and the long-term intended outcomes of the Beaver Hill Initiative bear considerable resemblance to those associated with the new paradigm for protected areas, including the gathering of diverse groups under one organization through collaboration and partnership.

- The process encompasses some of the fundamental principles of planning as a social learning process where participatory and learning-based approaches are focussed on task-oriented action through constructive behaviour change (Swinnerton 1999).

- Although Elk Island National Park staff initially took a lead role in advocating the need for a regional approach to the Beaver Hills, the Initiative's co-ordinating committee is currently following a round-table model where decision-making is by consensus.

- An evident strength of the Initiative is the commitment by the municipal politicians who represent the five counties in the Beaver Hills. Municipal governments provide a central role in determining the patterns of growth and land-use change across the broader landscape. In addition, as elected officials, they represent a diversity of interests, including individual landowners, and they reflect the relative balance of development and environmental stewardship.

- It is too early to assess the implications of the Initiative for the protection of the ecological integrity of Elk Island National Park or within the other protected areas within the Beaver Hills. To date, the park is seen as one of many equal participants in the Initiative. Moreover, protecting the essential

National Round Table on the Environment and the Economy. 2003. Securing Canada's natural capital: A vision for nature conservation in the 21st century. NRTEE, Ottawa, ON.

qualities of Elk Island National Park is recognized as being concurrent with managing the environmental, social and economic capital and benefits of the region.

- The long-term success of projects such as the Beaver Hills Initiative often depends on financial resources beyond the existing budget allocations of the partnering groups (see National Round Table on Environment and Economy, 2003). To make progress, the co-ordinating committee must be awarded significant funds.

Conclusions

The Beaver Hills Initiative illustrates the need for collaboration and partnership and the adoption of innovative approaches to successfully conserve a region's biodiversity and natural capital while ensuring the sustainability of local communities and their quality of life. Many of the underlying principles and approaches being followed exemplify the new paradigm for protected areas. Particularly relevant is the potential of the Beaver Hills Initiative to demonstrate the applicability of this new paradigm within the volatile environment of an urban centred region.

Acknowledgements

Thanks to the co-ordinating committee of the Beaver Hills Initiative and many others who contributed to the ideas presented here.

Life is a Classroom Without Walls: Naturalization of Schoolyards – The Earth Challenge Project

Karin Adshead, Earth Challenge Project Designer and Project Manager

Abstract

The Earth Challenge Project is curriculum-integrated, participatory eco-literacy in the public school system, and nature-based interpretation of the curriculum guidelines. It was designed to empower children to be responsible stewards of the earth, and active, thoughtful participants in our society; giving them the tools, confidence, and communication skills to aid our society in making significant change towards sustainability. The project revolves around dynamic, on-going, schoolyard naturalization concepts. Furthermore, through the community building that underlies the project, there is an opportunity to empower whole communities, inside and out of the school body to adopt nature-based activities.

Introduction

There are many reasons why some education programs have failed to achieve their goals. Projects may have been initiated by a teacher or a handful of parents. Parents carried the project until their children left the school or they accepted other commitments. In the case of the teacher, they accepted other commitments or were transferred to other schools. These projects were generally of benefit only to the students of that teacher. Another limitation is that the standard method of implementing projects, in Edmonton at any rate, is for an individual to receive a salary and sign over property rights for a teaching module which is published in a binder and then sold to schools. It is entirely up to the busy teacher to use the resource in class. Not all teachers feel a personal interest in environmental issues and field activities. Finally, many projects are restricted to private schools or their equivalent, which ignores the needs of the thousands of children in public schools.

Learning from These Experiences

Support from outside the day-to-day activities of the classroom is essential for vision continuity to overcome the hurdles of personal interest levels, and the difficulty of implementing something new. For major changes to be effective, changes must be supported every step of the way. There were three goals related to long-term learning and life skills that I hoped students would achieve. The pilot project was developed at the Minchau Elementary School in Edmonton, Alberta. Aspects of the Earth Challenge project that seek to overcome resistance to program implementation are given in Table 1.

Trees have been planted on school grounds for environmental reasons. This school yard has trees transplanted from a road-widening project (photo by Ross W Wein, 2004).

Table 1.
Earth Challenge: aspects of the project

This project seeks to overcome obstacles encountered by other programs through:

- Curriculum-integrated programming,
- On-going consultation and support for schools to implement the program,
- A focus on multiple intelligence applications of learning,
- Innovative programming, including collaboration with recognized local professional artists and facilitators,
- An umbrella approach, unifying existing quality environmental education programs,
- A holistic, upward spiral of knowledge regarding nature and environmental issues,
- A balanced representation and discussion of environmental and social issues,
- Emphasis on written, oral, visual, social and cultural communication skills,
- The daily integration of environmental education into all aspects of education resulting in overall heightened awareness.

Long-Range Goals for the Earth Challenge Project

The first goal was increased empathy for the environment, and a deeper understanding of our inter-connectedness with the natural world. We emphasized that all must start with the heart. You have to care before you will want to make change. The second goal was an increased capacity for critical thinking. Before you can visualize change, you need to have confidence in your ability to understand and act on the issues in an independent and creative way. The third goal was increased oral and written communication skills. All leaders of cultural and societal change have relied on their ability to impact society with their superior communication skills.

Earth Challenge Project Concepts and Themes

Table 2 suggests examples that encourage students to develop empathy for the environment. The concepts and themes increase in complexity through the grades; special needs students are given special consideration.

Earth Challenge Project Communication and Critical Thinking

In the following section, the communication and critical thinking goals are achieved through a range of activities by grade (Table 3).

Consequences of lifestyle choices

Landscape projects require long-term planning (e.g., present tree size vs. size at maturity). Students must think beyond the moment. Monitoring growth and changes makes it clear that change is inevitable. Using landscapes to teach this concept also emphasizes that change can be very slow – too slow to see on a day-to-day basis, but that change is happening. Studying environmental issues and sustainability makes for environmentally literate citizens. A good knowledge base empowers one to make good choices.

Table 2.
Suggested concepts and themes for schoolyard naturalization

Programs by Academic Year

Kindergarten and Grades 1 and 2	Concept: the butterfly garden Theme: personal transformation • Growing native Alberta flowers, shrubs • Growing a heritage seed vegetable garden
Grade 3	Concept: welcoming the birds (1) Theme: taking flight; exploring the earth • Building bird feeders and houses • Participation in Project FeederWatch
Grade 4	Concept: welcoming the birds (2) Theme: taking flight; exploring the earth • Designing and landscaping the school grounds in ways to enhance bird habitat, using native trees and shrubs • Growing six varieties of grains, which reflect the ethnic origin of students
Grade 5	Concept: wetland patrol Theme: building and understanding • Participation in Volunteer Land Stewards Program (designated wetland area) – clean up, habitat enhancement, protection, etc. • One-time construction of pond on school grounds
Grade 6	Concept: the shelterbelt Theme: reverence for the earth • Construction of a wildlife friendly shelterbelt on school grounds, to provide an opportunity to study bio-diversity close up • Community permaculture project: students will develop a demonstration garden on the school grounds according to the principles of permaculture
Special Needs Students	Concept: the sensory gardens Theme: overcoming adversity • Raised-box beds designed to be wheelchair accessible, containing plants, rocks, and small water features to stimulate senses

Children respond to activities that bring nature into the classroom, especially if concepts are reinforced outdoors (photo by Norma Keillor, 2004).

Communication skills

In order to share choices in sustainability, or concern for environmental issues, you need good communication skills. Communication will change the world we live in, and it will not all be based on who has the fastest web-link or most sophisticated cell phone. Technology is only as good as the people using it. Enter the ancient art of storytelling. In the process of telling a good story, a problem is usually resolved, and issues can be addressed in ways that allow the people concerned to save face. Time is slowed, as the story unfolds, which allows everyone listening the time to slow down, hear the message, appreciate the wisdom, and perhaps most importantly, to think with clarity. A well-told story also has a rhythm that can be meditative, resulting in a mental state essential to critical thinking. The person telling the story is making many evaluations of the body language of the audience, a valuable skill in inter-personal relations. The person telling the story must overcome their fear of public speaking, which is one of our societies' greatest barriers to effective communication. The audience has the opportunity to learn, regardless of reading ability – very important in a world where oral communication is critical. The vocabulary of the storyteller and the audience can be enhanced as they reach for new ways to develop their stories. The social skills of the storyteller and audience can be expanded as the storyteller uses body language to aid in communication and by the values promoted in the story.

Writing stories, poetry, songs, and plays provide other ways of expressing oneself in meaningful ways and can sometimes be used in unique ways to catch attention. Art in many forms (dancing, sculpting, painting, drawing, music) supercedes words and language and crosses boundaries. Artists are often at the forefront of change, using their talents to help make it happen. Artists are also often big picture thinkers, having refined the ability to see how the many parts make up the whole.

If students learn the alphabet in sign language or Braille, they are given a greater appreciation for the challenges some people face, as well as another means of communicating. Body language sets the stage for storytelling. Furthermore, this has been used successfully to teach students high in bodily kinaesthetic and spatial intelligences (multiple intelligence theory) to read. "By using gestures and hand signals to create letters, words, and concepts, children who find reading a chore can experience success." (Armstrong 2000).

Armstrong T. 2000. In their own way: discovering and encouraging your child's personal learning style. Distributed by St. Martin's Press, Los Angeles, CA. 211 pp.

Observation skills

Taking a walk in the woods with a group of students will quickly inform you of their level of observation skills. In our society of instant gratification and constant noise, children find it unrewarding to slow down and really see and hear what is

Primary school children on a field trip through the forests of the North Saskatchewan River Valley (photo by Jade Dodd, 2002).

happening around them. This attitude, carried into adulthood, may contribute to the insensitivity for much of the environmental degradation happening around us. Tracking animals and bird watching make a game out of being aware of your surroundings, and requires stillness and perseverance, as well as careful attention to detail and the use of more than one sense. So does the written nature journal, packed with notes and drawings. Spend an hour drawing a plant, and you become intimately aware of its every nuance. Monitoring the projects throughout the seasons enhances the sense of being part of the annual unfolding. Participating in a wide range of environmental monitoring programs such as the Watch programs (Plant Watch, Worm Watch, Frog Watch, Project FeederWatch) increases global awareness, and the sense of being part of the global picture (see Table 4).

Table 4.

Other programs included in the Earth Challenge program

SEEDS

EEC Conservation Action Program for Schools (CAPS)

PlantWatch (grade K – 2)

Project FeederWatch (grade 3)

BirdQuest (grade 3)

Worm Watch (grade 4)

Frog Watch (grade 5)

Volunteer Land Stewards (grade 5)

Critical thought

In order to make social, cultural and environmental change happen, critical thought is necessary. How do you teach about environmental issues without biasing students? What if their family depends on the manufacturer in question? How do you respect all points of view? How do you get real answers? Enter the detective.

Eco-mystery story writing assists students in acquiring the knowledge and skills that are necessary for functioning in a society constantly demanding decision-making. Through the vehicle of mystery story writing, students become detectives seeking answers about environmental issues, researching techniques for finding information and learning to analyze situations from an objective viewpoint. The stories, which are based on the crime/clues/solution formula, empower students to hone critical thinking, observation, and communication skills. The human element behind the issues and their witnesses are exposed, and students are encouraged to explore their own biases, as well as those of their information sources. Role-playing, and the concept of "the council of all beings" (where everyone must listen to all points of view), applied to a sample environmental issue, are powerful ways to put yourself in someone else's shoes. This is wrapped up with an exploration of creative strategies for change.

Tools for change

When speaking of tools for change, the boundaries blur. Every aspect of the Earth Challenge project is designed to provide those tools; however, some highlights could be:

- A thorough understanding of the workings of democracy, applied to local issues (this must be implemented with care, so as to allow students to form and voice their personal opinions freely),
- Speaking skills (storytelling), and song writing, as well as participation in an annual student-led conference,
- Knowing that change is possible by participating in it (dynamic landscape projects),
- Studying historic, current, and future environmental issues (learn from history),
- Connecting with nature in a significant way builds an understanding of needs, and instils a desire to protect nature in a meaningful way (we protect what we understand and appreciate),
- Co-operation: landscape projects require teamwork, planning, and the support of everyone involved, and group activities (such as plays, etc.) allow everyone the opportunity to contribute in a way that is personally meaningful.

Community building

The Earth Challenge Project is very much about community building. Making the school grounds an attractive place for people in community provides a neighborhood focus that extends beyond the school population. Reduced vandalism is a projected outcome of the pride in the projects, as well as of the shift in values regarding nature. Participating in the landscape projects means building a sense of place, which is so often lost in our fast-paced world.

Plays and other presentations do not need to be restricted to parents – they can also provide entertainment and education to other people in the community. Landscaping work bees and maintenance pull people together in a very traditional way, as do community suppers and dances. Family classes give moms and dads an inexpensive way to spend quality time with their families, and utilize the valuable resource of the school building in off-hours. There is also the opportunity to bring in volunteers from the community to teach various art programs, do demonstrations, etc. thus providing an outlet for community energy and gifts.

There is no sense in re-inventing approaches. Inviting other teachers and their programs to participate and assist in achieving a goal makes the best use of existing resources and people, and builds a community of peers as well (e.g. the eco-mystery writing workshop).

Self-esteem

These two words have the power to make or break people in terms of their willingness to share what they can do in and for the world. Applying the theory of Multiple Intelligence honours the individual learning styles of all students and helps them to achieve their academic potential. Developing confident, knowledgeable, and environmentally literate citizens is the ultimate goal.

Project Evaluation

The Earth Challenge project represents a means of imparting a philosophy, an outlook on life and living, which cannot be transmitted effectively to students in a one-hour annual field trip. Information relayed to them over the course of their elementary grades through eco-immersion makes this learning philosophy readily transferable to any school system, given due consideration to local issues, ecosystems, and talented people. This philosophy fills the need outlined in the United Nation's Agenda 21 regarding sustainable living education.

The real evaluation and reward is in the classroom, as children respond. Children who have absorbed these principles feel committed to protecting nature. They will not be the children and, later, adults who will be ripping limbs off trees or dumping oil in the back alley. The current methods of teaching environmental issues, as add-ons or extra-curricular activities, only serve to reinforce the belief that the needs of the earth can continue to be minimized and ignored – to everyone's detriment. Science today is beginning to acknowledge that we are not at the peak of some invisible pyramid; rather, we are an integral part of the web of life. Every action of ours affects countless others – both living and non-living. It is within our grasp to embrace our role in this beautiful web and work towards its health. Children who have worked profound change in their own piece of the world are ready to become adults who believe that they can and will make a difference in the bigger world. The Earth Challenge project is designed to give children a sense of the wonder of this web of life, as well as concrete examples of how to fully participate in it.

Conclusions

The importance of family and adult involvement needs to be emphasized. In the environmental movement, education and expectations are focused on children and all efforts are directed towards them with the assumption that it is too late for adults. It is an unhealthy attitude to exclude adults because it demonstrates an unwillingness to promote adult responsibility. In a family situation, it would be considered unhealthy to always ask the children for the solutions to all of our problems, to make all the decisions, to deal with the fall-out from our actions. In reality, we would say, "I will do what I can in this situation, and I will give you the tools you will need as an adult to deal with similar situations." There is a difference between modeling behavior, and absolving oneself of responsibility. The challenge to adults and families is to take up the Earth Challenge and work towards real and lasting change that will solve environmental problems and ensure a future for coming generations in our city.

Acknowledgements

Thanks to the Board of Directors of the Global, Environmental, and Outdoor Education Council (GEOEC) of the Alberta Teachers' Association, teachers, and students at the Minchau Elementary School for their interest in this project. The newsletter *Connections* of GEOEC is an important source of information that alerts teachers to environmental issues and programs.

Additional Reading

Gardner, H. 1993. Frames of mind: the theory of multiple intelligences. Tenth-anniversary edition. Basic Books, New York, NY.

Orr, D W. 1992. Ecological literacy: education and the transition to a post-modern world. State University of New York Press, Albany, NY. 210 pp.

Green Planning Policy and Partnerships in Edmonton

Bob Priebe, City of Edmonton Community Services Department

Abstract

Many cities are developing green planning strategies to retain conservation areas while dealing with diverse stakeholder and financial realities. Almost 20 initiatives that would enhance co-operation and planning among stakeholders are discussed for the city of Edmonton; the status of each is given. A key to the success of protected areas is the formation of a land trust.

Introducing Green Planning Policies

There has been active policy development for the protection of conservation areas in many cities. In western Canada, the cities of Edmonton, Calgary, Regina, Red Deer, Medicine Hat, and Saskatoon have different approaches to conserving natural sites. Calgary has developed criteria for environmental reserves and natural environment parks. Red Deer's neighbourhood guidelines state that a neighborhood area structure plan must include, among other things, a strategy aimed at preserving and interpreting the significant natural and cultural heritages on the site. The administration also targets lands in undeveloped quarter sections and tries to acquire them before development activity begins.

In Medicine Hat, the municipal development plan has specific policies regarding the natural environment as an endowment to be preserved, protected and enhanced. Saskatoon has, in bylaw, both objectives and policies for conservation of natural areas and archeological sites. Edmonton's policies and approaches are noted herein.

Some large American cities like Chicago, Illinois and Houston, Texas have identified the need for natural parks from a policy perspective. Houston has as one of its park types, nature parks. In Chicago, there are specific visions, objectives and policies for natural areas, greenways and wetlands.

One of the challenges is to evaluate these policies periodically to determine the effectiveness of the policy. Unfortunately, these evaluations are difficult to find.

Challenges to Policy Implementation

The challenges to effective policy implementation with the existing framework as we know it today in Edmonton include the following:

Voluntary nature of the policy framework

Policy C-467 (Conservation of Natural Sites in Edmonton's Table Lands – 1995) addresses current and potential protected area sites primarily beyond the river valley. The policy guiding the city's efforts is voluntary on behalf of landowners with the exception of providing information to the city regarding the ecological value of the sites. This voluntary nature can have positive and negative effects. A voluntary policy means that development interests make the final decision. Market forces that demand natural environments in urban areas help to shape the developers' decision making.

City of Edmonton. 1995. Policy C-467, Conservation of Natural Sites in Edmonton's Table Lands, approved by Edmonton City Council.

Because decisions are not imposed on them, developers may be willing to negotiate with the city or a land trust. The negative side is that preservation is at the discretion of the landowner/developer, although City Council ultimately approves all planning documents.

Alternatively, a mandatory preservation policy might mean that landowners would have no choice but to preserve a stand of trees on their land through the development process. However, in practice, the landowner could simply remove the trees before a planning application is made.

Lack of money for purchase of sites

Given the funding required to purchase sites in the current market, the City will not allocate enough money to acquire sites. Potential sources of funds include the City, the Province (through grants), philanthropists, or not-for-profit organizations such as a land trust. Only the City has dedicated funds at this time (Natural Area Reserve Funds) and those funds were $450,000 in 2003 and $500,000 in 2004.

No conservation co-ordinator office until recently

Policy C-467 references the importance of a conservation co-ordinator to organize internal and external efforts to save natural areas. Before the appointment of a conservation co-ordinator, there was a lack of cohesion internally in terms of providing a common city voice to site preservation and there was no formal mechanism to work with environmental non-governmental organizations (ENGOs) like the Sierra Club, Edmonton Natural History Club, or private sector organizations like the Urban Development Institute to develop proactive approaches to issues or sites.

Unco-ordinated public involvement

Citizens are typically aware of the threats to local sites. ENGOs like the Edmonton Natural History Club usually do not focus on broad policy issues. Each ENGO has its own mandate, is volunteer run, and often has insufficient resources to undertake this broader co-ordinating function. Consequently, public input has come too late in the process. Quite often that input is limited to a relatively small number of very dedicated and highly qualified volunteers. Unfortunately, proffered solutions can have major financial implications on others.

Past Protection Policy Implementation

Despite past successes in conserving sites, the net result of the preceding challenges was a reactive rather than proactive approach. This meant that conservation of sites was generally left to be addressed within the development process long after area structure plans and neighbourhood structure plans were approved. These plans most often did not identify sites to be protected since many of these plans were approved under C-467 which was passed in 1995. The public articulation of that dilemma included:

- ENGOs publicly criticizing developers and City Council for not conserving sites,
- Developers' approval timelines were extended as the city administration attempted to find ways to save sites. The development industry lost profits because of these delays,
- Citizens often were largely unaware of attempts to save sites until development occurred on these sites. Once it was known the site was to be lost, some felt betrayed by the development process,
- City Council members became involved in divisive arguments; other council business suffered.

The end result was that more sites than necessary may have been lost to development. An example was the Little Mountain Natural Area which was a 15 ha treed area.

As we look forward, it is important that we build on the foundation already in place. In the early 1990's, there was no policy framework to protect natural areas. The development of Policy C-467 spearheaded by Planning and Development included substantial dialogue with both the Urban Development Institute and ENGOs. Some sites have been saved by the private sector (Kinokamau Lake), by city action (Falconer Kettles in SE Edmonton), by community action (Graunke Park) and by assistance provided by the Province (Poplar Lake). It is now time to expand the effort to develop a much more co-ordinated multi-pronged effort to save more sites.

Future Protection Policy Implementation: Policy C467 and the 2001 Conservation Initiative

The Conserving Edmonton's Natural Areas document identified a number of initiatives that would see enhanced co-operation and planning among stakeholders (Westworth 2001). The key initiatives proposed in the report, and their status, are summarized below.

- The establishment of a community driven land trust. The land trust would give more options to landowners interested in conserving all or a portion of a property. It would also provide another way of fund raising to acquire sites through purchase. Secure financial support is necessary for the land trust.

  Status: *To date, there have been discussions among various interested parties around the formation of a land trust, but a land trust has not yet been established.*

- The appointment of a conservation co-ordinator by the City to work within the city organization and with external groups interested in conservation.

Westworth Environmental Associates. 2001. Conserving Edmonton's Natural Areas; A Framework for Conservation Planning in an Urban Landscape. Co-sponsored by the Alberta Environmental Network Society and the City of Edmonton.

Status: *A full time conservation co-ordinator has been hired and is actively working to save sites. Efforts to date have seen the development of guidelines for management plans, an atlas of natural areas, working with the administration to find ways to conserve sites, and the establishment of a governance model for the position.*

- The establishment of legacy leaders. These private sector partners would provide leadership and funding of initiatives and staff for a five year period.

  Status: *This was to be a community driven initiative and has not occurred because there is no focal point for the community initiatives at this time (no land trust organization).*

- The development of promotional materials to educate and encourage conservation activities, including the development of a book celebrating Edmonton's natural history.

  Status: *The office of the conservation co-ordinator is producing an atlas of natural sites. This was to be a community driven initiative.*

- A landowner outreach program to begin a dialogue with landowners around the benefits and value of conserving natural sites. This would be an educational program and could sow the seeds for future conservation arrangements if desired by landowners.

  Status: *The city has not initiated to date a broad based landowner outreach program.*

- Continue to use existing development process tools, such as municipal reserve, environmental reserve, public utility lots, etc. to best conservation advantage. In the development process, the city ultimately places a land-use classification on each parcel of land. Land will be designated for housing, commercial, parks, etc. In a new area the city can save a natural area using different kinds of tools. A water body, if used as a stormwater lake, can be designated a public utility lot. A tree stand can be taken as municipal reserve and dedicated as a park. Unstable land, be that ravine or river valley lands, can be designated as environmental reserve to perform a park-like function.

Status: *The city continues to use available tools, although this does not mean that all sites or all portions of sites have been conserved.*

- The development of a partnership protocol among ENGOs, city, and urban development industries. This protocol would discuss how the major players will cooperate and interact with the media.

  Status: *No partnership protocol exists today, in part because there is no land trust organization to participate. The city has on-going informed discussions with the development industry through the Urban Development Institute/General Managers Committee to resolve broader level conflicts, but is not specifically related to the natural areas planning issue. No funding to develop the protocol has been acquired.*

- Of the approximately 60 sites remaining on the original inventory of sites (Geowest 1995, Westworth 2001), a short list of 13 sites needing immediate conservation action is under consideration. Action was defined as meeting with landowners, determining their interest in conservation, and identifying options for them. The remaining 47 sites were considered important as well and all existing development process tools (municipal reserves, ecological reserves, etc.) should be used to conserve them.

  Status: *A large portion of one of the listed 13 sites has been acquired. The city and ENGOs continue to look for opportunities to save other sites as well. However, a broad based initiative has not occurred.*

Geowest. 1993. Inventory of Environmentally Sensitive and Significant Natural Areas, 1993, City of Edmonton. (Note this report was updated in 1995 and 1999).

Westworth Environmental Associates. 2001. Conserving Edmonton's Natural Areas; A Framework for Conservation Planning in an Urban Landscape. Co-sponsored by the Alberta Environmental Network Society and the City of Edmonton.

- A request for a five year approximately $2M dollar commitment from city council for natural area acquisition.
  Status: *The annual city contribution was $150,000 in the 1990s, $250,000 in the early 2000s and has risen to $450,000 (2003) and $500,000 (2004). The figure is reviewed annually through the capital budget process.*
- The development of a green spaces master plan. This plan would ensure, among other things, that there is a policy framework that includes the use of municipal reserve dedication to save natural sites.
  Status: *The city is developing the urban parks management plan that will look at the potential to create a green space master plan in some form. In addition, rules regarding the use of municipal reserve are also being revisited to reflect and include natural area preservation.*
- Development of a smart growth vision that includes what the city should look like in the long term.
  Status: *The city already has in place direction in a number of sources (Plan Edmonton, Integrated Services Strategy, Environmental Strategic Plan, etc.) that speaks to what the city may look like in the future and what it may include.*
- Development of an integrated fund development approach with the River Valley Alliance to promote retention of natural sites inside and outside the river valley.
  Status: *This city initiative has been acted upon to the extent that the alliance and City regularly communicate on strategies and initiatives. The City is part of the River Valley Alliance. The city seeks to ensure no counterproductive initiatives have occurred.*
- Development of detailed site inventories.
  Status: *Detailed site inventories continue to be provided*

City of Edmonton Community Services Department, May 2003. Urban Parks Management Plan. Acquisition, Construction, Preservation, and Animation, Municipal Practices Review. Internal working paper.

through the development process by the development industry.
No single comprehensive city-wide site inventory has occurred.

- Development of a corporate steering committee to review how current practices impact natural areas planning, and how the city might collectively change processes as appropriate.
  Status: *As part of the governance model for the office of the conservation officer, an internal corporate steering committee is operational. In addition, a council appointed natural areas committee has been appointed which advises the administration.*

- Undertake promotional events like natural heritage day/week on an annual basis to promote natural area preservation.
  Status: *This initiative has not been acted upon.*

- Sponsor an urban conservation award as part of the Emerald Award program to celebrate community or industry initiatives.
  Status: *This initiative has not been acted upon.*

- Undertake a benchmark attitude survey on land conservation and nature appreciation activities that provides statistically valid data.
  Status: *The urban parks management plan undertook a community consultation plan that looked at, among other things, the community's interest in natural landscaped type environments. That study indicated that the community would like to see a blend of natural landscapes and manicured type spaces (sports fields, sliding hills, etc.). Historically our park spaces have been more manicured than natural outside the river valley.*

City Council subsequently accepted the Conserving Edmonton's Natural Areas report as information on September 11, 2001. The recommendations were action items for both the community and administration. It should be noted that city support of some of those items was in keeping with the spirit of the recommendation but how the city would action them might be different than the recommendation proposed. For example, in dealing with the recommendation around action on the 13 sites, the city accepted the notion that the 13 sites could be considered, but that other sites could also be chosen for other reasons.

Future Timelines and Responsibilities

As we move forward, it is important to remember that this is an evolving initiative fraught with many challenges as well as opportunities. There is no particular timeline associated with the initiatives identified in the Westworth report, although all sides agree more concerted and co-ordinated action is necessary, and time is of the essence. The Office of the Conservation Co-ordinator will play a key role, however, time is limited given the wide mandate. The development of the community driven land trust organization will be the ultimate barometer of our collective success or failure. Without such an organization in place, alternative land options for landowners will be limited and land acquisition funding will be grossly inadequate. Clearly this is a situation where all players must be in the game and contributing for us to achieve any level of success.

Acknowledgements

This paper is partly based on (Westworth 2001) that was guided by a steering committee made up of Barry Breau (AEN), Lindsay Kelly (Urban Development Institute), Patsy Cotterill (Edmonton Natural History Club), John Wood (King's University College), Charles Richmond (citizen) and myself. The authors of this document were employees of the consultants: Westworth Associates Environmental, Dagny Partnership, IPS Consulting, Land Stewardship Centre, and Environmental Law Centre. Funding for the project was received from Alberta Lotteries.

Conservation Status of Strathcona County: Options for Private Landowners

Locke Girvan, Strathcona County

Abstract

Strathcona County has a wealth of natural landscapes and wildlife resources. The County places value on these resources and has expressed a desire to minimize the effect of development and subdivision. The Municipal Government Act gives limited opportunities to protect wetland and upland habitats through the dedication of municipal and environmental reserves. The restrictions on the amount of land dedicated under the Act, however, may be inadequate to maintain even the minimum ecological functions of these habitats (e.g. wildlife habitat, wildlife corridors, water quality enhancement). Municipal jurisdiction should consider other mechanisms for the conservation of natural landscapes and wildlife resources, particularly conservation easements. Providing incentives through the subdivision and development process can encourage a greater level of conservation applied to land where protection is justified for ecological reasons.

Introduction

Strathcona County is located within the transition between two natural regions, the boreal forest and the parkland. Generally soils in the parkland region are chernozems and in the boreal forest region are luvisols. Over 40% of Strathcona County, 47,805.6 ha, supports upland and wetland habitat; much of this is fragmented and/or isolated by lack of connectivity. Wetland resources cover 20,072 ha (17% of Strathcona County), including 7 permanent creeks, 15 named lakes, and 1 river.

The natural area resources of the area include:

- Environmentally Sensitive Areas – Infotech Services and Associates (1989) identified 40 environmentally sensitive areas in Strathcona County.
- Elk Island National Park – Federal park set aside in 1906, "to the people of Canada for their benefit, education and enjoyment ... to be maintained and made use of so as to leave them unimpaired for future generations." (Cool *et al.* 1999)
- Cooking Lake – Blackfoot grazing, wildlife and provincial recreation area – turned over to the Province in 1931, "to maximize grazing through intensive pasture management, to protect wildlife populations, and to provide a variety of outdoor educational and recreational pursuits." (Alberta Environmental Protection 1997)
- Ministik Lake Gamebird Sanctuary – Provincial bird sanctuary designated in 1911, for "the conservation of its wildlife resources, ecological values and for the benefit of future Albertans." (Alberta Environmental Protection 1998).
- Cooking Lake moraine – Southern extension of the boreal ecosystem into the parkland natural region. This area forms a macro-corridor for wildlife migration. There is concern for

InfoTech Services and Associates. 1989. Environmentally sensitive areas: County of Strathcona and M.D. of Sturgeon. Edmonton Metropolitan Regional Planning Commission, Edmonton. AB. 216 pp with maps.

Cool, N, K Brunner, R Chapman, B Fisher, K Green, R Kaye, R Larson, B McDougall, T Neufeld, W Olson, S Otway and L Walton. 1999. Elk Island National Park ecosystem conservation plan. Elk Island National Park, AB. 47 pp with appendices.

Alberta Environmental Protection. 1997. Cooking lake – Blackfoot grazing, wildlife and provincial recreation area management plan. Blackfoot Provincial Recreation Area, AB. 44 pp.

Alberta Environmental Protection. 1998. Ministik lake gamebird sanctuary wildlife management plan implementation strategy. Edmonton, AB. 13 pp with appendices.

fragmentation of connective links between, and in close proximity to, federal and provincial land resources.

The Community

Environmental protection and development activities are often in conflict. Economics and material culture motivate development often at the expense of the environment, individuals and community. Strathcona County's Outdoor Master Plan (1987) and Strathcona Tomorrow Report (1992) are strategic planning documents that involved extensive public input and reflect the community sentiment. Both documents express common recommendations to balance land-use planning with environmental enhancement, conservation and protection as a means of sustainability and to preserve the quality of life within the municipality. The Engineering and Environmental Planning Department's mandate is to identify potential environmental and community needs, and provide information to the approving authority on how these needs can be met. Prioritized Landscape Ecology Assessment (PLEA) 1997, a habitat based assessment, is used in the planning process to determine the relative significance of habitat units in the context of landscape ecology and conservation biology concepts.

Development Activity

The Municipal Development Plan (MDP) is an overall policy document for orderly development within a municipality. Strathcona County has sustained a high level of development and subdivision pressure in response to regional economic conditions over the past few years (Table 1).

Strathcona County. 1987. Outdoor master plan. Strathcona County, AB. 248 pp.

Strathcona County. 1992. Strathcona tomorrow executive summary project report. Strathcona County, AB. 43 pp with appendices.

Table 1

Numbers of subdivisions and developments approved by Strathcona County in recent years

| Year | Approvals | |
	Subdivision	Development
1997	83	1401
1998	100	1629
1999	99	1713
2000	85	1642
2001	72	1302

Mechanisms for Protected Areas

Land dedication

The Municipal Government Act (MGA) (Province of Alberta 1997), gives municipalities a limited opportunity to require the dedication of land for public utility lots and municipal and environmental reserves during the subdivision process. Dedication of land is without compensation and is taken within a framework of conditions outlined in the MGA and MDP based on municipal and community needs and environmental factors. This mechanism can be used to protect environmentally important elements of the landscape, but this is limited in the context that habitat and other landscape elements often cross property and jurisdictional boundaries. Weaknesses include the view by individual landowners that this is a land grab by government, the loss of municipal tax revenue, and the burden to the municipality for maintenance, enforcement, and liability. The mechanism also increases public access and therefore risk of negative impacts to the reserve or adjacent private property. Strathcona County currently manages 1795 properties made up of 5682 ha.

Province of Alberta. 1997. Municipal Government Act. Queen's Printer for Alberta. Edmonton, AB. 336 pp.

Municipal reserves

The strengths of this approach are that it provides land for a broad spectrum of municipal purposes (e.g. schools, recreation, buffers) and can be used to conserve wildlife habitat. The weaknesses are that dedication is limited to a maximum of 10% of the net amount of land considered for development and subdivisions of 16 ha or less. This has the potential to become a source of conflict between different interest groups.

Environmental reserves

The values of these reserves are that they maintain watercourses and their function, prevent development in hazardous lands, can be used to conserve wildlife habitat, and land dedicated as environmental reserve must remain in its natural state. There are several weaknesses. While the name infers land is dedicated for environmental protection, its purpose appears to be for the prevention of adverse affects to human habitation as a result of environmental factors. Under the MGA land can only be claimed as environmental reserve if it consists of a swamp, gully, ravine, coulee or natural drainage course; land that is subject to flooding or is, in the opinion of the subdivision authority, unstable; or a strip of land not less than 6 m in width, abutting the bed and shore of any lake, river, stream or other body of water for the purpose of preventing pollution, or providing public access to and beside the bed and shore. The environmental reserve cannot be used to protect lands other than as specified in the Act.

Public utility lots

This designation is applied to lands for walkways, utility corridors, and stormwater retention facilities but can be used to help conserve natural wetlands when they form part of a storm water management facility.

Conservation easements

The Environmental Protection and Enhancement Act was amended in September 1996 to allow the use of conservation easements for environmental enhancement, conservation and protection. Dedication of the easement must be voluntary; however, if municipalities, through their bylaws, require conservation/protection of natural features it can be a mechanism for a landowner. Strathcona County has adopted two incentive-based approaches to landowners wishing to subdivide lands that contain environmentally sensitive areas or important wildlife habitat to dedicate conservation easements. The first incentive is conservation easements in lieu of reserve. One acre of the municipal reserve owing may be waived for each three acres of land dedicated for conservation purposes The second incentive is related to density of housing: one additional lot, above the base density of 50 lots per 65 ha, may be approved for each three acres of land dedicated for conservation purposes.

In Strathcona County 44 easements have been registered conserving 486 ha and 13 are pending. In most instances landowners' needs, municipal interests and community values have been met through the use of conservation easements.

The strength of the easement is that the right of land ownership is not given up and only certain rights are relinquished. Landowners have direct input into how the land under a conservation easement property will be used in the future when their interest in the land is passed on to subsequent landowners. A landowner, as a member of

Province of Alberta. 1996. Environmental protection and enhancement act. Queen's Printer for Alberta. Edmonton, AB. 161 pp.

Strathcona County. 1998. Strathcona county municipal development plan bylaw 38-98. Strathcona County, AB.

a larger community, has an opportunity to help maintain rural landscape characteristics including vegetation, wildlife, aesthetics, and other features, which add to the quality of life and attract people to live in a rural environment. The easement can be applied in perpetuity affording a level of permanence similar to that of reserves. The landowner choosing this alternative does so on a voluntary basis, and thus may be eligible for a tax credit as a gift to the Crown. The procedure can be less costly to the landowner for survey requirements if achieved through descriptive plan and, at most, the same as for reserve dedication. There are other values to the municipality. The amount of land can exceed that taken under reserve dedication, the municipality retains the land-related tax base, and the municipality does not incur the cost of maintenance and enforcement. Agreements can be designed on a site specific basis to address landowner needs and can be applied to all levels of subdivision except urban.

Easements have some limitations. Voluntary dedication does not allow approval authorities to impose conservation easements as a condition of subdivision and some members of the community will not be satisfied with any mechanism which takes away or restricts their land and how they use it. There may be inconsistency between MGA and Alberta Environmental Protection and Enhancement Act easement provisions. Landowners, the legal sectors, and real estate sectors may lack understanding and may distrust government processes. Changes to Alberta's municipal tax system do not recognize conservation lands as a tax category. Also, the recent change to a market value based assessment for lands not used for agriculture has created an incentive for rural landowners to alter or remove natural landscape features to gain the benefit of the productivity based assessment afforded agricultural land and thus lower property taxes.

Other mechanisms that could be used include:

Land purchase – very expensive, generally not offered at undeveloped price but development price,

Restrictive covenants – expensive, very legalistic, needs a dominant tenement benefiting from a servient tenement,

Environmental reserve easement – applied under the same conditions as environmental reserve but the land must remain in a natural state, therefore there are fewer options for use.

Further Reading

Saxena, A, M Sherrington and J Bentz. 1997. Prioritized landscape ecology assessment of Strathcona County. Strathcona County, AB. 131 pp with appendices and maps.

Natural Processes and Urban Form: Can a Modern City Support Healthy Ecological Functions?

Bernard Amell, Earth Tech Calgary

Abstract

Citizens commonly consider many of the tangibles and intangibles as they make decisions in purchasing a home and in planning their recreational activities. The significance of nature in the city is not simply an issue for the environmental elite. Most modern municipal plans and policies express environmental values, but there is a moderate to negligible realization of them as development plans are designed and implemented.

Stormwater Pond in the City of Calgary is used as an example to describe a cluster of systemic, political, and marketing forces that can result in resistance to the effective integration of natural processes into a new development. Citizen apathy and cynicism about municipal planning and politics can easily develop. The best laid plans can be completely curtailed or reversed by these forces that include bureaucratic kingdom building, professional turf wars, environmental elitism, the dominance of short-term economic and political considerations over long-term, regulatory preference for the tangible/measurable, and the mediocraticizing effect of advocacy style debate. Strategies for counteracting these forces are addressed.

Introduction

Whether a modern city can support healthy ecological functions is examined by Spirn (1985) and Hough (1995). McHarg's (1992) work on the city of Woodland, Texas, is now over 25 years old and still valid. Arendt (Arendt and Harper 1996, Arendt *et al.* 2001) is innovative in environmental planning and restoration and landscape invention for more ecological protection (Baldwin *et al.* 1994). The knowledge and vision for innovative environmental planning are not missing.

While there are many design opportunities for natural areas to be integrated into subdivisions, and home purchasers, developers and marketers value native areas highly, there seems to be numerous barriers to increased incorporation of natural processes into suburban development. Most of these barriers are social rather than technical.

For example, one of southwest Calgary's new communities is built immediately adjacent to a highly valued trout habitat in the Bow River. Every advertisement for the area includes some mention of this amenity, yet this development has Calgary's largest outflow that discharges untreated storm water directly into the river.

It is tempting to think that consultants, developers and marketers are engaged in cynical subterfuge, but it is only when the public places a high priority on including more nature in their cities that we will witness real progress in protecting the environment.

Spirn, A W. 1985. The granite garden: urban nature and human design. Basic Books, New York, NY. 334 pp.

Hough, M. 1995. Cities and natural processes. Routledge, New York, NY. 292 pp.

McHarg, I L. 1992. Design with nature. The Natural History Press, New York, NY. 197 pp.

Arendt, R G and H Harper. 1996. Conservation design for subdivisions: a practical guide to creating open space networks. Island Press, Washington, DC. 203 pp.

Arendt, R G, M Clarke, A Hutchinson and K Foster. 2001. Growing greener ordinance language: visually enhanced zoning and subdivision models. Island Press, Washington, DC. 236 pp.

Baldwin Jr, A D, J De Luce, and C Pletsch (eds.). 1994. Beyond preservation: restoring and inventing landscapes. Minneapolis: University of Minnesota Press, Minneapolis, MN. 256 pp.

Stormwater Pond in Fish Creek Provincial Park, Calgary was designed to manage stormwater from the light rail transit south extension project right-of-way. The pond removes the sediment load and the water flows into an oxbow of Fish Creek (photo by B Amell).

Stormwater Pond in Calgary is an example of a small pond with a riparian wetland fringe, located in Fish Creek Provincial Park. It was created as part of the 2000 light rail transit south extension project and was designed to manage storm water from the right-of-way, as well as to serve as a retrofit system to treat water from existing suburbs. The new pond system removes the sediment load and the water overflows into an old oxbow with tree and shrub species that respond well to inundation. The result is that the filtered water becomes a groundwater source for the Creek, while enhancing wildlife habitat, aesthetics, and recreation.

Resistance to Change: Bureaucratic Turf Wars

It is easy to criticize bureaucrats and there is a widely held view that bureaucracies become insular and autocratic over time. But in the Stormwater Pond example both civic and provincial managers showed a willingness to work together beyond maintaining the status quo.

Recommendations

- Pursue multiple value plans and distribute plans to each bureaucracy in ways that are attuned to its specific issues and decision history. Avoid values with design features that are irrelevant to the agency.
- Give a conceptual plan to a specific person in each agency and allow them time to champion within their agency.
- Encourage understanding of the available planning choices. A veto approach can disarm creativity and force others into a defensive mode.
- Create collaborative interdepartmental review teams or project steering committees with real influence over decisions.
- Celebrate successes arising from collaboration between civic departments and agencies and among the public sector, private sector, and nonprofit organizations.
- Recognize, in the media, public agency personnel who embrace innovation.

Professional Turf Wars

Equally dangerous, but perhaps less visible, are other turf wars among professions in specialized disciplines. For example, the engineering profession can be pitted against biologists, landscape architects and others; there is no profession that is immune to this tendency. This conflict leads to a patched together plan that overlooks a synergistic designed opportunity that might be identified. In the example given above the hydrologist could have insisted on excluding design components for which there were insufficient data to run a computer model. This would have precluded the infiltration portion of the design that was of particular interest to the environmental designer.

Recommendations
- Allow each professional to express concerns early enough that the design outcome can be modified. Hopefully, an effective collaborative team will be open to design concepts from any source.
- For open and effective dialogue, professionals must learn to minimize the use of jargon from their field and from other fields.
- Seek willing collaborators before the project begins so that the plan will be developed in an interdisciplinary manner.
- Be conscious of building trust, sharing responsibility, and sharing credit for successful outcomes.

Land-Use Zoning

One of the most entrenched tools of urban planning is land-use zoning. With respect to environmental design, land-use planning has some severe limitations since natural processes and dynamic forces do not respect such arbitrary boundaries. In fact most natural processes operate along gradients and permeable boundaries rather than discrete ecosites. If a land-use zoning approach had been taken in our project example, the area might have been zoned ecological reserve and the storm water facility might have been considered only for public utility lot zoning. This may well have caused approval delays to the point that the project would not have been successful. Land-use zoning is unlikely to be replaced, since it offers a measure of assurance of development patterns and densities that have long been accepted by agencies responsible for infrastructure.

Recommendations

- Consider planning techniques beyond standard land-use bylaws, such as those proposed by Arendt and Harper (1996) and Arendt *et al.* (2001) and others.
- Interdisciplinary planning review teams could be given more latitude in influencing special case aspects of proposed land developments.
- The description of appropriate uses within each development district could be left more general and therefore more discretionary.
- There could be a composite land-use zoning, so that in our example the open water areas of the storm water storage facility could be given a public utility lot designation and the vegetated and upland areas could be given an ecological reserve designation.

Tangible Versus Intangible Considerations

There is a tendency for managers of regulatory approvals to be rather pragmatic in their outlook. Regulators tend to give preferential consideration to the tangible effects of the plan, such as long-term maintenance and risk management, while neglecting consideration of intangible factors such as education value and aesthetics. In our example, a pragmatic ruling might have led to a small pond and wetland and that no significant sized trees be removed. The result would have been an abrupt and unnatural shoreline shape and a gradient that would have diminished the aesthetic value and the wildlife habitat potential.

Recommendations

- Do not describe in detail the intangible values.
- Recognize that no draft plan will suit all audiences.
- Leave discussions about beauty and other intangible values until the project is a success.
- Be prepared to give costs for each item of your proposal.
- When describing aesthetic, environmental, and recreational amenity values to developers and other business people, be prepared with marketing and cost/benefit data.

Short-Term versus Long-Term Planning

Politicians and land developers measure success in time frames that are resolutely short-term, while ecological processes have much longer time scales. From an environmental conservation point-of-view we should recognize that there are players who take the long-term view. These include bureaucratic departments and agencies and also many nonprofit and citizen adviser groups. This could be the basis for a strategic alliance among public agencies and citizen based groups. Unfortunately, one more often sees the gulf of misunderstanding among these groups.

Recommendations

- Urban ecology activists should recognize the potential for collaboration with individuals in public agencies.
- Seek out politicians who have a long-term view and larger interests than the day-to-day issues.
- Ensure that the first stages of an urban ecology project generate some immediate and highly visible successes. This may require staging events for the media allowing local politicians to be visible and praising bureaucrats who were involved. This is

simply a necessity to counteract the dominance of short-term issues that so often put ecological issues on the sidelines.

- For public projects, advocate lifecycle cost analysis of all construction and mitigation components (Brown *et al.* 1991, Brown and Kane 1994, Hawken *et al.* 1999). A long-term economic view is often more likely to be congruent with ecological processes. These changes require some creative economic thought and advocacy and may require players including chartered accountants, investment advisers, lawyers, and other professionals.

Advocacy Breeds Mediocrity In Planning

We have a system of city planning that is based on the judicial model; opposing interests argue their cases before City Council or a planning commission, who decide on the best outcome. An assumption of this advocacy system is that there is equity of the opposing interests, but the urban ecology activists often struggle because of the financial imbalance between developers and nonprofit groups. Lacking financial resources, environmental interest groups often serve as their own advocates and rely on a combative stance and media attention. The advocacy system begins with an assumption of irreconcilable conflict and, using these approaches, environmentalists have won some battles. In adjudicating, the planning commission is often put into the position of striking a balance that rarely identifies absolute winners and losers. This art of compromise often results in the approval of projects that are suboptimal for all concerned. This can be called mediocratization. The process of review also consumes fees and time in a troublingly unpredictable way. Had this advocacy battle risen in our example project, the effort and potential for poor publicity could have preempted the design altogether.

Brown, L, C Flavin, and S Postel. 1991. Saving the planet: how to shape an environmental sustainable global economy. World Watch Institute, Washington, DC. 224 pp. http://www.worldwatch.org.

Brown, L and H Kane. 1994 Full house: reassessing the earth's population carrying capacity. World Watch Institute, Washington, DC 250 pp.

Hawken, P, A Lovins, and L Lovins. 1999. Natural capitalism: creating the next industrial revolution. Little, Brown. 416 pp. http://www.rmi.org.

Recommendations

- Become familiar with examples of successful alternative approaches.
- Discuss potential projects widely with local citizens, public agencies, service groups, and other potential stakeholders early enough to obtain real input and not just public lip service. This can deflect potential adversarial attitudes and community members can become local advocates of urban ecology initiatives.

Arcadian Beauty Versus Ecology

The term Arcadian beauty refers to the landscape aesthetic that we inherited directly from the development and underlying themes of European urban parks and estates. It is the vision of a green and pleasant landscape where nature is neat and contained, with songbirds and flowers. This inherited attitude can be a significant problem for urban ecology initiatives because ground squirrels, wasps, and mosquitoes are components of self-sustaining and diverse natural landscapes. In our project example there is a high-value condominium project directly overlooking Stormwater Pond. Fortunately, this naturalization project did not receive citizen criticisms that could have canceled the project.

Recommendations

- Give the natural landscape a clear and logical edge, but include some manicured landscapes near residences.
- Offer nature walks, write newspaper articles, host children's classes outside, and think of other ways that celebrate the spontaneous beauty and the seasonal changes offered by natural areas.
- Offer to take concerned people to developments similar to what is envisaged.

- Encourage good maintenance of trails in natural areas so that people will have positive experiences.
- Promote philosophies that promote some degree of randomness and decay. The Japanese aesthetic of Wabi-Sabi is one example (Koren 1994, Juniper 2003).
- Be patient. The philosophy of Arcadian beauty may diminish as people become increasingly more interested in path-oriented recreation, wildlife viewing, exercise, and health.

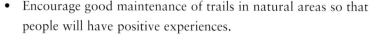

Koren, L. 1994. Wabi-Sabi: for Artists, Designers, Poets and Philosophers. Stone Bridge Press, Albany, CA. 96 pp.

Juniper, A. 2003. Wabi Sabi. The Japanese art of impermanence. Tuttle Publishing, Boston, MA. 176 pp.

Neveh, Z and A Lieberman. 1984. Landscape ecology: theory and application. Springer-Verlag, Berlin and Heidelberg Gmbh and Co. KG. 400 pp.

Wilderness Ethic and Environmental Elitism

Wilderness ethic is an extreme aesthetic shared by the most committed environmental activists. This is based on a reverence for nature that is unaffected by human forces; the vision excludes humans from the landscape and opposes intervention in natural processes. This philosophy may be appropriate on extensive landscapes that still have intact ecosystems, but application to urban natural areas ensures conflict. For example, if activist groups oppose the development of upgraded paths, the expanding network of trails may lead to excessive erosion. One cannot ignore the pervasive influence of humans on urban natural areas; there are too many people, domestic animals, and escaped garden plants. Open spaces are too precious and preserved at too great a cost to justify fencing people out. Given this reality, the wilderness ethic must be tempered to accommodate appropriate management activities.

Instead of attempting to identify the pristine conditions by such approaches as the listing of the number of native species, a more appropriate approach might focus on the restoration of self-sustaining natural processes such as energy flow, nutrient cycling, succession patterns and movement of plants and animals. This work has been explored in numerous writings on cultural landscape ecology (Neveh and Lieberman 1984).

334

There exists a wide constituency that is beginning to connect urban nature with their personal quality of life. We should be making such people partners in our efforts. Generating dialogue and facilitating many more urban ecology initiatives will occur if such people become partners in our efforts.

An Alternative Development Strategy to Protect Conservation Features in the Rural-Urban Fringe

Geoff S. Abma, Master of Environmental Design Student, University of Calgary

Abstract

Canada's population has more than doubled since 1950, growing from 13.7 million to over 30 million by 2000. Canadian cities are experiencing significant growth pressures as more than 78% of these people live within urban regions (United Nations Secretariat 2003). Urban development is inevitable and the present development models are detrimental to some of the natural features of the landscape that citizens appreciate. Economic analyses suggest that the models are also unsustainable in terms of long-term infrastructure replacement. Alternative development models and implementation frameworks are needed that will provide effective opportunities to ensure that ecologically viable natural areas are included in human development landscapes. Various mechanisms including business revitalization zones, preferential tax credits, transfer of development rights, protective zoning, and landowner

United Nations Secretariat. 2003. World population prospects: the 2002 population revision database. Accessed July 30, 2003. http://esa.un.org/unpp/.

compacts when creatively integrated can provide these opportunities to new suburbs.

Introduction

Suburbanization is the present and dominant development model in most North American cities. It is characterized by development dedicated to single land-uses of a low-density nature. This form of urban development utilizes large amounts of land, expensive infrastructure, and engenders a heavy dependence on the automobile as the primary means of transportation. Duany *et al.* (2000) describes suburban form in terms of its five segregating components. First, suburban housing developments are single-use areas consisting solely of single-family detached homes of a single economic class. Second, shopping areas are single-use areas separated from housing subdivisions, generally with low-rise buildings and an expanse of auto parking between the building and the roadway. Third, office and industrial areas are set aside solely as work environments, typically a building or collection of buildings surrounded by parking lots. Fourth, civic institutions in suburban areas are large, widely spaced, unadorned, infrequent and surrounded by significant amounts of parking. In contrast, older, traditional areas contain civic institutions that serve as neighbourhood focal points and monuments to the community. The fifth element of suburban form is the expensive and extensive networks of high-speed roads needed to connect the other four disassociated components.

Most cities today expand into landscapes that have long been converted from natural areas to agricultural land and more recently acreages. Any native ecosystems that remain have been heavily modified and fragmented; these ecosystems are found largely along wetlands, streams and rivers. The conventional suburban development process requires that most natural areas are removed or

Duany, A, E Plater-Zyberk, and J Speck. 2000. Suburban nation: the rise of sprawl and the decline of the American dream. North Point Press, New York, NY. 320 pp.

Much of the upland area around Edmonton was converted from natural vegetation (much biodiversity) to agriculture (less biodiversity). With conversion to suburbs (very low biodiversity) the economic benefits from local agriculture crops and farmers' markets is lost (photo by Ross W Wein, 2002).

filled-in to make way for construction. Natural areas that remain tend to be small and isolated from other natural areas. Some wetlands may be modified and incorporated as civic infrastructure, such as water retention ponds. More commonly, natural areas are replaced by other green spaces such as conventional parks, golf courses, or human-made lakes. A significant point is that once the subdivision is built there is little or no flexibility for future land-use changes such as introducing natural systems.

Problems with the Present Development Model

Suburban communities significantly diverge from the natural model of ecological functioning. Natural ecological systems are self-sufficient and comprised of cyclical processes whereas suburban systems displace nutrient cycles with linear human-controlled systems and consume massive amounts of energy and resources (White 1998). Sustainability implies that natural capital, any stock of natural assets that yields a flow of valuable goods and services into the future, should be used no more rapidly than it can be replenished. Replenishment of natural capital depends on the maintenance of the organizational integrity of the earth's ecosphere components, and the structural relationships between them, required for the continuous self-production and self-regulation of the ecosystems that provide these resources (Wackernagel and Rees 1996).

Under the current conventional development framework, natural or ecological capital has been reduced to simply an inventory of industrial resources for human consumption such as lumber and fossil fuels (Wackernagel and Rees 1996). Suburban residential heating/cooling and transport are the two largest consumers of fossil fuel energy and directly emit large amounts of harmful substances into the atmosphere, consuming the natural capital stock of clean air. Additionally, it is widely known that greenhouse gases have been linked to global climate change and suggests suburban form has a significant detrimental impact on the earth's climate.

The well-drained streets and civic places of suburban subdivisions are ecologically costly in terms of significant damage to terrestrial ecosystems, as well as eroding streams, flooding, eutrophication of ponds, and impairment of water quality downstream. Wetlands are often filled to make way for suburban development, changing the course and flow of water systems from meandering waterways to linear canals or underground drains. The prevention of infiltration of precipitation for groundwater recharge creates faster flows of water that contribute to sediment loading of downstream waterways. Combined with the absence of natural

White, J S. 1998. Beating plowshares into townhomes: the loss of farmland and strategies for slowing its conversion to nonagricultural uses. Environmental Law 28 (1): 113-143.

Wackernagel, M and W E Rees. 1996. Our ecological footprint: reducing human impact on the earth. New Society Publishers, Gabriola Island, BC. 176 pp.

Hough, M. 1995. Cities and natural process. Routledge, New York, NY. 292 pp.

Vojnovic, I. 1999. The environmental costs of modernism: an assessment of Canadian cities. Cities 16 (5): 301-313.

Slack, N E. 1996. Financing infrastructure: evaluation of existing research and information gaps. Canadian Mortgage and Housing Corporation, Ottawa, ON.

Freedgood, J. 2002. Cost of community services studies: making the case for conservation. American Farmland Trust, Washington, DC. 78 pp.

Daniels, T. 1999. When city and country collide: managing growth in the metropolitan fringe. Island Press, Washington, DC. 377 pp.

water purification by wetlands, concentrations of heavy metals, nutrients, suspended solids, and microorganisms are significantly higher in urban run-off than in natural streams. The removal of areas of biomass production, such as forest stands and grasslands, wipes out habitat for various plant and animal species and detrimentally impacts the trophic energy systems and the survivability of other species (Hough 1995).

The low-density, land-consumptive, and single-use of suburban development make the supply and maintenance of municipal infrastructure and services an expensive endeavor. Increased separation of land-use activities directly corresponds to an increase in municipal infrastructure and service requirements in the form of roads, water lines, sewage mains, sidewalks, etc. and operating expenditures for street cleaning, snow removal, street lighting, garbage removal, etc. (Vojnovic 1999, Slack 1996). With the majority of the $10 billion spent by governments in Canada each year on public infrastructure being provided by municipal governments, many municipalities are finding it more and more difficult to meet the increasing demand for more infrastructure at the same time as maintaining the existing infrastructure – much of which is in major need of repair (Slack 1996). According to cost of community services studies from more than 90 communities in North America, suburban residential communities cost more to municipalities than they generate in tax revenues and tend to be subsidized by commercial, industrial, farm and forest lands, and open space land-uses (Freedgood 2002).

In North America, relatively flat and well-drained agriculture tends to be the predominant land-use in the urban-rural fringe that is supplanted by suburbs because it tends to be less costly for the developer and home purchaser (Daniels 1999, Freedgood 2002). With only 11% of Canada's land mass capable of any form of agricultural use, the loss of prime agricultural land to expanding cities is significant. Of the 300,000+ ha of land converted to urban uses between 1966 and 1986 in 25 of Canada's largest cities, 58% was classified as land highly capable of agricultural production. Between 1986 and 1996 millions more acres of agricultural land were lost to other uses (Alberta Agriculture Food and Rural Development 2002). Overall, the loss of ecosystems and the loss of prime farmland to suburban development and the land-use conflict this generates, specifically in the urban-rural fringe, are some of the largest issues facing contemporary North American cities (Calthorpe and Fulton 2001).

A Revised Model Theory and Practice

An alternative long-term, sustainable development framework is needed where urban form, natural areas and agriculture can be incorporated in a development model for the benefit of citizens that includes recreation, health and education. This framework can also include new ecological infrastructure technologies that use natural areas to provide municipal infrastructure and services to urban communities such as stormwater management, wastewater remediation, and more (Van der Ryn and Cowan 1996). Unlike conventional municipal infrastructure, these technologies can partially mimic the ecological functioning of an area. Mechanisms that support the implementation of this alternative development model include the business revitalization zone (BRZ), protective zoning, preferential tax treatment, transfer of development rights, and landowner compacts.

In the rural-urban fringe, a formalized voice representing urban interests often overpowers the voices representing the interests of natural and agricultural areas. Application of the business revitalization zone concept, traditionally an inner-city development

Alberta Agriculture Food and Rural Development. 2002. Loss and fragmentation of farmland. AAFRD Resource Planning Group, Policy Secretariat, Edmonton, AB.

Calthorpe, P and W Fulton. 2001. The regional city: planning for the end of sprawl. Island Press, Washington, DC. 260 pp.

Van der Ryn, S and S Cowan. 1996. Ecological design. Island Press, Washington, DC. 216 pp.

tool, to the urban-rural fringe could provide that unified voice. Additionally, a BRZ could initiate research into the forms of conservation, recreation and agriculture that are compatible with urban development.

A major obstacle to protecting natural areas, recreation areas and prime agricultural areas is that the economic returns offered by suburban developers to landowners are far greater than for protection. Methods of allowing landowners to benefit from the increased equity of their land due to approaching development are imperative. Available opportunities can be created through the integration of preferential tax treatment, transfer of development rights, and protective zoning. A preferential tax credit program can provide benefits to the landowners of significant natural areas or enhance the viability of agricultural production. A transfer of development rights program provides a framework that purchases the development rights from landowners of natural areas and agricultural areas for use in areas designated for urban development. The natural areas and/or agricultural land are permanently protected from future development by this conservation easement. A protective zoning initiative could provide temporary protection from development until a transfer of development rights program can be fully implemented.

Another mechanism might be landowner compacts. With this mechanism, a group of landowners join together in a legal contract where their property lines are dissolved and a portion of the integrated land area is developed leaving the remainder as open-space agricultural land and natural areas. All property owners profit from the development based on the amount of land they contributed to the whole, even if the development does not occur on their property (Baetz 1994).

Baetz, B W. 1994. Creation of landowner compacts for sustainable community development. Journal of Urban Planning and Development 120(4): 174-183.

How to Make This Happen in Alberta's Cities

The implementation of an alternative development framework assumes the presence of a formal group that takes a special interest in quality of life issues in the community; an example might be a local community league. The implementation process begins with the creation of a business development zone (BDZ) to represent the conservation, recreation and agricultural voices who will promote a form of alternative development through a community-initiated process. A flow chart to the alternative development is depicted in Figure 1.

Once a business development zone (BDZ) association is created, it can commission the compilation of a land-use profile, which will provide the basis for planning alternative developments. The BDZ association could facilitate research into innovative business development opportunities. The BDZ can also assist in the creation of a community forum where stakeholder groups (may include the community league, natural conservation groups, developers, residents, and other landowners) can meet to discuss the developing plan. This forum would facilitate increased dialogue and potential co-operation. The above information can be used as a basis for a community design charette, where local stakeholders can work with design professionals to develop their alternative community-based development vision.

Based on the vision developed by the community design charette, a formal area structure plan (ASP) can be created. Integrated into this ASP would be the other mechanisms like the transfer of development rights program, preferential tax treatment, or landowner compact scenario. Once the ASP and its mechanisms are in place, private developers will then begin construction of the development, using ideas such as transit-oriented development and other mixed-use concepts, that will benefit from compatible land-uses, including natural areas.

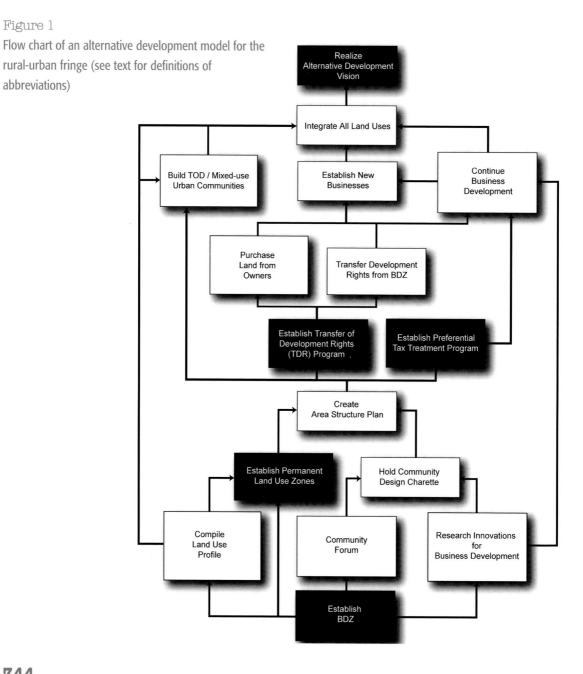

Figure 1

Flow chart of an alternative development model for the rural-urban fringe (see text for definitions of abbreviations)

The crucial elements of this implementation process are the community forum, design charette, active involvement by the municipal government, and involvement of the private development community. Private developers and construction companies are the groups primarily responsible for construction of municipal infrastructure; without their support and involvement, an alternative development vision will not be realized. The municipal government provides the zoning framework and overall direction to the development community and will most likely implement a framework conducive to alternative development if the community supports and initiates the process. Due to the considerable involvement of various stakeholder groups, creation of a process to guide alternative development is relatively free of conflict and creates win-win situations.

Conclusions

Including implementation mechanisms into a framework for the alternative development model provides opportunities to incorporate ecologically viable natural areas, recreation areas and agriculture areas into future urban development. It is clear that the current suburban development model does not provide a sustainable form of urban development nor is it one that will maintain or enhance the ecological functioning of the landscape. As Canadian cities accommodate future populations, alternative development frameworks, such as the one described here, may prove useful for incorporating networks of natural areas into future suburbs.

Acknowledgements

This work was developed as a Masters thesis at the University of Calgary (Abma 2003).

Abma, G S. 2003. An implementation framework for an agricultural business development zone: the case of Northeast Edmonton. Master's Degree Project. Faculty of Environmental Design, University of Calgary, Calgary, AB. 110 pp.

Establishing a Conservation Land Trust for the Edmonton Region

M. J. Salomons, University of Alberta

Abstract

The need for regional conservation land trusts for urban and adjacent rural areas has been recognized for some time because of growing land-use pressures. While many examples of land trusts are found across North America, there are relatively few urban-focused land trusts. Urban land trusts face a number of unique challenges, including: few and small available sites, high market value of land, low tax credit incentives, and high costs of stewardship. The available literature related to urban land trusts in Alberta, Canada, and the United States as a whole was reviewed and employees from selected trusts were interviewed to identify ideas that could be used in urban conservation land trusts and specifically for an urban land trust for the Edmonton region. Key ideas include partnership building with a wide range of stakeholders, engaging the public, seeking financial sustainability, promoting iterative planning, and program evaluation.

Introduction

In the 1800s Western Canada was characterized by large
expanses of prairie and forest with scattered populations of
Aboriginal peoples, explorers, fur traders and homesteaders.
Today, our countryside tends to be characterized more by acreage
developments, agriculture, and petroleum and forestry industries.
While much effort has gone into establishing protected areas, work
to date has mainly followed the global trend of focusing on large
and relatively untouched ecosystems located far from human
habitation (Chiesura 2004). Urban preservation of parks and open
spaces in urban areas has focused mostly on small, manicured
areas maintained as recreational spaces for residents.

A number of changes over the past two decades have
contributed towards a gradual change in urban conservation in
Alberta:

- In contrast to the largely rural populations of the past, today
  80% of Alberta's population is urban – compared to the 67%
  of the European population that lives in towns and cities
  (Chiesura, 2004).
- There has been a gradual shift from the perception of our cities
  as places apart from nature to an idea that nature can and
  should be nurtured, protected, and integrated into our urban-
  rural landscapes.
- Naturalization is emerging as a realistic landscaping alternative
  to not only residential lawns but also the parks and natural
  areas located in and around our cities.
- There has been a further expansion of municipal responsibilities
  accompanied by decreases in municipal transfer payments
  (Evergreen 2004).
- Alberta's municipalities, particularly in the Calgary-Edmonton
  corridor, are among the fastest growing in Canada.

Chiesura, A. 2004. The role of urban
parks for the sustainable city. Landscape
and Urban Planning 68: 129-138.

Evergreen. 2004. Evergreen Common
Grounds. Green Space Acquisition and
Stewardship in Canada's Urban
Municipalities: Results of a Nationwide
Survey. (available at:
http://www.evergreen.ca/).

Ryan, R and J Hansel Walker. 2004. Protecting and managing private farmland and public greenways in the urban fringe. Landscape and Urban Planning 68: 183-198.

Campbell, M C and D A Salus. 2003. Community and conservation land trusts as unlikely partners? The case of Troy Gardens, Madison, Wisconsin. Land Use Policy 20: 169-180.

Arendt, R. 1999. Growing Greener: Putting Conservation into Local Plans and Ordinances. Island Press, Washington, DC.

Greenaway, G. 2003. Conservation Easements in Alberta: Programs and Possibilities. Corvus Conservation. (available at www.corvus.ca).

Nature Conservancy of Canada. 2000. Stewardship Manual. Version 1. Nature Conservancy of Canada. (available at www.natureconservancy.ca).

- There is increased concern about loss of farmland and natural areas in and around our municipal areas.
- There is increased demand for more and better quality green space (Evergreen 2004) and public recreational space in our municipal areas (Ryan and Walker 2004).
- Public sentiment and the prevailing political climate of our times precludes large-scale government interventions (Ryan and Walker 2004) and sees private initiatives and privately owned land as vital to meeting public recreation and natural area demands.
- People have expressed dissatisfaction with the failures of public regulatory planning (Jacobs 2000, in Campbell and Salus 2003).

These changes have contributed to the growing popularity of conservation land trusts. Conservation land trusts are private, charitable organizations with the primary role of protecting land under their stewardship from undesirable change (Arendt 1999). Also known as conservation foundations or conservancies, land trusts have a century-old history in North America, with the first trust appearing in the eastern United States in 1891. The land trust concept was born out of a desire by local citizens to protect natural areas. These citizens would buy and jointly steward the open spaces they deemed critical to the quality of life in their community (Greenaway 2003). Although land trusts are usually involved in a wide variety of different activities, the three fundamental activities of land trusts are: selecting sites to conserve; securing sites by purchase, application of conservation easement or other means; and stewarding sites to ensure that they are protected in perpetuity (Nature Conservancy of Canada 2000).

Land trusts are the fastest growing segment of the conservation movement in North America today, with over 1,300 land trusts operating in the United States (http://www.lta.org), and well over 100 in Canada (http://www.uoguelph.ca/~claws). Land trusts have been successful in conserving parcels of rural and wilderness land across Canada thanks to the efforts of larger national trusts (the Nature Conservancy of Canada, Ducks Unlimited Canada), provincial trusts (The Land Conservancy of BC), and local trusts (Southern Alberta Land Trust Society).

Baker, T, Regional Manager, Lower Mainland, The Land Conservancy. 2004. Personal communication.

Challenges Facing Urban Conservation Land Trusts

In spite of the popularity and usefulness of land trusts, there are relatively few examples of urban conservation land trusts in North America. This is due in part to the trends outlined above. It is also due to some unique challenges that face conservation land trusts in urban environments.

Selecting sites that are of significant natural or environmental value is a challenge in an urban environment. The general societal perception that true nature or wilderness only occurs away from any human habitation or influence has resulted in ignoring sites in cities. For example, in Vancouver, where there is interest in protecting historic buildings within Vancouver, most conservation projects are on the periphery of the city (Baker 2004). Any natural site that is going to be conserved on a long-term basis must be of sufficient size and must be connected to other protected sites: both of these criteria can be a challenge in an urban or peri-urban setting. Finally, there is a significant amount of controversy associated with any conservation project located close to urban areas. As one individual with a long experience of working on conservation projects in Alberta noted, "In Edmonton there are, roughly speaking, two categories of people: those interested in land

Cameron, T, formerly with Alberta Sport, Recreation, Parks and Wildlife. 2004. Personal communication.

Greystone Consulting. 2004. Regional Land Trust Study – Executive Summary Phase 1: Analysis of Legal Issues, the Development of Governance Model and the Investigation of Partnerships and their Roles and Responsibilities. Prepared for the City of Calgary Parks Foundation: 2004 (available at www.landtrustproject.com).

Bennet, R, Ecological Gifts Coordinator, Environment Canada. 2004. Personal communication.

Burns, V, President, Boston Natural Areas Network. 2004. Personal communication.

speculation, and those interested in land conservation" (Cameron 2004). While this is obviously an oversimplification to make a point, it does highlight the tensions that influence urban conservation projects.

One of the main challenges to securing sites in the urban context is high land market values. Because of this, it is often a challenge to raise funds for natural area purchases, as an equivalent dollar amount can protect a much larger parcel of land in a rural or remote setting. The criteria for application of the ecological gifts program, a tool used by land trusts to increase tax benefits to land donors, are sometimes not applicable to urban natural area situations (Bennett 2004). Lands secured, either directly or indirectly, by the land trust can be subject to expropriation by a municipality under the Municipal Government Act (Greystone Consulting 2004). And finally, conservation easements are a relatively new and generally unknown tool for protecting land. As such, landowners are very cautious about applying conservation easements to their land, especially in an urban context where land values and pressures to develop are so high (Baker 2004).

There is both a need and an obligation to properly steward protected lands for the long-term. This includes developing and applying a long-term maintenance plan for the site, paying taxes and liability insurance, establishing a program of preventative maintenance, and building infrastructure (signs, fences, trails, etc.). For rural land trusts, stewardship of sites can often function adequately with volunteers. Urban lands, on the other hand, are often subject to a high level of abuse and misuse, and thus their stewardship requires a significant level of resources and time commitment (Burns 2004).

Examples of Urban Conservation Land Trusts

Even with the relatively few examples of urban conservation land trusts in North America, examples of successful management can be found.

Recommendations for Urban Conservation Land Trusts

From the examples of land trusts compiled in Table 1, there are many recommendations that are applicable to any urban land trust and certainly to a land trust tailored to the Edmonton region:

Develop and strengthen partnerships

While land trusts working in rural areas may have few stakeholders who safeguard important conservation areas, the many stakeholders of urban environments make the process more time consuming. To be successful, land trusts, and especially urban land trusts, need to value and nurture collaboration with a variety of partners (Millar 2003). This includes partnering with community groups, conservation organizations, the development community, and various levels of government.

Work at a regional level

Decisions about priorities for protection require working on a regional rather than site-specific basis (Calgary Parks Foundation 2004). Most of the environmentally significant natural areas of focus will be in the urban-fringes, and conserving these sites will necessitate working together with surrounding municipalities as well as with other local conservation groups.

Work at arms length, but in partnership with government

There are significant advantages to land trusts operating separately from government (Tarves 2004), including greater flexibility and

Millar, H. 2003. Successful Stewardship and Conservation Organizations – Case Studies and Best Practices. Commissioned Research for The Leading Edge: Stewardship & Conservation in Canada. Land Trust Alliance of BC.

Calgary Parks Foundation. 2004. Proposed Regional Land Trust: Summary of Public Input. February (available at: www.landtrustrproject.com).

Tarves, T, Senior Program Manager, Parks Foundation Calgary. 2004. Personal communication.

Table 1

Descriptions and lessons learned for North American urban conservation land trusts

Name	Description	Lessons Learned
Abbotsford Land Trust Society Web-site: www.abbotsfordlandtrust.ca	A locally based land trust working to protect important natural areas, historical and cultural sites, and other lands of community importance for the benefit of Abbotsford residents. The trust does this through the maintenance and promotion of healthy ecosystems, the development of educational programs, community outreach, and by acquiring or holding conservation easements on lands.	• Establish an arms length relationship to government: while the support of the city is important to the ongoing operation of the land trust, the close association of the two can hinder the effectiveness of the trust. • It is important to adopt land trust standards and practices (for example, those developed by the Land Trust Alliance of BC) (www.lta.org). (Fox 2004)
Habitat Acquisition Trust Website: www.hat.bc.ca	This is a regional land trust established to enhance the protection and stewardship of regionally significant lands on southern Vancouver Island and the southern Gulf Islands. The three main activities are: 1) Acquisition of significant lands; 2) Holding conservation covenants (easements); 3) Community projects aimed at environmental education and stewardship.	• Promoting land stewardship has proven to be an effective (and cost effective) tool for land conservation. • To maintain its effectiveness, while faced with the large number of conservation organizations in the Greater Victoria Area, the trust has focused its mandate and works in close partnership with other organizations and municipal governments.
The Land Conservancy of British Columbia (TLC) Website: www.conservancy.bc.ca	This trust works throughout British Columbia protecting important habitat for plants and animals in natural communities as well as properties with historical, cultural, scientific, scenic or compatible recreational value. The Land Conservancy operates in five regions, each with its own priorities based on local circumstances and opportunities.	• Factors contributing to the success of this trust include having an executive director who is highly personable and has a background in real estate and fund-raising, having some highly visible projects to attract public attention, and having an effective and dedicated board of directors.
Boston Natural Areas Network Website: www.bostonnatural.org	This trust works to make the Boston Urban Wilds (143 sites of natural beauty and environmental significance) a permanent part of a public open space network through public-park ownership.	• Support by public funds is critical to properly maintain and steward protected lands for the long-term (100 years plus); BNAN has focused on getting natural areas into public park ownership (Burns 2004). • Change focus from individual sites to a 'bundled' approach to creating corridors of green space incorporating reused industrial lands, railway lines, and existing parks.
Portland Trails Website: www.trails.org	This trust was founded in 1991 to create a 30-mile trail network within the Greater Portland Area, to serve as a public advocate for the protection of and access to natural places within the region, and to encourage the participation of neighbourhoods, schools and the business community in trail use and stewardship.	• Portland Trails has maintained a separation from government while at the same time has developed a strong partnership with government. This has maximized the flexibility of the trust, for example allowing them to own land not just within the City of Portland but also within neighbouring municipalities - thus maximizing the connectivity and use of trail systems (Cumming 2004). • Focusing on partnerships has been a key to success.

increased acceptance in the eyes of the public. At the same time, developing effective partnerships with various levels of government appears to be instrumental to success for urban-based land trusts. Collaboration with government is especially important when planning for long-term stewardship of natural areas.

Engaging the public at many levels is critical to the success of land trusts (photo by John R Wood, 2004).

Engage the public

Public awareness of conservation issues and activities is an essential component of a successful conservation and stewardship strategy (Evergreen 2004, Millar 2003, Wildlife Habitat Canada 2002), and successful organizations understand the needs of their communities and adapt their conservation priorities accordingly (Millar 2003). The support of community members is very important to leveraging public funds. An effective communication and education program is essential for developing public awareness, support, and engagement in conservation programs (Boon 1997). An important element of engaging the public is to begin protecting land, no matter how modestly, as soon as possible

Cumming, N, President, Portland Trail. 2004. Personal communication.

Wildlife Habitat Canada. 2002. Volunteer Sector Stewardship in Canada Summary Report. Wildlife Habitat Canada and the Voluntary Sector Initiative.

Boon, J. 1997. Land Trust Paper. The Land Centre: (available at: www.landcentre.ca).

Fox, L, Coordinator, Abbotsford Community Land Trust. 2004. Personal communication.

Cox, K and G Dorn. 1993. Wetlands Conservation in Canada and Saskatchewan: Lessons and Ideas to be used for Land Trust Formation. Second Interprovincial Land Trust Conference. Saskatoon, SK.

Simpson, L, Regional Director, Nature Conservancy of Canada Alberta Region. 2004. Personal communication.

Walker, D, Ontario Land Trust Alliance. 2004. Personal communication.

(Cox and Dorn 1993). Beginning organizations have a tendency to get too involved in planning, which can paralyze the organization. Success often breeds success, and success stories should be actively publicized (Baker 2004). Doing so will help to build the momentum of the organization, and will help to build the public awareness and support necessary for success.

Focus on financial sustainability

The stability of a land trust is essential for landowners to feel confident enough to donate land or easements to the organization. Perpetual protection needs to be ensured. A successful stewardship and conservation organization especially needs long-term financial stability in order to maintain its long-term programs, and to retain and train permanent staff and volunteers (Evergreen 2004, Millar 2003, Wildlife Habitat Canada 2002). This is particularly true if the organization holds any conservation easements that must be properly monitored and protected through enforcement of regulations. Financial planning for the organization therefore needs to start immediately (Cox and Dorn 1993, Millar 2003). An endowment fund to pay for staffing and to help with stewardship costs is ideal (Simpson 2004), and provides a guarantee of the long-term viability of an organization. A broad based membership with dues can also provide some of the financial stability needed for an organization. Generally, however, land trusts are involved in a substantial amount of fund raising, usually for specific projects and sometimes to help cover staffing and office costs as well. Diverse funding from a variety of sources is a strong indicator of an organization's success (Millar 2003). One group has suggested aiming for 45% of funding coming from the community, with the rest from private foundations and government sources (Walker 2004).

Keep the mandate broad, yet be focused

Unless urban conservation land trusts are set up specifically to address the conservation of a specific site or area, they should strongly consider keeping the terms of reference for the trust broad, including provisions for the protection of agricultural land, heritage buildings, recreation land, wildlife corridors, and possible other lands (Cameron 2004). Having a broad mandate attracts a broad range of interests, encourages a wide and more stable base of support, and creates a greater range of opportunity for the trust (Turner 2004). Most large urban centres have a variety of different groups working to address urban environmental issues. This can lead to a subtle form of competition between groups for the limited human resources and amount of available funding (Baker 2004). Success in this situation relies on working in conjunction with other organizations where possible. Often the best way to do this is to avoid organizational overlap by focusing mandates and by establishing mutually complementary and more specific mandates (Eliason 2004). For example, an urban land trust organization could focus heavily on selecting sites, securing sites, forming partnerships with other organizations for the stewardship of sites, and on related activities such as environmental education.

Get good advice

While there are many options available for the organizational structure of a land trust, it is very important that the governing body of the land trust have good advice on conservation priorities and practices, on business and the real estate market, and on funding and fund-raising. Finding and keeping board members or outside advisors with the expertise, skills, and willingness to assist will aid greatly in the long-term success of the trust.

Turner, B. 2004. Protecting British Columbia's Cultural Heritage: the rewards and challenges of conserving built heritage. The Kingfisher, Vol. 8, Spring: pp 1-4.

Eliason, J, Stewardship Coordinator, Habitat Acquisition Trust. 2004. Personal communication.

Develop a plan

It is essential to develop a strategic plan for the trust, along with a specific time-line and implementation schedule. This includes determining which lands to secure (site selection), how and when to secure them (site securing), and how to manage them (site stewardship). The steps in this process include conducting an inventory of sites to conserve, developing a master plan at a regional level for conservation of these sites, establishing priorities, and collecting all of the planning and legal tools available to the trust to help in the conservation of these sites.

Establish and implement a communications and education plan

A communications and education strategy is an essential element of a successful land trust. This should not be left to chance, as it is in many conservation organizations, but should be developed and implemented at the early stages of the trust. Education can be an excellent way for land trusts to meet their conservation objectives. For example, promoting good land stewardship has proven to be effective, both in terms of meeting objectives and reducing costs (Eliason 2004). Public speaking tours, the establishment of a speaker's bureau, the development of a website, and the publication of newsletters and an annual report are all tools for education.

Start protecting land as soon as possible

Once specific goals and objectives have been established, it is important to not delay in protecting land (Cox and Dorn 1993). First impressions are important, so actions should be taken immediately to build the type of image desired. This may involve doing something soon that makes it clear to others what the organization can do for the community. If at all possible, this should entail having a website prepared as soon as the land trust is launched. This will help build membership and the support of non-members in the public and in government agencies. It is also essential to building financial support for the organization, which is much easier with a successful example of the organization's work (Cummings 2004). A proactive approach should be taken in terms of land selection. Consult people dealing with land and develop partnerships using the conservation tools developed (Baker 2004).

Evaluate program effectiveness
Evaluation is not just based on the effectiveness of achieving specific conservation targets, but should also focus on how well the organization is working and on improving it. This is important not just to make programs and projects more effective, but also to demonstrate measurable outcomes to donors and constituents (Millar 2003).

Acknowledgements

Thanks go to the many individuals who provided valuable advice and background information for this paper, and Dr. Ross W. Wein, Ernie Ewaschuk and Adele Mandryk, who kindly reviewed drafts of this paper and provided valuable advice and input. Additional thanks are due to the Alberta Sport, Recreation, Parks and Wildlife Foundation who generously provided funding, and the Land Stewardship Centre of Canada, who had the vision and willingness to financially partner to undertake much of the background research for this report.

A Naturalist's Bibliography for Edmonton

Archaeology

Pyszcyk, H W. Undated. Archaeology: guide and tour of Greater Edmonton Area. Royal Alberta Museum, Edmonton, AB. 57 pp.

The Physical Environment

Godfrey, J D. 1993. Edmonton beneath our feet: a guide to the geology of the Edmonton Region. Edmonton Geological Society, Edmonton, AB. 150 pp.

Wheaton, E E. 1998. But it's a dry cold: weathering the Canadian prairies. Fifth House Ltd., Calgary, AB. 185 pp.

The Biota

Bovey, R B and E Pluciennik (illus.). 1990. Birds of Edmonton. Lone Pine Publishing, Edmonton, AB. 128 pp.

Fisher, C and J Acorn. 1998. Birds of Alberta. Lone Pine Publishing, Edmonton, AB. 384 pp.

Johnson, D, L Kershaw, A MacKinnon and J Pojar. 1995. Plants of the western boreal forest and aspen parkland. Lone Pine Publishing and the Canadian Forest Service, Edmonton, AB. 392 pp.

Joynt, A and M G Sullivan. 2003. Fish of Alberta. Lone Pine Publishing, Edmonton, AB. 176 pp.

Kershaw, L, J Gould, D Johnson and J Lancaster (eds.). 2001. Rare vascular plants of Alberta. Alberta Native Plant Council, University of Alberta Press, Edmonton, AB. 484 pp.

Nelson, J S and M J Paetz. 1992. The Fishes of Alberta. The University of Alberta Press and The University of Calgary Press, Edmonton and Calgary, AB. 437 pp.

Packer, J. 1983. Moss's Flora of Alberta. 2nd ed. University of Toronto Press, Toronto, ON. 687 pp.

Pattie, D L and C Fisher. 1999. Mammals of Alberta. Lone Pine Publishing, Edmonton, AB. 240 pp.

Russell, A P and A M Bauer. 1993. The amphibians and reptiles of Alberta: a field guide and primer of boreal herpetology. The University of Calgary Press and The University of Alberta Press, Calgary and Edmonton, AB. 264 pp.

Stelfox, H and C Fisher. 1998. A winter birding guide for the Edmonton region. Edmonton Natural History Club, Edmonton, AB. 56 pp.

Enjoying Nature

Chapman, R. 1991. The discoverer's guide to Elk Island National Park. Lone Pine Publishing and the Friends of Elk Island Society, Edmonton, AB. 96 pp.

Griffiths, D. 1979. Island forest year Elk Island National Park. The University of Alberta Press, Edmonton, AB. 357 pp.

Milholland, B. 2002. North Saskatchewan River guide. North Saskatchewan Watershed Alliance, Edmonton, AB. Unpaged.

Saley, H, D H Meredith, H Stelfox and D Ealey. 2003. Nature walks and Sunday drives 'round Edmonton. Edmonton Natural History Club, Edmonton, AB. 80 pp.

Subject Index

Bold page numbers refer to special features, such as photographs, diagrams, charts, and tables.

legislation to protect, 29, 47, 103

lifestyle in fur trade era, 34–42

maps of site densities and distributions, **23**, **27**, **29**, **35**

pottery styles and dating, **25**, 37–38

site density (site/km^2), 27, **29**

sites, near/away from river, **30**, 30–32, **32**

stone tool making, 26, 31, 33–34

See also Aboriginal peoples

arctic fox, 125

aspen

in Edmonton surrounding area, 60, 64, 215, 233, **233**

in river valley, 12, **13**, 17, 62, 109, 137, 148–49, **149**

map of land cover classifications, **10**, **147**, 148, **214**, **215**

as owl habitat, 109

Aspen Parkland Ecoregion, 89, 145

Assiniboine people, 37–38

Astotin Creek, 169, 170

Astotin Lake, 64, 164, 166

Athabasca/Smoky River

map of archaeological sites, **29**

Atim Creek, 181

Australia

first national park, 259–60

avocet, 194

awareness

See perception; spirituality and nature

B

Baird's sparrow, 60–61

bald eagle, 193

balsam poplar

as Edmonton surrounding area, 215, 233, 234

in river valley, 62, 63, 109

as owl habitat, 109

See also poplars

Banff National Park

headwaters of N. Saskatchewan River, 48, 55

barred owls, 113

bats, **99**, 100, 101, 117

beaked hazelnut, 64

bears, black, **93**, 109

beaver

in Elk Island National Park, 94, 168–69, 170–71

in river valley and surrounding area, 63, **96**, 213

surveys of, 93–94, **99**

Beaver County, 289, 291

Beaver Hills/Cooking Lake Moraine

about features of, 64, **286**, 286–88, 318–19

archeological sites, 28

development in area, 169–70

ecosystem in area, 64

map of area, **163**

Beaver Hills Initiative, 283–92

about mandate and actions of, 283–85, 290–92

See also Beaver Hills/Cooking Lake Moraine

bees, 100–101

Belgravia Ravine, **225**

bibliography, 359–60

Big Lake Environment Support Society, 196–98

Big Lake Management Group, 199–200

Big Lake Natural Area, 191–201

about location and features, 191–95, **192**

future planning, 197–200

history of development, 195–97

biophilia, 261

See also spirituality and nature

bioregional conservation networks, 53

birch, 62, **146**, 215

birds

climate change and, 125

educational programs, 297, 299–301

in Big Lake Natural Area, 193

in Central Parkland Natural Subregion, 60–61

in Clifford E. Lee Nature Sanctuary, 174, 176

in Elk Island National Park, 91

in Little Mountain area, 233

in Wagner Natural Area, 184

inventory in Christmas Bird Count, 94–96, **95**, 117

inventory of river valley, 90–91

migration and seasonal changes, 89, 98, 111, 114–15

nuisance species, 91–92, **98**

perception of, 264–67, 299–301

as urban wildlife, 61–62, 117

use of corridors, 74, 141–42

use of stormwater ponds, 84–86, **85**

See also Ministik Bird Sanctuary

birds of prey, 95

bison

depletion of, 36, 42–44

early presence of, 25

impact on Central Parkland Natural Subregion, 60

in Elk Island National Park, 94, 162–64, **164**, 166, 168

black bears, 93

land renewal, **154**

land-use categories, 119, 128

management of turf, 97–98

management of wildlife, 102

management plan for urban parks, 314–15

natural areas reserve fund, 20, 241–42, 248, 309

surveys by citizens (of birds, mammals, etc.), 123

surveys of citizens, 90, 251, 315

tourism promotion of, 157, 251

utilities and watershed conservation, 278, 280

voluntary nature of policies, 308–9

Westworth report (2001), 20, 103, 139, 245

Westworth report (2001) implementation, 160, 218, 245, 311–16

See also North Saskatchewan River; North Saskatchewan River, urban park system (ribbon of green); North Saskatchewan Watershed Alliance; wetlands, lost

Edmonton, City of, legislation and policies

about history of, 18–20, 90

bylaws for conservation, 18–19, 90, 252, 322, 330

bylaws on Big Lake area, 197

bylaws on domestic pets, 93

City of Edmonton Policy C-467 (1995), 20, 235, 308–11

Edmonton Natural History Club

about mandate of, 310

conferences of, 252

Little Mountain area partnership, 231, 236, 239–40, 242, 247

See also environmental non-governmental organizations

Edmonton Parks Master Plan (1970–1980), 18

Edmonton Public Schools

nature education at Minchau Elementary School, 294, 295, **295**, **298**

See also Earth Challenge Project

Edmonton Regional Plan (1972), 18

Edmonton Regional Planning Commission

Big Lake Natural Area and, 195, 197

education, environmental

activities in, 296–303, **297–98**, **300**

ATA specialist council newsletter on, 305

barriers to success of, 294

conservation nets and, 157–58

for families and communities, 303, 305

for landowner outreach, 312

for special needs students, 297, 299

in Big Lake Natural Area, 197

in Clifford E. Lee Nature Sanctuary, 175–76, 178

in conservation land trusts planning, 356

in Wagner Natural Area, 185, 187

on landscape aesthetics, 333–34

on perception of wildlife, 264–67, 299–301

as purpose for green spaces, 257

See also Earth Challenge Project; human interactions with wildlife; spirituality and nature

elk

in Edmonton, 109

in Elk Island National Park, 94, 162, 164, **165**, 166

Elk Island National Park, 162–72

about features of, 64, 162–63

about history of development, 165–66, 169–70, 286–87, 318

archeological sites and climate change evidence, 28, 36, 168

management and partnerships, 166–70, 287–89, 291

map of area, **163**

surveys and inventories, 91, 94

wildlife in, 94, 162–64, **164–67**, 166, 169–70

See also Beaver Hills Initiative

Elk Point/Frog Lake area

Aboriginal reserves in, 42–44, **44**

archeological sites, 30, 30–32, **32**

Ellerslie Road

wildlife corridors at, 83, **84**

Emily Murphy Park, 106

empathy with nature, 296

See also Earth Challenge Project; spirituality and nature

endangered species, 120–21

English sparrow, 92

ENGOs

See environmental non-governmental organizations

ENHC

See Edmonton Natural History Club

environmental education

See education, environmental

environmental non-governmental organizations (ENGOs)

advocacy system and, 332–33, 355

Grand River Conservation
Authority, 277–78
Grassland Natural Region, 5, 58, 59
grasslands
in Alberta, 36, 57–58, **58**, 60
in maps of land cover
classifications, 10, 59,
147, 149, 214, 215
gravel pits and gravelled areas
in valley area, **14, 17, 31**
renewal of land, **154**
great blue herons, 194
great horned owls, 65, 106, 113
Great Smoky Mountains National
Park, 268–69
greenways
aesthetics of, 258–60, 333–34
in urban planning, 2, 81, 88,
250, 347–48
purposes for, 257, 268–73
as wildlife corridors, 81–84, 135
Groat Creek and Ravine, 224
grosbeaks, 61, **95**
ground squirrel, Richardson's, 92
grouse-like birds, **95**
gulls, 111

H
Habitat Acquisition Trust, 352
habitat fragmentation
about threat of, 135
conservation nets and, 88, 136–37
greenways as habitat links, 135–36
impact on mice and voles, 73–74
in river valley, 148–49, **149**
small patch effects, 69–71, **72**
use of transportation corridors
due to, 102–3
See also conservation nets;
corridors for wildlife;
urban planning for
urban wildlife

hares
See rabbits and hares
hawks, 61
Hawrelak Park, 154
hazelnut, beaked, 64
Head-Smashed-In Buffalo Jump,
Fort Macleod, 46
heritage buildings, 349, 355
Hermitage Park, 80
Highway 16, 185–86
highways
See roads and highways
Historical Resources Act, 29, 47
Horsehills Creek area, 208–19
about location and features,
210, 213, 213, 215
history of area, 211–12
land cover types in, **214–15**,
215–16
threats to, **216**, 216–19
house mouse, 92
house sparrows, 94, **95**
Hudson's Bay Company, 211
human interactions with wildlife,
96–102, 105–18
benefits of, **96**, 96–97
health hazards, 97, 100–102
in conservation net buffer zones,
143
night wildlife in Edmonton, 106,
109–18
nuisance species, 92, **98**, 98–100
perception of wildlife, 264–67
purposes for green spaces, 257,
268–73
surveys of human use of
greenways, 90, 251
vehicle collisions with wildlife,
69, 82–83, 91, 92, 99,
100–101, 103
wilderness concepts and, 107–8,
334–35

wildlife adaptations to urban
areas, 120–21
with mosquitoes and insects,
100–101
with plants, 97–98
with saw whet owls, 106,
108–9, 113
with white-tailed jackrabbits,
123, 126, 132
See also education,
environmental;
spirituality and nature
human spirituality and nature
See spirituality and nature

I
Inland Cement area, 204–6
insecticides, 101–2
insectivorous plant species, 65
insects
in Clifford E. Lee Nature
Sanctuary, 175
in urban areas, 100–102
Integrated Pest Management, City
of Edmonton, 102
interconnectedness with nature
See Earth Challenge Project;
spirituality and nature
*Inventory of Environmentally
Sensitive and Significant
Natural Areas* (1993),
19–20, 247

J
jack pine, 65
jackrabbits, white-tailed
See white-tailed jackrabbits
Japanese landscape aesthetics, 334
Jasper Yellowhead Museum and
Archives, jasper, 46
jays, 95

Minchau Elementary School, Edmonton
schoolyard naturalization project, 294, **295, 298**
See also Earth Challenge Project
Ministik Bird Sanctuary, 163, 169, 206, 318
moose
in Edmonton area, 109, 194
in Elk Island National Park, 94, 162, 166, **166**
vehicle collisions with, **100**
Moran Lake, 216
Morgan Creek, 186
mosquitoes, 100, 102, 188
mosses and lichens, 90–91, 184
moth, giant atlas, in Thailand, 111–12
Mount Pleasant Cemetery area, 31
mountain ash, 110
mountain lion, 109
mouse, house, 92
mule deer
in Edmonton area, **94,** 109
in Elk Island National Park, 162, 170–71
Municipal Government Act (MGA)
land reserves under, 317, 320–22
public utility lots under, 312–13, 320, 322, 329–30
municipal reserves
about use of, 321
as development tool, 312–14, 321–22
municipalities
about urban planning trends, 3–5, 326, 347–48
advocacy system difficulties for, 332–33, 355
conservation easements under EPEA, 322–23
development tools under MGA, 320–22

intangible values, treatment in planning process, 330–31
land-use zoning, 329–30
planning turf wars, 328–29
population pressures on, 336
short-term *vs.* long-term planning, 331–32
See also Edmonton, City of; Edmonton, City of, conservation efforts; Edmonton, City of, legislation and policies; Municipal Government Act (MGA); rural/urban development issues; urban planning for urban wildlife
mysticism and nature
See spirituality and nature

N

narrow-leaved meadowsweet, 234
National Institute for Urban Wildlife, 85
National Round Table on the Environment and the Economy (2003), 285
Native people
See Aboriginal peoples
Natural and Protected Areas of Environmental Protection Branch (Alberta), 175
Natural Areas Advisory Committee, City of Edmonton, 20
Natural Areas Implementation Committee, City of Edmonton, 20
Natural Areas Reserve Fund, City of Edmonton, 20, 241–42, 248, 309
natural subregions
map of vegetation, **59**

See also Boreal Forest Natural Region; Central Parkland Natural Subregion; Grassland Natural Region
nature, spiritual response to
See spirituality and nature
Nature Centre, John Janzen
See John Janzen Nature Centre
Nature Conservancy of Canada
Elk Island National Park partnership with, 170
land conservation trusts, 289–90
Little Mountain area development, 236
See also conservation land trusts
night wildlife
See human interactions with wildlife; white-tailed jackrabbits *(L. townsendii)*
North America
conservation land trusts in, 348–49, **352**
conservation nets in, 144–45
green spaces in, 250, 258–60, 308
watershed planning, 277
white-tailed jackrabbits in, **132**
North Saskatchewan River, 48–56, **52–53, 63,** 159
about the river and watershed, 48, 50–52
as Canadian Heritage River, 4, 48, 55
conservation nets in valley, 146, **148,** 148–58
ecosystem stability and, 52–56
floods of, 17
history of protection, 12, **13–16,** 17–20
inventory of species, 90–94, **94,** 102

nuisance species, 91–92
stormwater ponds, 84–86, **85,
222, 327,** 327–28
tolerance for urban habitats, 87,
120–21
wilderness concepts and, 107–8,
334–35
zones of urban areas, 88
See also conservation nets;
corridors for wildlife;
habitat fragmentation;
human interactions with
wildlife
urban streams
about urban streams, 208–11,
217–19
See also Horsehills Creek area

V

Vancouver, City of
watershed planning and
development, 221–22,
278
vegetation
impact of drought on, **146**
impact of loss of bison herds on,
36
in Central Parkland Natural
Subregion, 60–61
in Horsehills Creek area, 213
in Little Mountain area, 233
in natural regions, 145–46
in river valley, 90–91, 148–49,
149
in river valley, on north and
south banks, **58,** 61, 62,
109
map of vegetation in natural
subregions, **59**
non-native species, 92–93, 146,
146, 156

seed dispersal in corridors, 153
See also plants
vehicle collisions
with wildlife, 69, 82–83, 91, 92,
99, **100–101,** 103
Victoria Park area
brick production in, **14**
vole, meadow, 92
vole, red backed
in Elk Island National Park,
169–70
study on impact of fragmented
habitat on, 73–74
volunteers
about use of, 66, 310, 350
for Earth Challenge Project, 303
for Little Mountain
conservation, 238, 240,
246
for Wagner Natural Area, 188
See also environmental non-
governmental
organizations (ENGOs)

W

Wagner Natural Area, 180–90
about location and features, 65,
180–81, **182, 183**
biodiversity in, 65, 181, 184
cross-section of fen and swamp
during deposition, **183**
history of protection, 185–89
wetlands during deposition
(chart), 181
Wagner Natural Area Society,
185–88
walleye, 194
Wanuskewin Heritage Park,
Saskatoon
Aboriginal displays, 46
warblers, 115

Washington, Seattle area
watershed planning in, 277
wasps, 100–101
watch programs
on plants, worms, birds, frogs,
etc., 300–301
watchable wildlife sites (Alberta
designation), 176
water arum, 64
**Water for Life: Alberta's strategy
for sustainability,** 209
water spider, 184
waterfowl
in Beaver Hills area, **286**
in Christmas Bird Count, 94–95,
95
use of stormwater ponds, 84–86,
85
watersheds
government programs, 218
planning in N. America, 277–78
See also Horsehills Creek; North
Saskatchewan River;
North Saskatchewan
Watershed Alliance;
urban streams
waxwings, 94, **95,** 110
Wayne Gretzky Drive, 102–3
Wedgewood Ravine Bridge, 83
Weir Industrial Park, 226
West Nile virus, 102
Western (Boreal) toads, 65
western snowberry, 60
Westworth report
See *Conserving Edmonton's
Natural Areas*
(Westworth report,
2001)
wetlands
environmental education on,
297
impact of suburbanization on,
339